The Daily Telegraph

THE QUIET PINT

D0812901

A Guide
to
Quiet Pubs

The Daily Telegraph

THE QUIET PINT

Compiled and Edited by
Derek and Josephine Dempster

"Q" Publications Limited
3 Harnet Street
Sandwich
Kent CT13 9ES
Tel: 01304 613547 Fax: 01304 613548

Cover Design

Concept by Derek and Josephine Dempster
Graphic design by Claire Limbrey
Watercolour of The White Swan, Richmond, by Alan W. Palmer

Typography & Design by SandwichDeSign

The contents of this book were believed to be correct at the time of going to press, However, because public houses and wine bars are subject to changes of ownership, management and policy, the publishers accept no responsibility for any differences that may occur between the information given in this Guide and the actuality.

Directors: Edwin Peat, Derek Dempster, Josephine Dempster, Roger Viner, Nicholas Irwin.

Printed by
BPC Wheatons Ltd
Hennock Road
Marsh Barton
Exeter EX2 8RP

THE QUIET PINT is affiliated to the Pipedown Campaign,
6 Kingsley Mansions, London W14 9SG. Tel/Fax: 0171 385 5811

CONTENTS

FOREWORD 7

INTRODUCTION 8

THE PIPEDOWN CAMPAIGN 10

ACKNOWLEDGEMENTS 11

ENGLAND:

Bedfordshire & Cambridgeshire 13
Berkshire 24
Buckinghamshire 33
Cambridgeshire, see Bedfordshire 13
Cheshire 46
Cleveland see Northumbria 256
Cornwall 52
Cumbria 62
Derbyshire & Staffordshire 76
Devon 89
Dorset 110
Durham see Northumbria 256
Essex 122
Gloucestershire 135
Greater Manchester see Lancashire 209
Hampshire 154
Hereford, Shropshire & Worcestershire 166
Hertfordshire 185
Kent 193
Lancashire, Greater Manchester & Merseyside 209
Leicestershire, Lincolnshire & Nottinghamshire 221
Lincolnshire see Leicestershire 221

Merseyside see Lancashire 209
Midlands (Northamptonshire, Warwickshire & West Midlands) 236
Norfolk 244
Northamptonshire see Midlands 234
Northumberland see Northumbria 256
Northumbria (Cleveland, Durham, Northumberland, Tyne & Wear) 256
Nottinghamshire see Leicestershire 221
Oxford 270
Shropshire see Hereford 166
Somerset 288
Staffordshire see Derbyshire 76
Suffolk 305
Surrey 319
Sussex 329
East & West Tyne & Wear see Northumbria 256
Warwickshire see Midlands 234
West Midlands see Midlands 234
Worcestershire see Hereford 166
Wiltshire 354
Yorkshire, North, West & South 365

LONDON 386
London Pubs by Postal District 419

SCOTLAND 420

WALES 440

Wine Bars and Pub Groups 454

Pub nomination forms 462

BARLEY MOW INN
Kirk Ireton
Ashbourne
Derbyshire

FOREWORD

By Julian Lloyd Webber

THE QUIET PINT has got off to a wonderful start! Its first issue was favourably compared with the plethora of other pub guides and sold well enough to place it alongside the two leaders in this crowded field. I am not surprised. For far too long the minority (majority?), who like to be able to order a drink without having to scream at the bar-staff to make themselves heard above some God-awful racket, had been forced to suffer in anything but silence. At last THE QUIET PINT came to their rescue.

And now it is back – with an even greater selection of these wonderful establishments which have bucked the trend of inflicting that most pernicious of aural pollutants – muzak – on their long-suffering customers.

THE QUIET PINT has made an important impact and, for the first time in many years, it is now easier in cities, towns and villages across Britain to find a pub with good food, drink and conversation without having to endure someone else's choice of muzak.

The tide has turned!

Julian Lloyd Webber

INTRODUCTION

It doesn't matter what you do in life, you win some, you lose some. In its first year THE QUIET PINT won praise for originality, quality and wit - a successful combination that called for a reprint within less than two months of its launch in October 1995. It won again when The Daily Telegraph chose it to be a Telegraph Book - and then to co-publish this and future editions.

As you might expect, this Edition is bigger than the last: 250 pubs that did not feature in the original volume are included and described. We lost 49. Most had to be eliminated because they were taken over by owners or licensees who believe muzac is good for business. Some closed down.

Changes of owner or licensee are a problem for any public house or restaurant guide. While the information contained in a guide might be totally correct at the time of going to press, it is impossible to escape the fact that changes in pub managements will erode its accuracy. Guide users may therefore find on occasion that they are patronising inns that no longer fit the descriptions given about them in the Book. Life's like that. Here today and gone tomorrow.

That is why we appreciate hearing about any changes, and thank all readers who have have written in. They are our auxiliary eyes and ears which help us to be as up-to-date and informative as an annual publication cycle allows.

A pub's reputation depends very much on the people who run it. We know of several establishments that thrived under certain managers, but slumped when they left. Like fairy godmothers waving wands, they then moved on to transform dingy, run-down old ale houses elsewhere into successful and popular meeting places.

One of our new entries, The Wat Tyler Inn, was just such a place until 1992. Bang in the middle of busy Dartford, Kent, it attracted so little custom that it would close each evening and Sundays. Playing standard background music and with a well-used juke box, "it was", says the present landlord, "like a teenager's bedroom!" Refurbished, restored, devoid of music and serving a range of reasonably priced beers, the pub is now open from 10 am to 11 pm seven days a week and thriving with escapees from the other musac-infested pubs around. The formula is such a success that he's bought another pub elsewhere in Kent.

What so may publicans fail to appreciate is that atmosphere is not created by music. One can understand how it can "take the chill off" bleak and unattrative surroundings for the staff before opening times, but at other times it is intrusive, no matter whether the selection is from the Top Ten or a classical selection - and it's still bleak and unattractive.

There are many different types of pub in this book. They cater for many different tastes. Each one is someone's favourite local. Some are the sort of bloke-ish places that will suit some, but perhaps not the kind auntie would appreciate. We are not judgemental : we are concerned with telling you where to find pubs without background music; passing on what our reporters tell us and doing our best to verify all they have said by speaking to the landlords.

We hope this Book contains something for everyone. We think it does, and we're bound to hear if it doesn't!

Derek D. Dempster

9

PIPEDOWN

By Nigel Rodgers
Honorary Secretary

One of the chief reasons for originally starting Pipedown was the difficulty of finding a pub not filled with piped music (aka canned music, elevator music, muzak, muzac) blaring from every speaker and making conversation all but impossible. Brewers and landlords, in misguided attempts to 'improve' pubs, have wrecked many of them with bogus themed interiors. But almost certainly worse than this is piped music, which is regarded as enhancing the 'atmosphere' of a pub. This is utter nonsense, as any right-minded pub-goer knows, so I warmly welcome the second edition of THE QUIET PINT. I often use it myself, finding it witty, informative and astonishingly useful. Pipedown The Campaign against Piped Music, does not just fight piped music in pubs of course, but also in shops, restaurants, hotels, doctors' sugeries, railway and bus stations, airports (and on trains, buses and aeroplanes), in public swimming pools and especially down the telephone when kept on hold. We have scored some notable successes in our brief existence, helping to persuade Gatwick Airport to discontinue its piped music and Sainsburys not to install it when thinking of doing so. Concerted efforts by members concerned have recently freed Cambridge Station of piped music at least at rush hours – a small feat but is shows what can be and is being done. Pipedowns's aim is to establish the right not to have to listen to other people's choice of music be it good bad or indifferent. The same principle applies to piped television. Membership of Pipedown costs £10 a year (£15 for those living abroad, £50 for life membership) and brings quarterly newsletters detailing the fight against piped music worldwide along with muzac-free guidings, and (in any resonable number) four types of protesting card and five types of sticker. Local groups are being set up across Britain, as are sister-bodies in other English-speaking countries (where the pun can be appreciated). If you wish to join the fight against piped music, please fill in the form below and send it, with a cheque for £10 made out to Pipedown and a SAE please, to 6 Kingsley Mansions, London W14 9SG. Alternatively, if you would like more information, please just send an SAE. (There's an application form at the back of the Book).

ACKNOWLEDGEMENTS

We are very grateful to those who wrote to us nominating new pubs for the 1997 edition of THE QUIET PINT. Some of the nominations had to be discarded; music was being played, perhaps not at the time they were visited, and perhaps very softly, but this meant they did not qualify for an entry. Those who wrote to us are listed here. Many asked to remain anonymous, many were anonymous as they sent unsigned postcards. By whatever means you informed us about our new pubs, we thank all of you.

N.R. Alexander, Keith Allen, J. Arkinstall, Mrs E. Bagge, Cmdr. Gerald Barnett, Andrew Barr, C.P. Bowyer, Russ Broadbent, Dr. Thurstan Brewin, J.A. Cheal, B.A. Clarke, Jeremy Condliffe, Ian Ashley-Cooper, R. D. Dewhurst, John Deacon, D.T.J. Doughan, Bob Eardley, Stuart Eltham, Dave Esson, J.E. Evens, John Freestone, D.E. Goodall, John Gray, M.J. Green, Diana Griffith, Marie Hobson, John Hogarth, Roscoe Howells, R. Johnson, Dave Jones, Mrs R.D. Knight, Geoffrey Lawrence, G.G. Lawrence, John Litchfield, Sydney Lyle, W. Marsh, Barbara Martin, Diana Maultby, Lynda Mitchell, Peter Merrington, Owen Mortimer, Mrs Eileen Pittard, Col. D.D. Ranft, B.H. Rogerson, Mrs H. Rookes, Alan Seymour, Lynn Sharpless, Geoffrey Shaw, J.H. Shore, P.J. Sims, Dr G.J. Standwell, Robert Stevens, R.G.R. Stickland, A.W. Stutchbury, Ann Sugden, K.W. Sykes, John Tredgett, Mrs R. E. Vestey, Capt. R. Hayward-Wills, Maurice Whitehouse, Geoffrey Wylie.

The following friends and supporters did a wonderful job researching a number of pubs for us in their own areas: Jim Braye, Dierdre Bryan-Brown, Stan Coates, Nick Corbould, Andrew Cruikshank, Hugh Denham, David Dowse, Martin Ellis, Joy and Hugh Gardiner, Lynda King-Taylor, Anne and Michael Marwood, Susie and Ben McDowell, Ian Ponsford, Jacqui and Darrol Stinton, Ann and David Watkins, and Gavin Whitehead.

Lastly, many thanks to Audrey Lang who did a last minute check for any vital changes.

B

BEDFORDSHIRE & CAMBRIDGESHIRE

BOLNHURST

Ye Olde Plough   Tel: 01234 376274

Kimbolton Road, Bolnhurst, Beds MK44 2EX
Free House. M J Horridge, licensee.

Not only is there a good choice of home-made food and real ales in this 500 year old pub, but also the added bonus of a lovely garden and long terrace – where you can sit and look over the pond – and a landlady who (it is rumoured) will let all you keen gardeners take cuttings of anything you fancy. Let's hope there isn't too much demand; one has visions of a denuded garden. The restaurant upstairs and the bar share the same menu which changes weekly and could include, soup, paté, local sausages, home-baked ham vegetarian pasta, steak kidney in ale pie, fillet of salmon in green peppercorn sauce, steaks, interesting puds. Ruddles Best, Courage Directors and Butcombe Bitter on hand pump. Buck's Fizz in summer – so civilised! Two resident cats, two dogs. No cats up trees, please, so watch your dogs!

OPEN: 12–2.30 (3 Sat). 7–11.
Real Ale. Restaurant Fri, Sat eves & Sun lunch only.
Well behaved children until 9. Dogs on leads.

BYTHORN

White Hart   Tel: 01832 710226

Bythorn, Nr Huntingdon, Cambs CB2 3QN
Free House. Bill & Pam Bennett, licensees.

This 17th century village inn is really more of a restaurant than a pub. Having said that, you don't need to have more than a beer or a glass of wine with a nut or a crisp. Food is served in the bar as well as the restaurant and a no-smoking dining room. The menu is very creative and popular: home-made

13

soup, ploughman's, duck liver terrine, fresh scallops, venison casserole, game in season, loin of pork in orange sauce, steaks, home-made puddings. Big Sunday lunches. Greene King IPA and Abbot ales. Wines by the glass. Seats and tables outside in the garden.

OPEN: 11–3. 6–11. Closed Sun eve and all day Mon. Real Ale. Restaurant. No-smoking dining room. Children welcome. No dogs. Morris dancers occasionally.

CAMBRIDGE

Champion of the Thames   Tel: 01223 352043

King Street Cambridge Greene King. David Green, licensee.

An atmospheric, busy, friendly, town pub. As you would expect, it quickly fills up with University dons, students, businessmen and anyone else wanting to enjoy a quiet pint. Just two bars, one called the 'hamsters cage' as it is no more than a tiny snug. Monday to Friday, lunchtime snacks only – bacon doorsteps, cheese and onion rolls and soup in winter. As the landlord says " we're a pub, and pubs sell beer". Which they do very well. All the beers are from the Greene King range. N.B. Lunchtimes are always quiet, but blues tracks played some evenings.

OPEN: 11–11
Real Ale.
No children. Dogs. Yes, if the landlord likes the look of you.

CAMBRIDGE

Cambridge Blue   Tel: 01223 613582

85–87 Gwydir Street, CB1 2LG.
(Side st. off Mill Road) Nethergate. Nick Winnington, licensee.

If you want to meet the local Monster Raving Loony party candidate, now is your chance. He is the one leaning on the bar waiting to serve you. More power to his elbow, say I. A late Victorian pub with a large garden complete with a model railway (G scale, if you want to know) and chickens. One called Hetty is frequently in the pub. There is a no-smoking bar, a small snug and a conservatory. Pub menu and bar snacks – large filled rolls, lamb and vegetable samozas, Mexican bean stews, home-made pies and daily specials. Nethergate IPA, Bitter, Golden Gate and Old Growler. Always two guest beers, these vary, but one of them is always a mild ale. The Cambridge Blue was CAMRA Cambridge pub of the year in 1995.

N.B. Just in case you go there first thing in the morning, when all is quiet, the landlord may be listening to the radio – it will be turned off soon.

OPEN: 12–2.30, (3.30. Sat) 6–11. No eve meals Sunday.
Real Ale
Children in conservatory area. Dogs on leads.

CAMBRIDGE

Eagle   Tel: 01223 301286

Bene't Street, Cambridge, Cambs CB2 3QN
Greene King. Peter & Carol Hill, licensees.

Originally The Eagle and Child, this lively rambling 16th century town pub was built on land bequeathed to Corpus Christi College in 1525 . A lot of the interior is still intact: 17th century fireplaces, some mullioned windows, wall paintings and original pine panelling. More up to date are the names of British and American airmen written on the ceiling in lipstick or whatever else came to hand during World War 2. They have been left intact although the ceiling has been given a little wash. Simple, good range of bar food: a variety of salads, quiches, pasties, roast lamb, chicken, seafood pancakes etc. Greene King ales on hand pump. Many wines by the glass. There are seats and tables in the cobbled, galleried yard at the entrance to the pub.

OPEN: 11–11; Meal/snacks 12–2.30; 5.30–8.45. not Fri, Sat, Sun.
Real Ale.
Children welcome. No dogs. Except guide dogs.
Wheelchair access.

IN THE LICENSED TRADE BACKGROUND MUSIC POLICY CAN CHANGE OVERNIGHT

The entries in this Edition of the Quiet Pint were correct at the time of going to press. However, changes can occur very quickly in the licensed trade and a pub that has been free of background music can adopt a different policy overnight. The editors cannot therefore be held responsible for such changes and we rely on our readers to keep us informed.

CAMBRIDGE

Free Press   Tel: 01223 68337

Prospect Row, Cambridge, Cambs CB1 1QU
Greene King. Christopher Lloyd, lease.

No need to fear you'll be press-ganged into training for the next University boat race when you enter this totally non-smoking pub, which is registered as a boat club and has walls covered in rowing blades and appropriate photographs. Originally a terraced house, it became a pub in 1840 and was named after a failed local paper of the same name (I am quoting Jill, the jolly barmaid) which, as you can see, has nothing to do with boats! There are five home-made soups daily, one of which is vegetarian, hot chilli, lamb casserole, several vegetarian dishes and home-made puddings. Ales are Greene King and there is a range of malt whiskies. Seats in the sunny, sheltered garden which is a home to the extras from Watership Down.

OPEN: 12–2.30. 6–11.
Real Ale.
Children welcome. Dogs on leads

CAMBRIDGE

Tap & Spile   Tel: 01223 357026

14 Mill Lane, Cambridge CB2 1RX
Pubmaster. Peter Snelgrove, manager.

By the river, with a terrace overlooking the mill pond from where you can hire a punt to practise your skills. One big bar serving eight different ales: Adnams Bitter is permanent; all the rest are constantly changing guest beers. Traditional bar food: steak and kidney pie, ocean pie, fish and chips. All home-made – nothing frozen. There is an outside drinking area on the green nearby.

OPEN: 11–11
Real Ale
Children only at mealtimes. Dogs not at mealtime.

COLMWORTH

Wheatsheaf   Tel: 012324 376370

Wilden Road, Colmworth, Beds, MK44 2NJ.
Free House. K.J. Graham, licensee.

A very old country pub on the South side of the village. Inside there are low beamed ceilings, an inglenook fireplace with big winter log fires and just so you know, a juke box in the public bar. There is a restaurant within the building, but the facility has been rented out – it supplies all the bar snacks and pub meals. Our reporter says it is good. Please let us know.. Draught Bass is on permanently and there will be two other guest beers.

OPEN: 11–2.30. 6–11
Real Ale. Restaurant run independently.
Children in garden. No dogs.

FEN DRAYTON

Three Tuns   Tel: 01954 230242

High Street, Fen Drayton, Cambs. CB4 5SJ
Greene King. Michael & Eileen Nugent, tenants.

Exceptional 15th Century carvings on the tie beams suggests this was an important local building. It is thought to have been Fen Drayton's guildhall. (Known as Fenny Dreiton in 1285). The pub has been considerably altered and extended over the years. The present bar was built onto the side of the original building. Heavily beamed and with inglenook fireplaces, it is filled with interesting bric à brac and old photographs. Food is cooked to order – short varied menu offering: fried whitebait, chicken satay, grills, fish, home-cured ham, chicken curry, salads, sandwiches and choice of puddings. Greene King IPA, Abbot and Rayments Special Bitter. Range of malt whiskies. Tables on the lawn at the back of the pub amongst the fruit trees.

OPEN: 11–2.30. 6.30–11.
Real Ale.
Children in eating area until 8. Dogs in garden only.

FOWLMERE

Chequers   Tel: 01954 230242

High Street, Fowlmere, Cambs. SG8 7SR
Pubmaster. Norman Rushton, lease.

How to be in two places at once: depending on which address you read, this pub is either in Cambridgeshire or near Royston, Hertfordshire. You may be forgiven for thinking this is the reason the inn sign is one colour one side, another on the reverse – confusion is everywhere. However, the answer is all to do with Fowlmere Aerodrome and the proprietor will be only too pleased to tell you all about it. The Chequers is a very civilised old coaching inn with a considerable reputation for an interesting variety of food: home-made soups, mussels in garlic butter, duck and pork paté, cassoulet, vegetarian dishes and home-made puddings. The blackboard menu changes daily. Two cosy rooms and a galleried restaurant. Tetleys and Tolly Cobbold Original. Good choice of wines, ports and brandies. Seats in the pretty, flowery garden.

OPEN: 12–2.30. 6–11.
Real Ale. Restaurant.
Children welcome. No dogs.

HORNINGSEA

Plough & Fleece   Tel: 01223 860795

High Street, Horningsea, Cambs. CB5 9JG
Greene King. Kenneth Grimes, tenant.

This small, lively 200 year old pub is a great favourite with locals and visitors alike. It has a beamed public bar with oak settles and tables and a no-smoking dining room. There is a good choice of bar food: sandwiches, home-made soups, omelettes, Suffolk Hot Pot, etc., good puddings. Always a roast at weekends. Greene King ales; choice of malt whiskies and vintage ports. Tables in the garden.

OPEN: 11.30–2.30. 7–11.
No food Sun or Mon eves. Real Ale: No-smoking restaurant.
Children over 5 in restaurant only. Dogs on leads.

KEYSTON

Pheasant   Tel: 01832 710241

Village Loop Road, Keyston, Nr Bythorn, Cambs. PE18 0RE
Free House. John Hoskins & Martin Lee, licensees.

There's just one room, but two distinct areas in this well kept, pretty
thatched pub. Originally the village blacksmiths it is decorated with horsey
artefacts. Heavily beamed and comfortable, it has a no-smoking area in the
restaurant. Martin Lee is the new chef/patron . Using the best local produce,
like fresh fish and game in season, it has an interesting menu which changes
every couple of weeks. The menu includes an extensive list of starters and
light snacks – wild boar sausages, breast of pigeon, poached fillet of hake,
etc. Over ten puddings to choose from. Roast sirloin on Sundays. British
cheeses. One menu serves both the more casual (paper napkins) and more
formal (linen napkin) sides of the pub. Adnams Best and three guest beers.
Good wine list, a considerable number by the glass. Tables outside.

OPEN: 12–3. 6–11.
Real Ale.
Children welcome. No dogs.

MADINGLEY

Three Horseshoes   Tel: 01954 210221

High Street, Madingley, Cambs CB3 8AB
Free House. R Stokes & John Hoskins, licensees.

Try not to ask for anything flambé here. This whitewashed, thatched pub,
with a single bar has been burnt down three times, so they say. It was last
rebuilt in 1911. The menu emphasises Mediterranean style food, both in the
restaurant and on the blackboard menu in the bar. Home-made soup,
tomato and basil tart, fresh crab salads, boeuf en daube, duck breast with
mint and caper dressing. Interesting British cheeses. Good puddings. Wide
ranging wine list, 75% of the customers are wine buffs. Adnams Best and
three guest beers are on hand pump. Tables in the flowery garden during the
summer.

OPEN: 11.30–2.30. 6–11.
Real Ale. No restaurant Sun eve.
Children welcome. No dogs.

NEWTON

Queens Head   Tel: 01223 870436

Newton, Nr Cambridge, Cambs. CB2 5BG
Free House. David & Juliet Short, licensees.

This is a charming, traditional 17th century village inn. A painting of the
goose on the pub sign depicts poor Belinda, keeper of the car park, now in
residence in the public bar – stuffed. One beamed, main bar with a big log
fire in winter and a smaller cosy saloon. Simple good bar food complements
the fine ales and country wines. Wide choice of sandwiches, all cut to order,
home-made soup, filled baked potatoes. Evenings and Sunday lunchtime
there is a selection of cold meats, salads, etc. Adnams Bitter and Broadside
with Adnams Old Ale in winter – all tapped from the cask. Country fruit
wines, farm cider. Seats at the front of the pub or on the green.

OPEN: 11.30–2.30. 6–11.
Real Ale.
Children in Games Room. Dogs on leads. Well behaved, both of them.

PULLOXHILL

Cross Keys   Tel: 01525 712442

High Street, Pulloxhill, Beds MK45 5HB
Charles Wells. Peter & Sheila Meads, tenants.

Typical English country pub; architecturally pleasing, white painted and
flower-bedecked. Heavily beamed interior with large log-filled fireplaces.
Dating back to the 15th century, there is a legend that the ghost of a slain
Cavalier stalks the pub by night. A satisfying lunchtime bar snack menu
provides soups, ploughmans, salads, scampi, trout and Virginia ham. Daily
specials and more substantial dishes are on offer in the restaurant: steaks,
mixed grills, chicken Kiev and a variety of fish. Good choice of wines.
Charles Wells and Adnams ales. Seats in the garden. Serious jazz sessions
on Sunday nights with the likes of Kenny Baker, Charlie Galbraith, Acker Bilk
and that ilk.

OPEN: 11–3. 6–11.
Real Ale. Restaurant. Specially priced lunches for senior citizens Mon–Fri.
Children in own room. No dogs.
Jazz every Sun eve.

RADWELL

The Swan   Tel: 01234 781351

Felmersham Road, Radwell, Beds. NK43 78S
Charles Wells. John Olsen, tenant.

Some parts of this thatched pub date back to the 13th century, more bits
were added in the 17th century creating the building you see today. It now
has three rooms with lots of beams; the restaurant seats 20 – the quiet
lounge the same number – and the public bar will take however many you
can squeeze in. Well thought out pub food and bar snacks. The Charles
Wells range of ales and guest beers in summer.

OPEN: 12–2.30. 5–11
Real Ale. Restaurant. No food Sunday evening.
No children. Dogs in garden only.

SOMERSHAM

The Black Bull   Tel: 01487 843681

High Street, Somersham, Huntingdon, Cambridgeshire Free House.
Anthony Harris, tenant.

On the edge of the Cambridgeshire Fens, not far from St. Ives and
Huntingdon (birthplace of Oliver Cromwell), Somersham is a relatively quiet
village. Near the centre of the High Street the Black Bull was totally
renovated over the last few years, re-opening in 1995. A friendly,
straighforward, well run pub, serving generous portions from extensive
lunchtime and evening menus. The soup is always freshly made and you
could have pie of the day, skate with black butter and capers or a salmon
and broccoli lasagne. Morlands Old Speckled Hen, Courage Directors and
Courage Best. Seats in the garden.

OPEN: 11–3. 6–11. (12–4. 7–10.30 Sun)
Real Ale
Children welcome. Dogs on leads.

SUTTON

John O'Gaunt Inn   Tel: 01767 260377

30 High Street, Sutton, Sandy, Beds SG19 2ND
Greene King. Les Wall, tenant.

Sutton is the High Street, or the High Street is Sutton was how it was put to us. You enter this delightful village across a 13th century packhorse bridge or through a ford, which, with any luck, is still full of water. The pub – with a public and lounge bar – dates back to the mid 18th century. The public bar has table skittles and an un-used shove ha'penny board; the darts aren't too popular either. Have these old English pub games lost out to the Gallic Boules the local league plays on the pub's outside court? An extensive bar menu offers, among other things: sandwiches, filled jacket potatoes, cottage pie, moussaka, three different Balti dishes, vegetarian dishes and daily specials. Sunday lunches too. Greene King IPA and Abbot ales, plus the Greene Kings seasonal ales, about five or six a year, as, and when, they come out.

OPEN: 12–3. 7–11.
Real Ale.
Children by appointment. Dogs in public bar.

TODDINGTON

Sow & Pigs   Tel: 01525 873089

19 Church Square, Toddington, Nr Dunstable, Beds. LU5 6AA
Greene King. Roger Martin, licensee

The unpredictable Sow & Pigs Pub has a notice pinned to the doors stating "No footballers," which encourages any lingerer to enter and find out why. Not many concessions to comfort in the minute public bar – nor in the lounge either. Bar snacks are freshly prepared. There is a Victorian style dining room which is used for special occasions. As the name suggests, you will find plenty of pigs – some even flying. A sense of humour is useful. The landlord is a splendid and ebullient man, popular with local eccentrics and farmers discussing their poverty. There are occasional poetry or jazz evenings upstairs. The ales come from Greene King and there are some guest beers.

OPEN: 11–11.
Real Ale.
Children welcome. Dogs on leads.

WANSFORD

Haycock   Tel: 01780 782223

Wansford, Peterborough, Cambs. PE8 6JA
Free House. Richard Neale, licensee.

Situated next to the river and more of a hotel than others on our list, it is nevertheless a well-run, friendly and appealing place for a drink and a meal. The Haycock has a flagstoned hall, an attractively panelled main bar, sitting room at the front with a big log fire and a garden room opening out onto a sunny terrace. There are two no-smoking areas. The bar food includes open sandwiches, home-made soup and home-made puddings. There is also an interesting, more formal restaurant menu: ravioli of scallops, smoked salmon or terrine of chicken liver paté are among the starters, followed by either fish or roast quail, pan fried saddle of venison, roast sirloin of English beef, along with other choices for the main course. Impressive selection of wines, some by the glass, and vintage ports. More down to earth, the regular ales are Ruddles Best and County, also Adnams ale together with a guest. There are boules and cricket pitches if you're feeling energetic and can muster a team.

OPEN: All day 10.30 onwards.
Real Ale. Restaurant.
Children welcome. Dogs on leads.
Wheelchair access available. Bedrooms.

WOOTTON

Chequers   Tel: 01234 768394

Hall End Road, Hall End, Wootton, Beds. NK43 9HP
Charles Wells. Eddy Finch, tenant.

This one is a 16th century Grade II listed, coaching inn. As you would expect from its age there are lots of low oak beams, an inglenook fireplace, two other open fires and shiny brasses to compliment the oak beams. Two bars and a small restaurant. Sandwiches and pizzas etc. on the bar snack menu, the restaurant offers fish, steaks, duck and chicken dishes, with choice of starters and puds. Skittles inside – the ceilings are too low for darts – boules outside in the large garden. Charles Wells Bitter and Fargo, Mansfields Riding Mild and two other guest ales which change every three months.

Open: 11–3. 5.30–11
Real Ale. Small restaurant.
Children in restaurant. Dogs in bar or garden only.

B
BERKSHIRE

ALDWORTH

Bell   Tel: 01635 578272

Aldworth, Nr Reading, Berks. RG8 9SE
Free House. H E Macaulay, licensee.

This 14th century pub is a popular stop for locals and energetic people walking the Ridgeway Path. Grade 1 listed, it has been in the same family for two centuries. Nothing much has changed over the years; heavily beamed, with panelled walls and traditional furnishings – no bar counter, just a hatch through which you are served. Food is limited to hot crusty rolls filled with ham, cheese, smoked salmon, salt beef, Devon crab, or spicy prawns; a nice crisp salad tossed in a garlic mayonnaise; home-made soup during the winter. Ales are: West Berks Ol' Tyler – a new local ale – Morrells Bitter, Dark Mild and Arkells BBB and Kingsdown. Wines from Berry Bros. A good claret and a house medium dry white always on offer by the glass. Seats in the attractive garden next to the cricket pitch.

OPEN: 11–3. 6–11. Closed Mon (Open Bank Holiday Mon)
Real Ale.
Children in Tap Room. Dogs on leads.
Occasional Morris Dancing.

BRACKNELL

The Old Manor   Tel: 01344 304490

Grenville Place, High Street, Bracknell, Berks.
Wetherspoons. Norma Hardesty, manager.

Originally the Old Manor House, re-born as a town centre pub, still retaining its original oak beams. Escape tunnels and hidey holes dating back to the Reformation were found during the alterations. The result is a large drinking area, a third of which will be no-smoking. There will be a choice of five or six

24

reasonably priced beers plus a changing guest from one of the smaller breweries. As with all Wetherspoon outlets, they serve good reliable food.

OPEN: 11–11
Real Ale
No Children. No dogs.
Wheelchair access.

BRAY

The Fish at Bray   Tel: 01628 78111

Old Mill Lane, Bray, Berkshire SL6 2BG
Free House. Jean Thaxter, licensee.

Bray is a delightful Thameside village, and The Fish an attractive white painted building about 150 years old. The appealing interior has old parquet wood floors covered with rugs and lots of old oak furniture. Well spaced tables allow plenty of room for dining, and of course supping your pint. There is a no-smoking conservatory at the back of the pub. A Brasserie type menu with lots of different bar snacks; full meals are available at both lunchtime and in the evening. With a name like The Fish at Bray no prizes for guessing what takes pride of place on the menu – fish. There could be: red snapper, cold poached salmon with lemon mayonnaise and new potatoes, monkfish and prawns with lime, coriander and coconut on wild rice, whole baked lemon sole with herb topping, Caesar salad with fresh anchovies to start with or baked giant mussels stuffed with herbs and garlic. Pastas, salads, char-grilled lamb and breast of chicken on spinach with gruyere sauce. All the dishes, with an emphasis on fish, appear on the daily changing blackboard. Lots of vegetarian dishes too. All the food is fresh with the exception of the prawns, bread and spinach. Brakspears Special, Flowers IPA and Guinness. At least 6 wines by the glass, lots more by the bottle. Picnic tables in the walled garden.

OPEN: 11–3. 6–11.
Real Ale. Restaurant.
Children welcome. Dogs on leads.
Parking available.

CHEAPSIDE

The Thatched Tavern   Tel: 01344 20874

Cheapside Road, Ascot SL5 7QG
Greene King. Robert King, Johnathan Mee, licensees.

Handy for the Guards Polo club in Windsor Great Park or a brisk walk around
Virginia water. No longer thatched, but inside you still have low ceilings,
beams, flagstone floors, an inglenook fireplace and a general feel of well
being. A huge blackboard menu lists everything from a sandwich and home-
made soup to steak and kidney pudding, fish (various) and vegetarian
dishes. Proper puds too. Greene King ales and a choice of wines. Seats
outside on the sheltered lawn.

OPEN: 12–3. 6–11.
Real Ale. Restaurant. Bar meals and snacks lunchtime only.
Children, not in the bar. No dogs.
Car park.

COOKHAM

Bell & The Dragon   Tel: 01628 521263

High Street, Cookham Village, Berks SL6 9SQ
Free House. Mr Malcolm Tall & Pam Bader O.B.E. licensees.

Licensed since the 15th century, the Bell was established as a house of
refreshment for people attending Cookham Church, parts of which date
back to 1040. Inside are three rooms, one of which is no-smoking. Lots of
beams and a friendly atmosphere. Bar food – served in the lounge bar –
includes sandwiches, quiche, toasties, omelettes, steak & kidney pie and
other hot dishes – all home- made. Full meals are served in the restaurant,
in which, it is important to note, there is MUSIC. Brakspears ale, tapped from
the cask. Choice of wines. Seats in the garden and on the terrace. The
Stanley Spencer Gallery is virtually opposite and well worth a visit.

OPEN: 11–2.30. 6–10.30 (11 Sat)
Real Ale. Restaurant closed Sun eve. Sandwiches only.
Children welcome. Dogs on leads in bar only.
Wheelchair access to the pub.

CRAZIES HILL

Horns Tel: 01734 401416

Crazies Hill, Wargrave, Berks. RG10 8LY
Brakspears. Andy & Clare Hearn, tenants.

Originally a Tudor hunting lodge – the stags' antlers are still above the front door! It's a friendly country pub, white painted with beams outside, inside more beams and big open fires. Typical lunchtime menu includes filled rolls, soup, salads, pasta and other hot dishes which vary daily. Meals are served in the restaurant on Friday and Saturday evenings. For the rest of the week evenings are devoted to conversation, pub games and a friendly drink. Brakspears ales and lots of malt whiskies. Good choice of wines. Lucky them, the Horns has a big garden of several acres.

OPEN: 11–2.30 (3 Sats). 5.30–11.
Real Ale. Lunchtime food only. No food Sun or Mon. Brasserie meals Friday and Saturday evenings – Must book.
Children in pub barn. Dogs on leads.
Live Music Mon eves.

FINCHAMPSTEAD

Queen's Oak Tel: 01734 734855

Church Lane, Finchampstead. RG40 4LS
Brakspear. Raymond Barker, tenant.

The Romans hung around here for quite some time. The Roman road which passes through this area is known as the Devil's Highway – and, no, I haven't found out why. Next to the parish church of St. James, the origins of this old pub go back into the mists of time. One of its walls has been dated as 17th century, but apparently there has been a drinking house on the site since the Romans. The pub also boasts the oldest non-smoking bar in Berkshire. Good traditional bar food: sea food platter, ham and chips, a fish dish or two, but you would really come here for the speciality of the house – pizzas. Brakspears range of ales – Bitter, Special and Old.

OPEN: 11.30–2.30. 6–11. (12–3. 6.30–11 Sat).
Real Ale
Children in garden only, along with the dogs on leads.
Barbecues in the summer.

FRILSHAM

Pot Kiln   Tel: 01635 201366

Frilsham, Nr Hermitage, Berks. RG16 0XX
Free House. Philip Gent, licensee.

It's unspoilt, old-fashioned, tucked away down a country lane, and popular
with the locals and passing ramblers. No counter, just a hatch for your
orders in the tiny entrance hall. A good fire keeps the customers warm in
winter and a simple bar menu sustains them. Home-made soup, filled rolls,
ploughmans and daily specials. Ales are: Morlands Original, Old Speckled
Hen, Brick Kiln, made for the Pot Kiln by Dave Madds at the back of the pub
and Arkells BBB. Tables in the big, sheltered garden. Good walks nearby.

OPEN: 12–2.30. 6.30–11.
Real Ale. Limited food Sun & Tues.
Children in dining room. Dogs on leads.
Live Music 3rd Sun of month.

HOLYPORT

Belgian Arms   Tel: 01628 34468

Holyport Street, Holyport, Maidenhead, Berks. SL6 2JR
Brakspears. Alfred Morgan, tenant.

To give meaning to this pub's name, illustrations of Belgian army uniforms
and other military prints adorn the low-ceilinged bar. The pub has a dining
area in the conservatory, used as an overflow for the busy lunchtime trade.
Bar food includes sandwiches, plain and toasted, pizzas with various
toppings, ham and eggs and other daily specials. Brakspears ales and
several malt whiskies are available. Seats in the garden overlook the pond
and village green.

OPEN: 11–3. 5.30–11 (6 Sat)
Real Ale. No food Sun eve.
Children in restaurant. Dogs on leads.

CHRISTMAS

Pub opening times at Christmas can vary. Some don't open at all. A
few open all day, while others open at mid-day only. If you plan to visit
one at Christmas, check by calling them on the telephone.

KINTBURY

Dundas Arms   Tel: 01488 658263

53 Station Road, Kintbury, Nr Newbury, Berks. RG17 9UT
Free House. David A Dalzell Piper, licensee.

A pub for over 200 years, the Dundas Arms enjoys an enviable situation by
the Kennett & Avon Canal. Its attractive terrace is very popular during the
summer and the dining room overlooks the canal. The menu reflects the skill
and enthusiasm of the owner/chef who offers a three course luncheon menu
and an à la carte dinner. But you can eat less ambitiously in the small bar:
fish soup with croutons, crab au gratin, paté, potted duck with sweet red
pepper relish, home cured gravadlax with mustard and dill sauce and potted
shrimps. A wide variety of wines from the cellar. Morlands Bitter and Charles
Wells Bombardier are the permanent ales; Hampshire Ironside, Morlands Old
Speckled Hen and Ushers Spring Fever are the guests.

OPEN: 11–2.30. 6–11.
Real Ale. Restaurant
Children to stay. No dogs.
Bedrooms.

KNOWL HILL

Seven Stars   Tel: 01628 822967

Knowl Hill, Berks RG10 9UR
Brakspear. Robin & Lyn Jones, tenants.

There is a picture in the saloon bar showing the Seven Stars as it was before
the imposition of the Window Tax in the early 18th Century. The Tax caused
many a building to change radically in appearance: to reduce the tax bill,
inessential windows were blocked up. The Seven Stars, one of the oldest
licensed houses on the Old Bath Road, was thought to have started out as
a hunting lodge in what was then part of Windsor Forest. It was the haunt
of several notorious highwaymen who found travellers on the Bath Road a
very profitable target. Welcoming and friendly, the pub has beams, panelling,
log fires and traditional furnishings. Bar food ranges from sandwiches,
ploughmans and vegetarian dishes to daily specials. Brakspears ales;
choice of wines. Seats in the large garden. Go on the right night and you
may be lucky enough to see one of the four ghosts said the haunt the area.

You have the choice of a headless woman, a white lady, a white dog and last, but not least, a phantom horseman.

OPEN: 11–2.30. 5–11. (12–3. 7–10.30 Sun)
Real Ale.
Children welcome. Dogs on leads.

MAIDENHEAD

Hand & Flowers   Tel: 01628 23800

15 Queen Street, Maidenhead, Berks SL6 1NB
Brakspear. Jane Page Warner & Keith Warner, tenant.

A small, one-bar Victorian pub in the middle of the town. Very popular at lunchtime; all the food is home-made: spicy sausage casserole, roast beef and other dishes, sandwiches have up to thirty three different fillings, eight more than last year. Very imaginative. They also make a point of not serving any frozen food, chips or jacket potatoes. The well kept beers are Brakspears Bitter, Special and Old.

OPEN: 11–3. 5–11.
Real Ale.
Dogs most welcome, with well behaved owners.

READING

Sweeney & Todd   Tel: 01734 586466

10 Castle Street, (off St. Mary's Butts) Reading, Berkshire
Free House. Mrs June Hayward, licensee.

A small pub at the back of a pie shop. You have a choice of a vaste range of home-made pies with adventurous fillings. Exceptionally busy at lunchtimes. As our researcher said "until I discovered the Sweeney and Todd, we had to return home for lunch, now we know where to have a bar snack and beer." Wadworths 6X, Adnams Bitter, Eldridge Pope Royal Oak and a guest beer.

OPEN: 11–10.30
Real Ale
No children. No dogs.

WEST END

Plough   Tel: 01734 340015

Plough Lane, West End, Waltham St. Lawrence, Twyford, Berks, RG10
09R. Badger. John Dowsett, lease.

Well over 400 years old, The Plough was originally a keeper's cottage for
Windsor Great Park. Low ceilings but no beams. Just as well as if there
were, the landlord, who at 6ft is only fractionally shorter than the ceiling
would have to remember to " bend-ze- kneez." A small rural local with a a
good restaurant seating 25. Wide ranging menu from basic pub grub to
steak au poivre, T-bone steaks, mixed grills, steak and kidney pie, fresh fish
every day – depending on what is available – and about 30 specials, all
home-made. The Badger range of ales including their new Best Bitter –
Dempseys. Charles Wells Eagle is the current guest. Extensive wine list –
Australian and other New World wines plus some excellent Riojas. Two acres
of garden, which is kept as a garden – not a play area for children. This pub
advertises itself as a quiet pub. People go there because it doesn't have
musak. "If you haven't the art of conversation, don't bother to come".

OPEN: 12–2.30. 6 –11. (12–3. 7–10.30 Sun).
Real Ale
Children in garden and restaurant only. Dogs in garden on leads.
Four well-marked walks.

WOKINGHAM

Queens Head   Tel: 01734 781221

23, The Terrace, Wokingham, RG40 1BP (at the top of station road)
Morlands. Jacqui Taylor, licensee.

This delightful old pub dates back to 1430. Small, with one bar, low ceilings
and beams. The one room boasts two fireplaces, but because of fire
regulations the pub is denied a real fire – you get fake flames instead.
Traditional bar food menu – ploughmans, filled jacket potatoes, basket
meals; specials Monday to Friday. Morlands IPA, Old Masters, Old Speckled
Hen, Tanners Jack and one guest ale. At the back of the pub are eight picnic
tables in a big walled garden, also a couple of tables at the front so you can
watch the world go by.

OPEN: 11–3, 5.30–11
Real Ale
Children in garden only. Dogs welcome.

WOKINGHAM WITHOUT

Crooked Billet Tel: 01734 780438

Honey Hill, Wokingham, Berks. RG40 3BJ.
Brakspears. Mr. G. Ill and Mrs P.K. Jack tenants.

On the rural edge of Wokingham, the Crooked Billet – originally a private house – has been licensed for the last 130 years. Low beamed ceilings, and a real fire. (You obviously have to be "without" Wokingham to have a fire – see above). Plenty of room for eating and drinking. A choice from any of the menus – à la carte, table d'hôte, bar menu and the two specials board can be eaten anywhere in the pub including the no-smoking restaurant. Lots to choose from – anything from soup to a fillet steak, home-made pies, curries, pastas, various fish dishes, vegetarian meals and puds. Brakspears range of ales, and two guests: Theakstons and Boddingtons. Seats in the garden.

OPEN: 11–11
Real Ale. Restaurant.
Children in restaurant and garden. Dogs in bar and garden.
Ample car parking.

YATTENDON

Royal Oak Tel: 01635 201325

The Square, Yattendon, Nr Newbury, Berks. RG16 0UF
Free House. Paul Marshall, manager.

This popular creeper-clad pub – with its pretty panelled bar and comfortable lounge with big log fire – has gained a reputation for serving high quality, imaginative food. Home-made soups, poached mussels in creamy garlic and chive sauce, spicy vegetable and mushroom ravioli, and patés, complement the daily specials and home-made pies. Wadworths 6X, Ruddles Best are on hand pump. Normally the attractive garden is reserved for residents, but comes into general use as the bar overflow in summer.

OPEN: 12–3. 6.30–11.
Real Ale. No-smoking restaurant. Closed Sun eve.
Children welcome. Dogs on leads.

B
BUCKINGHAMSHIRE

AMERSHAM

Kings Arms   Tel: 01494 726333

30 High Street, Old Amersham, Bucks HP7 DJ0
Free House. John Jennison, licensee.

Old Amersham High Street is a wonderful mix of Georgian houses, timbered inns and old courtyards leading to thatched cottages. Along the High Street you'll find the black and white timbered Kings Arms. A film star in its own right. That was the outside of The Kings Arms you saw in Four Weddings and a Funeral, pretending, as all good film stars do, to be something else, namely "The Lucky Boatman". Behind the floral displays you'll find a 15th century inn; originally two separate timber-framed open hall houses; still with a wealth of beams, supporting timbers, inglenook fireplaces and lots of little nooks and crannies. Traditional bar snacks – maybe mushroom and tarragon soup, ploughmans, filled baguettes, sandwiches, garlic mushrooms, Caesar salad, spicey lamb and salad in pitta bread, a choice of pasta dishes, daily specials on the blackboard and no chips; you can even order from the restaurant menu if you are really pushing the boat out. They do cream teas too. Greene King IPA, Benskins Bitter and Ind Coope Burton. Wines by the glass. Seats in the flowery courtyard or on the lawn.

OPEN: 11–11 (12–3. 7–10.30 Sun)
Real Ale. Restaurant.
Children welcome, they have their own area. Dogs on leads.
Car park.

BEACONSFIELD

Greyhound   Tel: 01494 673823

33 Windsor End, Beaconsfield, Bucks, HP9 2JN
Freehouse. Jaimie Godrich, licensee.

Situated on a tree lined road opposite the parish church at the older end of

Beaconsfield near the old coaching road. The Greyhound – thought to date back to the 15th century and originally to be a drovers pub – is all you would expect. Unspoilt, with low ceilings, beams, open fires and loads of atmosphere; two bars and a restaurant, both serving reliable and interesting food. Quite a large choice ranging from a sandwich to elaborate fish, steak and chicken dishes, home-made pies and a daily changing blackboard menu. Courage Best, Wadworths 6X and Fullers London Pride; two guest ales change weekly. No children during the week. They like dogs, "part of a pub" says the landlord. Absolutely. Seats in the garden. Good walks, once you've crossed the motorway!

OPEN: 11–3. 6.30–11
Real Ale. Restaurant.
Children Sat. and Sun. lunchtime only. Dogs on leads.

BEACONSFIELD

Old Hare   Tel: 01494 673380

41 Aylesbury End, Beaconsfield, Bucks HP9 1LU.
Allied. Neil Whittle, manager. Neil Burgess, asst manager.

This rambling old pub dates back to 1707, though it is believed to be even older than that. Pictures of hares (what else?), photographs and prints of the pub decorate the rooms. Interestingly varied food with daily specials on the blackboard; home-made puddings. The beers are well kept and include Ind Coope Burton, Benskins Best, Tetleys Yorkshire and guest beers. Selection of whiskies and house wines. There is a large sunny garden.

OPEN: 11–11. (12–10.30 Sun)
Real Ale. No food after 5 Sun.
Children in eating area. Dogs on leads.
Occasional Morris Dancing.

BELLINGDON

The Bull   Tel: 01494 758163

Bellingdon Road, Bellingdon, Bucks HP5 2XU
Pubmaster. John Welford, tenant.

An attractive brick, cottagey pub dating back to the 16th century. Between Chesham and Tring, The Bull actually was a cottage – well, farm cottages actually – and has been licensed for about 170 years. Only one room with the bar at the end, typical of its age: low, beamy ceilings and a large inglenook fireplace. Food is important here, but locals are catered for, and you can still enjoy your pint. Bar snacks are limited to the ploughmans variety, but the blackboard menu will list lots of fresh fish, steaks, pan fried tuna with cajun spices, vegetarian dishes, moussaka etc. Burton Ale, Benskins Best Bitter and Tetleys. Wines by the glass. Seats in the large garden.

OPEN: 12–3. 6–11
Real Ale
Children welcome, so are dogs.

BLEDLOW

Lions of Bledlow   Tel: 01844 343345

Church End, Bledlow, Bucks. GP27 9PE
Free House. F J McKeown, licensee.

Ideally situated in good walking country; in fact, all the best used tracks seem to converge on this sixteenth century pub, making it an ideal place to start or finish a long walk. In summer you can relax on the sheltered terrace and admire the views; in winter, warm yourself by the fire in the comfortable beamed bars. On the menu are home-made soup, filled rolls, steak pie, some fish dishes and daily specials. John Smiths, Courage Best, Marstons Pedigree and Wadworths 6X ales on hand pump.

OPEN: 11–3. 6–11.
Real Ale. No food Sun eve. Restaurant open Wed–Sat eves.
Children in side room & restaurant. Dogs on leads.

BOLTER END

Peacock   Tel: 01494 881417

Lane End, Bolter End, Bucks. HP14 3LU
Allied. Peter Hodges, lease.

Located opposite the common, the 17th Century Peacock is popular, friendly and traditionally furnished. The imaginative bar food ranges from ploughmans, with a choice of interesting cheeses, to Aberdeen Angus steaks, home-made Peacock pie, (no, not real peacocks!) and daily specials.

The poultry is free range. Fresh fish on Fridays. Roast Angus Beef on Sundays. Quite a choice of puds and Dorset Farm cheeses to finish. Brakspears Bitter, Wadworths 6X, Tetleys and ABC Bitter are complemented by guest beers and a good choice of wines. Seats in the garden during summer.

OPEN: 11.45–2.30. 6–11.
Real Ale. No food Sun eve.
No children. Dogs on leads.

CHALFONT ST. PETER

Greyhound   Tel: 01753 883404

High Street, Nr. Chalfont St Peter, Bucks. SL9 9RA
Courage. John Harriman, lease.

Named The Greyhound in 1490, this creeper-covered old coaching inn is actually a century older than its name. Inside are low beams, dark panelling and a big log fire. Bar food ranges from sandwiches to filled baked potatoes and a choice of three roasts from the carvery. Part of the restaurant is no-smoking. John Smiths, Marstons Pedigree, Courage Best and Directors, Ruddles County and Wadworths 6X. There are seats in the courtyard at the front of the pub and on the grass by the river.

OPEN: 11–11.
Real Ale. No food Sun eve.
Children in eating area & restaurant. Dogs on leads.

COLESHILL

Red Lion   Tel: 01494 727020

Village Road, Coleshill, Bucks. HP7 0LN
Allied Lyons. Christine & John Ullman, lessees.

Tucked away down a country lane about two miles from Amersham, The Red Lion – which at first glance looks like a 1930's villa – is very popular with all age groups, not only for its well kept beers, but also for its reliable bar food: freshly made sandwiches, ploughmans, salads (real ham – off the bone), creamed sardines on toast, daily specials such as chicken and mushroom pie, meatballs in red wine and tomato sauce and salmon quiche. There will be a roast on Sundays. Good selection of puddings. Flowers IPA,

Tetleys and Fullers London Pride, and sometimes Morrells Oxford ales. Some wines by the glass. Tables at the front of the pub in summer and barbecues in the garden at the back.

OPEN: 11–3.30. 5.30–11 (11–11 Sat).
Real Ale. Only bar snacks Sun eve.
Children welcome. Dogs on leads.

FINGEST

Chequers   Tel: 01491 638335

Fingest, Nr Henley-on-Thames, Bucks. RG9 6QD
Brakspears. Bryan Heasman, tenant.

In winter there's a huge log fire warming up this attractive 15th century brick and flint village pub. The comfortable lounge has French windows leading into the garden, which has a lovely view of the Hambleden valley. You can eat in a small no-smoking room and the popular bar food ranges from: sandwiches and soup to freshly caught trout, steaks, salmon and vegetarian dishes. A more ambitious menu features in the restaurant. Brakspears PA, SB and Old Ale. Varied wine list, some by the glass. Seats in the flowery garden. This is a good walking area.

OPEN: 11–3. 6–11. (12–3. 7–10.30. Sun).
Real Ale. No food Sun eve.
Children in eating areas. Dogs in garden only.

FORD

Dinton Hermit   Tel: 01296 748379

Ford, Nr Aylesbury, Bucks. HP17 8XH
Free House. John & Jane Tompkins, licensees.

The hermit was a local man who lived at Dinton Hall. He was clerk to one of the Judges who was responsible for condemning Charles I to death. The rest of his life was one of repentance for the part he played in the death of the King. Set in attractive countryside, this 15th century stone inn is a busy local, attractive not only for its well kept ales but for the above average home-cooked food. Soups, sandwiches, saucy mushrooms, kidneys in cognac sauce, chicken curry, veggy hotpot, choice of salads, a very popular asparagus omelette, fruit pies and a special bread pudding. There is a greater choice of fish and grills in the evening. (You must book). ABC Best Bitter, Adnams and Wadworths 6X. Lovely views of the surrounding countryside from here and lots of walks nearby.

OPEN: 11–2.30. 6–11.
Real Ale. No food Sun or Mon, nor for three weeks in July.
Well behaved children welcome. No dogs.

FORTY GREEN

Royal Standard of England   Tel: 01494 673382

Forty Green, Nr Beaconsfield, Bucks. HP9 1XT.
Free House. Philip Eldridge and Peter & Gill Carroll, licensees.

Renamed in 1651 when Charles II, fleeing after the battle of Worcester, hid in the pub rafters to escape the Parliamentarians. Interesting interiors with splendid oak panelling, fireplaces and magnificent oak beams. There is a splendid buffet of cooked ham, beef, turkey, salmon and various salads, pies, quiches and a choice of hot dishes. All the bread is home-baked. Marstons Pedigree and Owd Roger (originally brewed at the Inn), Morlands Old Speckled Hen and regular guest beers. Good choice of malt and Irish whiskies; also fruit wines.

OPEN: 11–3. 5.30–11.
Real Ale.
Children in eating area. No dogs.

FRIETH

Prince Albert   Tel: 01494 881683

Mores End, Nr Henley-on-Thames, RG9 6PX.
Brakspears. Frank & Joss Reynolds, licensees.

Surrounded by attractive, wooded country with lots of wonderful walks, this tiny, 250 year old pub has built a reputation for serving quality bar food. Brown rolls with lots of different fillings, ham and eggs and other hot dishes – really good well-made food. Brakspears Bitter, Special, Mild and Old on handpump. Good choice of wines and decent whiskies.

OPEN: 11–3. 5.30–11. Mon opens half an hour later.
Real Ale. Food available lunchtime only.
No children. Dogs on leads.

GREAT HAMPDEN

Hampden Arms   Tel: 01494 488255

Great Hampden, Nr. Great Missenden, Bucks HP16 9RQ
Free House. Terry and Barbara Matthews, licensees.

An interesting note for all you collectors – as am I – of useless information;
Hampden House, on the Hampden estate, used to be owned by Hammer
films, who made all those horror movies there. The quite normal Hampden
Arms, opposite the common, is over 400 years old and the first licensee was
the Earl of Buckingham. Two rooms, one with the bar. You can eat and drink
in both – that's if you can find the space. Standing room only in summer. You
must book if you want to sit and eat inside. Outside there are lots of tables,
so hope the weather is fine if you hit a busy period. Over 50 main courses
to choose from – so there should be something for everyone – plus a range
of starters and snacks. Abundance all round. You can start with avocado
Tahiti, hot Norwegian salad – scrambled egg with smoked salmon served
with salad and French bread or devilled whitebait. Steak Diane or Duck
Moderne – breast of duck in a brandy and orange sauce and finish with
strawberry vacherin. Lots, lots more. Wadworths 6X, Greene King Abbot Ale,
Tetleys, Eldridge Pope Thomas Hardy and Addlestones draught cider.

OPEN: 12–3. 7–11. (12–10.30 Sun)
Real Ale
Children welcome. Dogs on leads.
Car Park. Wheelchair access.

GREAT KINGSHILL
Red Lion   Tel: 01494 711262

Missenden Rd, Great Kingshill, High Wycombe, Bucks HP15 6EB
Pubmaster. Pepe Cabrera, tenant.

More of a restaurant than a pub, as you will find when you go inside. All the
table are set for dining. Señor Cabrera is also the chef and his speciality is
lots and lots of fish – all sorts, from a fresh sardine to skate. You can be sure
the only relationship between the fish here and the fish from your average
fish and chip shop will be the word fish. Even the chips are properly made.
Ansells and Tetleys ales and wines by the glass.

OPEN: 12–3. 6–11 Closed Sun evening.
Real ale. Restaurant.
Children welcome. No Dogs.

GREAT MISSENDEN

Cross Keys   Tel: 01494 865373

40 High Street. Great Missenden, Bucks. HP16 0AU
A143 Wendover to Amersham Road.
Fullers. R. Martin Ridler, licensee.

Two bars in this 500 year old High Street local, full of antiques, which, according to the landlord, includes him. It has a good range of snacks at lunchtime – soups, seafood pasta, salads and daily specials from the blackboard. When we spoke to the landlord, he was thinking of giving his menu an Italian accent. Whatever he had decided by the time you get there, you can at least be sure that the quality of food will be as reliable as ever. In the evening food is served in the bistro/dining room and not in the bar. Fullers complete range of ales, no guests. Picnic tables on the terrace.

OPEN: 11–3. 5.30–11.
Real Ale. Restaurant.
Children at the landlord's discretion. Dogs on leads in bar.

GREAT MISSENDEN

George   Tel: 01494 862084

94 High Street, Great Missenden, Bucks HP16 0BG.
Greenalls. Guy & Sally Smith, tenants.

A pleasing pub that was built towards the end of the 15th century as a hospice for the nearby Abbey. Listed Grade II, the bars still have their original heavily beamed ceilings. Home-made soup, deep fried mushrooms and steak and kidney pies are just a few of the dishes on the menu. Adnams, Wadworths 6X and two guest beers. Sangria in summer and mulled wine in winter. They have a lovely large garden.

OPEN: 11–11.
Real Ale. Food served all day. No-smoking restaurant.
Children in eating areas. Dogs on leads.
Bedrooms.

HEDGERLEY

One Pin   Tel: 01753 643035

One Pin Lane, Farnham Common, SL2 3RD
Courage. Doug Spence, licensee.

Built on a slope, Hedgerley is a pretty, well kept village. The One Pin is full of treasures, among them the customers, says the daughter of the house. A traditional two bar pub dating back to 1760, and still with the original cow-hair plaster ceiling between the beams in the saloon bar. Usual, reliable bar food is served Monday to Saturday. Courage Best and Directors, no guest beer. Seats in the garden. Good walks nearby.

OPEN: 11–3.30. 5.30–11.
Real Ale
Well behaved children away from the bar. Dogs in public bar.

HEDGERLEY

White Horse   Tel: 01753 643225

Village Lane, Hedgerley Village, Nr. Slough, SL2 3UY
Free House. Jess Hobbs, landlord/licensee.

At the end of the village, behind the window boxes, you'll find this attractive 14th century village pub. It retains the original small public bar and a larger lounge bar. Home-cooked food, a hot and cold bar menu. A refrigerated cold tray keeps the salads fresh. Hot food could include steak and mushroom pie, chilli, fish pie, quiches and some chicken dishes – the menu changes. Eight or nine ales: Greene King IPA and Rayments Special Bitter and Charles Wells Eagle are permanent: the others change from week to week. Lovely views from the big garden. Good walks nearby.

OPEN: 11–3. 5.30–11.
Real Ale.
Children and dogs allowed in the garden.

LITTLE MISSENDEN

Crown   Tel: 01494 862571

Little Missenden, Nr. Amersham, HP7 0RD
Free House. Trevor How, licensee.

So many of these charming Buckinhamshire pubs were cottages in their previous lives, including The Crown. Owned by the same family for about 70 years, they believe it was already a pub when they bought it. Dating back to the 17th century, it has just one bar decorated with old farm implements. Snack menu at lunchtime – simple home-made food, steak and kidney pies, salads, ploughmans, sandwiches – that sort of thing. Morrells Varsity and Hook Norton Best Bitter. Adnams Broadside could be the guest beer. The River Misbourne runs along the bottom of the garden, eventually flowing into Shardloes Lake.

OPEN: 11–2.30. 6–11. (12–2.30. 7–10.30 Sun).
Real Ale.
No children. Dogs on leads.

LITTLEWORTH COMMON

Blackwood Arms   Tel: 01753 642169

Common Lane, Littleworth Common, Bucks. SL1 8PP.
Freehouse. Colin & Valerie Whale, licensees.

This is a beer drinkers' paradise – over 1000 ales last year. Every Friday there are approximately 16 different beers to try, and two days to sober up! To soak up this embarras de richesses, there is a good choice of home-made food: filled rolls, omelettes, home-cured ham, steak and ale pies etc. Evening extras could include lamb aux fines herbes and salmon in champagne and cream sauce. There is always a Sunday roast. Among the beers you may try are Black Sheep Special, Hambleton, Mauldons Black Adder, Orkney Skull Splitter and Woodfordes Nelson's Revenge. Belgian beers, farm ciders and a choice of malt whiskies. Good head-clearing country walks nearby.

OPEN: 11–2.30. 5.30–11. (Fri & Sat 11–11)
Real Ale, lots of it!
Children if well behaved. Dogs on leads.

MARLOW

Clayton Arms   Tel:01628 478620

Quioting Square, 16, Oxford Road, Marlow, Bucks SL7 2NL
Brakspear. Ron and Rita Green.

A little gem of a pub, which used to be the stop-over for waggon loads of chairs from the local furniture industry (a Chair Museum just outside High Wycombe gives you all the history). Horses were stabled overnight and the load left in the yard before being taken to the railway stations at Maidenhead or Reading. The courtway arch into the old stable yard had to be raised to accomodate the high loads. Now, a quiet peaceful pub." No music or bandits" says our informant, "though it does get very lively on Sunday mornings when the dominoes, cards and darts appear"! Brakspear Mild,Bitter Old and Special.

OPEN: 11–2.30. 5.30–11. (11–3. 6–11 Sat. 12–3.30. 7–10.30 Sun)
Real Ale.
Children not in front bar. Dogs welcome.

MARSH GIBBON

Greyhound   Tel: 01869 277365

Marsh Gibbon, Nr Bicester, Ox/Bucks. OX6 0HA.
Free House. Richard Kaim, licensee.

Four hundred years old, extended two hundred and fifty years ago, this old stone pub has seen some changes in its lifetime. Now, someone with a love of Thai cooking is orchestrating the food and it has become a favourite meeting place for those interested in South East Asian food. There are a few traditional bar snacks, but you will be more likely to find spring rolls or spare ribs in a special sauce, chicken satay, beef in oyster sauce and entrecote teriyaki than anything else. Fullers London Pride, Greene King Abbot and IPA, Hook Norton Best and McEwans 80/- on handpump. Seats in the pretty small front garden – more room at the back.

OPEN: 12–3. 6–11.
Real Ale.
Children if well behaved. No dogs.

NORTHEND

White Hart   Tel: 01491 638353

Northend, Henley-on-Thames. RG9 6LE.
Brakspears. Derek Passey, tenant.

Still a foody pub, the emphasis here being on the quality of the food, but if
you just want a drink and bar snack you will be more than welcome. An
attractive 16th century inn with low ceilings, panelling and a big log fire. Just
before we went to press we learnt that there was a change of tenant. We
only had time to be told that the pub will be run much as before, "only
posher". So...I'm sure you'll let us know. Brakspear PA, SB, Old and Mild
beers on handpump. Bound to be a new wine list too – you can't cook
wonderful food without offering wine. Lots of walks in the beech woods.

OPEN: 11.30–2.30. 6–11 (6.30 winter)
Real Ale. No food Sun eve.
Children in eating area. Dogs on leads (if pub not too busy).

SKIRMETT

Old Crown   Tel: 01491 638435

Skirmett, Nr Henley-on-Thames RG9 6TD.
Brakspears. Peter Mumby, tenant.

A charming 17th century village pub. Three heavily beamed rooms, all of
which are non-smoking; open fires, lots of paintings, antiques and
interesting bric-a-brac. The pub does get extremely busy so you need to
book to be sure of a table in the evenings and at weekends. All the food is
home-made, from soups, steak, kidney and mushroom pie, poached
Scottish salmon with a prawn and dill sauce, to fresh sea bass. Beer from
the barrel is served through a hatch: Brakspear PA and SB. Moderately
priced wines. Pretty flower tubs on the terrace. There are seats in the garden
which has a fish pond.

OPEN: 11–2.30. 6–11. Closed Mon except Bank Holiday Mondays.
Real Ale
No children under 10. No dogs.

WEST WYCOMBE

George & Dragon   Tel: 01494 464414

West Wycombe, Nr High Wycombe, Bucks. HP14 3AB.
Courage. Philip Cass Todd, lease.

Dating back to the 15th century, this former coaching inn on the old London Oxford road was added to and modernised in 1720. Full of atmosphere, it has huge beams, sloping walls and big log fires. The ghost of a servant girl is reputed to haunt the handsome staircase. Well prepared food: soup, herby mushrooms, duck or pigeon pies, potted stilton, steaks, game from Wycombe Park and home-made puddings. Courage Best and two others chosen from Directors, Gales HSB, Ushers or Wadworths 6X. Good wine list and a selection of malt whiskies. Culture at West Wycombe Park (Hellfire Caves and all that!). Interesting walks nearby.

OPEN: 11–2.30. 5.30–11. 11–11 Sats.
Real Ale.
Children in own room. Dogs on leads.
Bedrooms.

C
CHESHIRE

BARTHOMLEY

White Lion

Tel: 01270 882242

Barthomley, Nr. Crewe, Cheshire CW2 5PG
Burtonwood. Terence Cartwright, proprietor.

The White Lion is an extremely attractive, thatched, timber-framed, early 17th Century inn. Opposite, is a 15th Century church where Robert Corke, who was landlord at the time of the Civil War, must have watched what has come to be recorded in history books as the Barthomley Massacre. According to the present landlord – Terry Cartright, who is the 19th since the pub was first licensed in 1614 – evidence discovered a year or two ago shows that the incident was blown up out of all proportion. The "massacre" was used for propaganda purposes preparatory to the trial of Charles I. The men smoked out of the bell-tower and severely beaten up were actually a bunch of contemporary "Skinheads" – rather than "Roundheads" – who had been hurling drunken abuse at a King's Troop. The White Lion's three beamed rooms, some with panelling and one with a bar, have not changed much in appearance over the centuries. The fare they offer today is undoubtedly as popular as it ever was. They serve very reasonably priced lunchtime food, including soups, filled French sticks, hot beef sandwiches, home-made hotpot, cheese and onion oatcakes or an open prawn sandwich. Saturday & Sunday: pies and rolls only, available. The pub gets very busy over weekends, but they can always find you a pie and a pint. Burtonwood Bitter, James Forshaws Bitter and Top Hat and Buccaneer on hand pump.

OPEN: 11.30–11. Closed Thurs lunchtime.
Real Ale. Lunchtime meals & snacks.
No children in main bar. Must be gone by 8.30. Dogs on leads.
Bedrooms.

CHESTER

Albion   Tel: 01244 340345

Park Street (off Newgate Street) Chester CH1 1RN
Free House. Michael Mercer, licensee.

The best preserved walled city in England. Medieval buildings, galleried streets, glorious Tudor houses and a magnificent cathedral make Chester one of the treasures of the country. Another little treasure is the Albion. Tucked under the city walls this friendly pub has some WW1 memorabilia including a collection of contemporary pictures. "A warmly eccentric landlord with an eccentric collection." Artifacts from the 40's and 50's too in the Edwardian style rooms. An interesting choice of bar food, "an inventive menu" says our researcher, " and no chips." Greenalls Mild and Original, Cains Bitter and Stones Bitter.

OPEN: Mon.11.30–3. 5.30–11. (11–3 5–11 Tues.Wed.Thurs. 11–11 Fri. 11.30–3. 6–11 Sat. 12.2.30. 7–10.30 Sun)
Real Ale
Children if well behaved. Dogs in public bar.

DELAMERE

Fishpool Inn   Tel: 01606 883277

Fishpool Road, Delamere, Nr Northwich, Cheshire. CW8 2HP
Greenalls. Richard & Maureen Lamb, tenants.

The name Delamere is taken from the Norman forest which used to cover much of Cheshire. The present forest is largely coniferous and man-made but very popular, as it has many marked paths for walkers. The fish pool is still there in the form of a pike-filled lake, which centuries ago was fished by the monks from the local abbey. This rambling, beamed old pub has probably been a centre great of activity for all its 300 years. Good wholesome bar food available: sandwiches, pies, Cumberland sausages, fresh salmon steaks, etc. Greenalls Bitter, Mild and Original on hand pump. Choice of wines.

OPEN: 11–3. 6–11.
Real Ale.
Children in eating area. No dogs.

GEE CROSS

Grapes Hotel   Tel: 0161 3682614

Stockport Road, Gee Cross, Hyde, Ches SK14 5RU
Robinsons. Brian Samuels, tenant.

On the bend of the steep hill in the old village of Gee Cross, opposite an imposing Victorian-Gothic (dissenting) church, the pub, a large, gabled and bay windowed building in the "Stockport" style of architecture, has leaded lights and engraved Edwardian windows. It has four large carpeted rooms with red ceilings, brass light fittings, and tiles from bar top to floor. Cheerful and friendly staff and customers. Robinsons traditional ales stocked, including Bitter and Best Mild. A bowling green is attached to the pub so you can while away the time encouraging the experts.

OPEN: 12–3. 5–11
Real Ale.
No children. No dogs.

HARTFORD

Hartford Hall   Tel: 01606 75711

81 School Lane, Hartford, Northwich, Cheshire CW8 1PW
Scottish & Newcastle. Livingston Evans, manager.

For those of you who like to know these things, towns ending in "wich" were salt producing towns. The salt from Northwich was initially shipped along the River Weaver, but after 1875 the boats were lifted, by a newly constructed hoist at Anderton, from the river to the Trent and Mersey canal. Hartford Hall, on the A556 between Northwich and the ancient walled city of Chester is a 16th century building, with additions; originally a manor house, later a nunnery. You can get a light lunch in the lounge bar: soup, a selection of sandwiches, ploughmans with ciabatta roll, or black pudding in a creamed whole – grain mustard sauce, deep fried popcorn prawns in a sweet and sour sauce, gammon steak in a Cumberland sauce, grilled swordfish with lemon mayonnaise, grilled steaks or vegetable curry with rice and pitta bread. If you want a full meal, there is an à la carte restaurant. Theakstons ales, Beamish stout and a fine wine list. There will be somewhere to sit in grounds of two acres.

OPEN: 12–2. 6–11
Real Ale. Restaurant.
Children welcome. Dogs on leads.
Bedrooms. Wheelchairs with help from staff.

HALEBARNS

Unicorn Hotel   Tel: 0161 980 4347

329 Hale Road, Hale Barns, Altrincham WA15 8SS
Hydes Anvil. George Davis, manager.

Another place that isn't sure where it is. Some think this is in Cheshire, others Greater Manchester. Not that it matters really except that Cheshire sounds more rural. Looking very smart – the Unicorn has been "done-up" – it is a comfortable, extended Hotel. Right on the road and only two miles from Manchester Airport. Very useful if you are coming or going. Bar, dining room. games room – even a conference room, but unless you want a conference, all you really want to know is that they have a good menu both in the bar and restaurant: roast beef, steak in ale and good curries, and you can get a drink. Hydes' Anvil – a family run Manchester Brewery – Mild and Bitter.

OPEN: 11.30–3. 5.30–11
Real Ale.
Children welcome. No dogs.

MOBBERLY

Bird in Hand   Tel: 01565 873149

Knowles Green Village, Mobberly, Cheshire WA16 7BW
Sam Smiths, Guy Richardson, licensee.

On the very edge of Mobberly, towards the wooded escarpment of Alderley Edge. Legend has it that knights on white horses wait in the Wizard cave for the call to save the country – we may well need them! But before you go to search them out, prepare yourself by stopping off at The Bird in Hand. Behind the hanging baskets are four rambling rooms, one bar, lots of sitting areas and a non-smoking room upstairs. Standard bar menu features hot sandwiches, welsh rarebit, scampi, steak and ale pie, fish and chips, vegetarian dishes and steaks. From the specials board there could be a lamb and mushroom curry, duck in orange sauce, liver and bacon and a 'dinghy' which is an enormous Yorkshire pudding. Samuel Smiths range of ales – no guests. Lots of malt whiskies. Good country walks nearby.

OPEN: 11–11
Real Ale
Children in eating area. Dogs on leads.

SMALLWOOD

Blue Bell Inn   Tel: 01477 500262

Smallwood, Nr Congleton, Cheshire
Greenalls. Robert Slack, tenant.

Situated off the beaten track in lovely countryside is the black & white 16th century Bluebell Inn. Open log fires in the beamed bar and lounge, a room for children, and a very attractive garden. Bar food is limited, but there is always soup and a sandwich or two. Greenalls Ales and a selection of malt whiskies.

OPEN: 11–11. Pub closed Mon lunchtime.
Real Ale.
No Children. Dogs on leads.

SUTTON

Ryles Arms   Tel: 01260 252244

Hollin Lane, Higher Sutton, Nr Macclesfield, Ches. SK11 0NN
Free House. Frank Campbell, licensee.

The landlord tells us that he threw out piped music many years ago and certainly nobody has missed it since. Food is important here; more a dining pub now, though you are still welcome to drop in for a drink and a little something from the bar menu. Traditional bar food: soups, sandwiches, ploughmans, potted shrimps, herrings in sour cream, chicken and mushroom pie, seafood platter, roast duckling with orange sauce, salads, chicken curry, steak & kidney pie and much more. Specials on the blackboard. Puds too. Part of the dining area is non-smoking and there is also a no-smoking family room. Ruddles Best, County, Marstons Pedigree and John Smiths on hand pump, plus a guest beer. Seats on the terrace and in the garden.

OPEN: 11.30–3. 7–11.
Real Ale.
Children in family room until 8. No dogs.

WINCLE

Ship   Tel: 01260 227217

Wincle, Nr Macclesfield, Cheshire SK11 0QE
Free House. Andrew Harmer & Penelope Hinchcliffe, licensees.

Thought to be one of the oldest pubs in Cheshire, The Ship was renamed in 1911 after Shackleton's Antarctic-Expedition. His ship – Nimrod – is depicted in the pub sign. Deep in the lovely Cheshire countryside, this comfortable old pub offers a good range of bar food: from soup, sandwiches, grilled trout, steaks to Venison casserole. Fresh fish Wednesday and Thursday, and they do a very popular gammon and eggs. Brown bread & butter ice cream. The house speciality is fondue bourgignon. Titanic Bitter from Burslem and a changing guest beer on hand pump. Selection of wines. Good walking country.

OPEN: 12–3. 7–11. Closed Mon Nov–March
Real Ale.
Well behaved children in family room. Dogs on leads.

C
CORNWALL

CONSTANTINE

Trengilly Wartha Tel: 01326 40332

Nancenoy Constantine, Nr Helston, Cornwall TR11 5RP
Free House. Nigel Logan & Michael Maguire, licensees.

Situated in a valley close to the Helford River, this charming old farmhouse has only been licensed since 1950. The unusual pub name means the settlement above the trees. The farmhouse, now the pub, dates back to the 18th century. There is one low beamed main bar, lounge, an eating area off the bar and a no-smoking family conservatory. A pretty garden, with picnic tables during the summer. Lots of home-made bar food: soups, home-made garlic bread, smoked fish platter, locally smoked ham with other cold meats and pickles, ploughmans with home-made pickles, salads and daily specials from the blackboard which usually features lots of fish dishes, maybe rabbit pie, lamb meatballs with curried lentils and other dishes; don't forget the delicious puds. There is also an imaginative restaurant menu. Furgusons Dartmoor Best, Exmoor Ale, Cotleigh, Butcombe and Sharp's Cornish Coaster or Doom Ale; other guests from the small independent breweries. Ciders, big selection of malt whiskies, and good choice of wines by the bottle or glass.

OPEN: 11–2.30. 6–11 (6.30 in winter).
Real Ale. Restaurant.
Children welcome. Dogs on leads.
Bedrooms. Occasional live music.

FALMOUTH

Seven Stars Tel: 01326 312111

1 The Moor, Falmouth, Cornwall. TR11 3QA
Free House. The Rev. Barrington-Bennett, licensee

The ancient port and leading holiday resort of Falmouth is in a splendid setting; walk along the spectacular cliffs with views of the wooded countryside and you will appreciate the fine natural harbour, deep enough for big ships to moor inland as far as King Harry Ferry. Falmouth was, for 200 years, the first port of call and the last stopping place for all Atlantic shipping. After appreciating the glorious surroundings you can make your way to The Seven Stars, a blissfully quiet pub. Built in 1660, it has been in the landlord's family since 1873. The Rev. Barrington-Bennett, who was ordained into the Anglican Church four years ago, is the last of the line. His son is following his own career as a press photographer. No food except for a Cornish pastie or two. Draught Bass and Sharp's Own from the cask. Tables on the forecourt.

OPEN: 11–3. 6–11
Real Ale
No children, Dogs in the back bar.

GUNWHALLOE

The Helzephron   Tel: 01326 240406

Gunwalloe, Helston, Cornwall, TR12 7QB
Free House. Harry & Angela Thomas, licensees.

Gunwhalloe is on a narrow lane, south of Helston towards Church Cove; the pub's Cornish name means "hell cliffs". Everything points to the fact that this area had more than a nodding aquaintance with the smuggling and wrecking that went on in the past. Much of the wood in this solidly built, 500 year-old stone pub comes from ships that were wrecked in the waters below. Very popular, it is packed to the gunnels during the season, not only for its well kept beers but food which is above the ordinary. One menu for both the bar and the no-smoking restaurant, ranges from the usual pub favourites to home-cooked dishes: good soups, sandwiches, ploughmans, paté, vegetarian dishes and specials from the daily changing blackboard menu. Fergusons Dartmoor Best Bitter, Sharp's Own and an interesting wine list. Wonderful views from the pub across Mount's Bay towards Penzance and Lands End.

OPEN: 11.30–3. 6–11 (6.30–11 winter eves)
Real Ale. Restaurant
Children in family room and restaurant. No dogs – cats.

HELSTON

Blue Anchor   Tel: 01326 562821

50 Coinagehall Street, Helston, Cornwall
Free House. Kim Corbett & Simon Stone, licensees.

Strong own-brew Spingo Ale is the feature in this granite and thatched 15th century pub. It is thought that beer has been brewed here for the past 400 years. Brewing was originally started by the local monks and continued after the dissolution of the monasteries. Locally very popular, the Blue Anchor has two bars and a family room. Home-made soups, filled rolls, home-made Cornish pasties and a changing selection of hot meals make up the menu. Ales here are in-house so to speak: Medium, Best, Spingo Special and Extra Special. You can see around the brewery some lunchtimes by arrangement.

OPEN: All day.
Real Ale.
Children in family room. Dogs on leads.
Live bands Fri eves

LANLIVERY

Crown Inn   Tel: 01208 872707

Nr Bodmin, Cornwall, PL31 30BT.
Free House. R.D.Williams, licensee.

In a country village off the Lostwithiel road, you'll find this attractive 12th century pub. Lots of rambling, beamed rooms, a sizeable restaurant and a couple of friendly spirits, of the ethereal kind. The usual variety of bar snacks. On the blackboard the chefs' specials are changed twice a day, and there is a frequently changing à la carte menu in the restaurant. No typical dish: "you name it, we do it". Sharps, Draught Bass and Worthington ales. Picnic tables in the garden. Lovely views.

OPEN: 11–3. 6–11
Real Ale. Restaurant.
Children welcome. Dogs too.
Wheelchair access.

LUDGVAN

White Hart   Tel: 01736 740574

Ludgvan, Nr Penzance, Cornwall TR20 8EY
Devenish, Dennis Churchill, tenant.

Unspoilt, quiet and appealing, this friendly 14th century village pub has small beamed rooms, full of interesting objects, pictures and photographs. Rugs on the floor; two big wood burning stoves for warmth; fine old seats and tables. Good, reasonably priced bar food: sandwiches, home-made soup and real Cornish pasties, salads, omelettes, steaks, daily specials and fresh fish. There is a no-smoking section in the eating area. Flowers IPA and Marstons Pedigree from the barrel, plus one guest ale during the season.

OPEN: 11–2.30. 6–11.
No food Mon eves, Nov–May. Real Ale.
Children in restaurant. Dogs on leads.

MANACCAN

New Inn   Tel: 01326 231323

Manaccan, Helston, Cornwall. TR12 6AJ
Greenalls. Brenda Steer, licensee.

Built of cob, under a thatched roof, the New Inn is a traditional Cornish building. Only one bar with a small working fireplace, the big fire doesn't work, which is why there is a table and chairs in it! A small pub that can just about seat 29; you get more in if they all stand up. The home-cooked food is above average: ploughmans and sandwiches of course, fresh salmon pie, gammon in cider, steaks and some chicken dishes, daily specials too. Whitbread Flowers IPA from a barrel behind the bar, Castle Eden and a guest beer.

OPEN: 11–3. 6–11
Real Ale
Children, if very well behaved. Dogs welcome.

MORWENSTOW

Bush Inn   Tel: 01288 331242

Morwenstow, Nr Bude, Cornwall EX23 9SR
Free House. Mrs B. Moore, licensee.

One of the oldest pubs in Britain, and thought to date back to the 10th century, the Bush Inn is in a hamlet near the coastal path and spectacular Vicarage Cliff. The ship's figurehead in the churchyard, surrounded by the graves of 40 unknown men, bears witness to the ferocity of the weather in this part of the Cornwall. Once a monastic guesthouse, this little pub is full of fascinating items including a propeller from an old De Havilland Gypsy Moth aeroplane. The landlord, Mr J. H. Gregory, who was well over pensionable age, sadly died last year. Mrs Moore, who had helped him run the pub for the last 28 years, now holds the licence and tells us she is "running the pub in the same way as Mr Gregory did". Lunchtime bar food only – home-made soup, pasties, ploughmans with home-made pickle, home-made stews, daily specials and good school puddings such as Spotted Dick. Beers include St Austell HSB and Winter Brew (January and February only) on hand pump and guest beers. Draught Guiness and cider. Seats outside in the courtyard.

OPEN: 12–3. 7–11. Closed Mon Oct–Apr except Bank Holidays.
Real Ale. Lunchtime food only but not Sunday.
No children. No dogs.

MYLOR BRIDGE

Pandora   Tel: 01326 372678

Restronguet Creek, Mylor Bridge, Nr Falmouth, Cornwall TR11 5ST
St Austell, Helen Hough, tenant.

There aren't many pubs where you can sail straight in – not quite into the bar except on a very high spring tide – but certainly up to the jetty. A very pretty 15th century thatched pub, which even has showers for visiting yachtsmen. There will be a permanent audience in good weather, sitting out front, waiting for you to make a hash of tying up. Having found your land legs, the pub offers a choice of three bars, non-smoking restaurant and two no-smoking areas. Bar food includes home-made soup, stuffed pancakes, fish pie, crab thermidor and daily specials. St Austells ales and Bass on hand pump. Malt whiskies and a large selection of wines. If you are coming by road, remember parking can be a bit tight at the height of summer.

OPEN: 11–11 summer. 12–2.30 (3 Sun). 7–11 winter.
Real Ale. Food till 10pm summer; restaurant open all year.
Children in eating area. Dogs on leads.
Wheelchair access to pub.

PELYNT

Jubilee Tel: 01503 220312

Pelynt, Nr Looe, Cornwall PL13 2JZ
Free House. Tim Williams, licensee

The crowns on the pillars outside this handsome 16th century inn give an indication of the royal memorabilia that can be found inside. Renamed the Jubilee to celebrate the first 50 years of Queen Victoria's reign, you will find old prints, Staffordshire figures of the Queen and Prince Albert, also Windsor armchairs! Big log fires in winter, lots of flowers in summer. Here you can get some of the best Cornish cooking, the emphasis being on the fresh fish and shellfish straight off the boats at nearby Looe. The wood-panelled bar has an extensive selection of bar snacks from traditional pasties and ploughmans, to steak & kidney pies. The very attractive restaurant offers an impressive choice of dishes and afternoon Cornish teas. Locally brewed Trelawneys Pride and Bass on hand pump. Choice of malt whiskies and a good wine list. There is a flowery courtyard for sitting in during the summer. Barbecues, children's play area.

OPEN: 11–3. 6–11. N.B. Musak in the public bar.
Real Ale.
Children welcome. Dogs on leads (and they can bring their bed).
Bedrooms. Wheelchair access.

PHILLEIGH

Roseland Tel: 01872 580254

Philleigh-in-Roseland, Truro, Cornwall TR2 5NB
Greenalls. Graham Hill, tenant.

Home to the Roseland Rugby Club during the winter months, the pub also has a choir practice twice a week. So any singing you do hear is real. One low-ceilinged bar in this typically 17th century pub, with a big log fire in winter. During the summer you can sit in the sunny courtyard. Home-made food includes soup, filled baked potatoes, salad nicoise, real Cornish pasties, local clams in the summer, seafood pancakes, sandwiches and lots of salads. There is a greater selection in the evenings: sirloin steak with cream and whisky sauce and local fish dishes. Greenalls Bitter, Marstons Pedigree and Draught Bass. Farm cider in the summer; a good range of malt whiskies.

OPEN: 11–3. 6–11. (11.30–3. 6.30–11 winter).
Real Ale.
Children welcome. Dogs on leads.
Wheelchair access.

ST BREWARD

Old Inn   Tel: 01208 850711

St Breward, Bodmin, Cornwall. PL30 4PP
Free House. Ann & Iain Cameron, licensees

Parts of this friendly old pub date back to the 12th century; some of it must be old as it is reputed to have been the beer hall for the masons who built the church in 1072. It has a two-roomed bar with flagstoned floors and low oak beams; an inner room with a log fire and a games room where children are allowed. Generous home-made bar food includes soup, sandwiches, fresh fish, pie of the day, vegetarian dishes, mixed grills and various puddings. Large range of malt whiskies. Bass, John Smiths Best, Ruddles County and a guest beer on hand pump. Seats outside in the low stone-walled garden – the walls protecting you from the free range sheep and cattle.

OPEN: 12–3. 6–11 (winter may close 2.30).
Real Ale. Restaurant.
Children in eating area, children's room & one bar. Dogs on leads.
Sometimes live groups.

ST JUST IN PENWITH

Star   Tel: 01736 788767

1 Fore Street, St Just in Penwith, Cornwall TR19 7LL
St Austell. Rosie & Peter Angwin, tenants

Near to the coastal path, this welcoming, apparently 18th century pub must be older than it looks. Legend has it that it was built to house the men building the church. However old it is, it has remained unchanged for years. The L-shaped bar with its mining memorabilia reminds the visitor that you are in what was once a prosperous tin mining area. Through the bar there is a separate snug, with a toy box for the children. No piped music, but there is a jukebox – just hope no one plays it. Food is served all day, but only pasties and rolls between 3 and 6. Food includes soups, pasties, French bread topped with chilli or garlic mushrooms, ploughmans, vegetable curry and daily specials such as chicken in wine and cream sauce. St Austell Tinners, HSD , XXX Mild and Trelwney Pride from the cask. Mulled wine in winter, cider in the summer. Seats on the pretty back terrace.

OPEN: 11–11.
Real Ale. Food served all day but only rolls & pasties 3–6.
Children in Snug. Dogs on leads.
Bedrooms.
Celtic folk music Mon eves.

ST. KEW

St. Kew Inn   Tel: 01208 841259

St. Kew, Nr. Wadebridge, Cornwall PL30 3HB
St Austell. Steve & Joan Anderson, tenants.

Plenty of space to park in the old stableyard of this friendly, stone built 15th century inn, situated in an attractive wooded valley. Inside there are two bars and a public lounge. The very popular bar food ranges from: soups, sandwiches, lasagne, smoked salmon, steaks and King Prawns in garlic to a Sunday roast and children's menu. (They pride themselves on a secret recipe for their sirloin steaks). The beers are St Austell Tinners and HSD served from casks behind the counter.

OPEN: 11–2.30. 6–11.
Real Ale. Restaurant.
Children (well behaved, in restaurant & own room; none under 6 in eves).
No dogs.

TREBURLEY

Springer Spaniel   Tel: 01579 370424

Treburley, Nr. Lauceston, Cornwall, PL15 9NS
Free House. John Pitchford, licensee.

Named after the landlord's Springer Spaniel, Bertie.(We are pleased to hear
he has a black Labby too, just like us). Formerly the Sportsman's Arms, it
has been transformed into a popular pub with seriously good food. The bar
menu, written on the blackboard offers home-made soups, filled French
bread rolls, cold meats with pickles, a choice of fish and salads, also starters
from the full restaurant menu. Hicks Special Draught and Dartmoor Best
Bitter with occasional guest beers. Good list of New World Wines to go with
the good food.

OPEN: 11–3. 5.30–11.
Real Ale. Restaurant.
Children welcome. Dogs on leads.

TYWARDREATH

New Inn
                                                       Tel:01726 813901

Fore Street, Tywardreath, Cornwall.
Free House. John Milan, licensee.

Stone built with a slate roof, this is a popular 18th century village pub, the
only one in this small village. Two bars; the saloon bar is now the childrens
room. Not far from the coast and the wonderfully safe beach at Par Sands.
If you can't get to the beach, the New Inn has a big garden you can relax in.
No food, but people come from miles around for the Draught Bass tapped
straight from the barrel. Other beers are St Austell XXXX Mild, Tinners and
the seasonal Winter Warmer.

OPEN: 11–2.30, 6–11
Real Ale
Children welcome. Dogs on leads.

ZENNOR

Tinners Arms   Tel: 01736 796927

Zennor, Cornwall TR26 3BY
Free House. David Care, licensee.

Zennor is a small village in a wild landscape 300ft above the sea. The Tinners Arms, over 400 years old, is a stone built pub which used to be the tin miners' local. A hostelry was originally built on this site to house masons working on the church of St Senara in the 12th century. Continuing the tradition of feeding and watering the populace, this comfortable old pub offers good simple bar food: smoked mackerel, lasagne, ploughmans, chicken and ham pie, vegetarian dishes. The menu changes with the season. St Austells ales from the barrel – Hicks Special during the winter and Tinners Ale or Trelawneys Pride in the summer.

OPEN: 11–3. 6.30–11. Summer 11–11.
Real Ale.
Children, but not in main bar. Dogs on leads.

C
CUMBRIA

AMBLESIDE

Golden Rule   Tel: 015394 33363

Smithy Brow, Ambleside, Cumbria LA22 9AS
Hartleys (Robinsons). John Lockley, tenant.

If you are out for one of those character-building walks, this pub is in just the right place for a welcoming, refreshing drink and sustaining snack. Popular with walkers, climbers and paragliders – the landlord being a paragliding instructor – the Cumbria Soaring Club meets here. Hang gliders take off from the ridges around the pub, but whether you fly or walk in, you will find: Hartleys XB, Robinsons Hatters Mild and Old Stockport Bitter, light snacks and meals. There was a brew house on the site in 1630. Seats outside in the pretty garden.

OPEN: 11–11.
Real Ale. Children welcome. Dogs on leads.
Parking difficult (very).

APPLEBY

Royal Oak   Tel: 017683 51463

Bongate, Appleby-in-Westmoreland, Cumbria CA16 6UN
Free House. Colin & Hilary Cheyne, licensees.

Opposite an old church, and close to the River Eden with its gently wooded valleys, you'll find the long, low, white-painted Royal Oak. In the summer there are seats among the flower-filled tubs at the front of the pub. Inside, you will find beamed and panelled rooms where you can enjoy a well-kept pint, or choose a dish from the imaginative menu: home-baked bread to go with the soup, home-cooked ham and beef to go in the sandwiches, filled crêpes, pork fillet in cream and madeira sauce, fresh fish, steaks and daily specials. Children's menu. There are two restaurants, one of which is non-smoking. Ten beers are kept on hand pump and, in summer, a traditional cider. Theakstons Best Bitter and a local beer such as Bongate Special Ale. The Hesket Newmarket Brewery brews ales especially for The Royal Oak. Guests include interesting beers from small breweries in the north of England and Scotland that perhaps are not too well known. Lots of lovely walks nearby and you are also near the wonderful Settle / Carlisle Railway which is well worth a trip.

OPEN: 11–3. 6–11.
Real Ale. Non-smoking Restaurant.
Well behaved children welcome. Dogs on leads.
Bedrooms.

BASSENTHWAITE LAKE

The Pheasant   Tel: 017687 76234

Bassenthwaite Lake, Nr Cockermouth CA13 9YE
Free House. W.E. Barrington Wilson, licensee.

You can't actually see the lake from The Pheasant, but you know it isn't far away; four miles long – the quiet is to be appreciated – motorboats are banned from this stretch of water. The Pheasant a solid, comfortable Cumbrian Inn has been in the same capable hands for years. There is an enviable, timeless quality about the bar, quickly filling up at lunchtime with people coming to sample the excellent bar menu: home-made soup, cheese or meat platter, potted Silloth shrimps, Cumberland sausages, Cumberland pork and ham pie, smoked local trout, local lamb and much more. If you want to push the boat out and have a full meal, there is an à la carte menu in the no-smoking restaurant. Theakstons Best, Morlands Old Speckled Hen, Youngers Scotch, Bass and Guinness ales. Wines by the glass and half bottle. A choice of whiskies. There is a lovely garden, surrounded by woodland which you can walk into from the grounds of the hotel.

OPEN: 11–3. 5.30–10.30. (11. Sat). 11.30–2.30 winter mornings.
Real Ale. Restaurant.
Children in eating area. Dogs in bar only.
Bedrooms. Wheelchair access.

BOWNESS-ON-WINDERMERE

The Hole in t'Wall   Tel: 015394 43488

Lowside, Bowness-on-Windermere, LA23 3DH
Hartleys (Robinsons). Andrew Mitton, tenant.

Once the local smithy, which probably explains the bellows and general air
of rustic-ness, the Hole in t'Wall is reputed to be the oldest pub in Bowness.
On two levels, the upstairs room has the juke box, so for glorious quiet, stay
downstairs with the bellows and enjoy your pint and dish of the day. The
menus change constantly, depending on what is available and what inspires.
You can, however, be assured that it will be competent, interesting and
worthwhile. Robinsons Hatters Mild, Old Stockport Bitter, Hartleys XB, Best
Bitter, Frederic's and Old Tom. Seats on a sunny sheltered courtyard at the
front of the pub.

OPEN: 11–11
Real Ale Children in family room. Dogs on leads.

BROUGHTON MILLS

The Blacksmiths Arms   Tel : 01229 716824

Broughton Mills, Broughton-in-Furness Cumbria
Free House. Andrew Wood, licensee.

Situated in the Lickie Valley, one of the prettiest valleys in the Lakes, the
Blacksmiths Arms is an out-of-the-way, basic, traditional pub, serving the
local farming community and everyone else nearby. However, it has
tremendous character – 300 years old with beams and flagstone floors. Very
popular with climbers and walkers as well as ordinary travellers. Not smart,
but a good pint and sandwich is all you will need to sustain you. If you can
stand a bit of ribbing from the locals, an evening here can be an entertaining
and rewarding experience. Theakstons range of ales.

OPEN: Extremely flexible hours
Real Ale
Children tolerated Dogs – depends on the Landlord.
Bedrooms.

BUTTERMERE

Bridge Hotel   Tel: 017687 70252

Buttermere, Nr.Cockermouth, Cumbria CA13 9UZ
Free House. Peter McGuire, manager.

Originally a simple, two-storey ale house, it has over the years been extended and improved, resulting in the attractive and comfortable hotel you find today. Very much geared up to walkers and the erratic Cumbrian weather – it even has a drying room! Muddy boots? – then make for the walkers' bar and its flagstoned floor. If they're really muddy, it's best to leave them where the carpet begins. Good selection of bar food from the walkers' snack corner: from simple soup, sandwiches and ploughmans to the cosmopolitan – prawns, smoked salmon in seafood spicy sauce, Cumbrian hotpot, mad stag and bobtail pie (hare, venison and rabbit topped with puff pastry), chicken breast cooked in herbs and garlic, chef's daily specials and vegetarian dishes. Sunday roast. The restaurant is no-smoking. Black Sheep Best Bitter, Theakstons Ales and a summer guest beer. Wines by the glass. A selection of malt whiskies. Seats outside on the terrace and wonderful walks.

OPEN: 10.30–11.
Real Ale. Evening restaurant.
Children welcome. No dogs.

CARTMEL

The Cavendish Arms   Tel: 015395 36240

Cartmel, Cumbria LA11 6QA
Free House. Tom & Nick Murray, licensees.

Very much a locals pub, but you are surrounded by serious walking country so there are plenty of visitors to this popular, friendly well run old place. Just off the main square with it's 18th century market cross, The Cavendish has its very own brewery. So as well as the good familiar bar food – there will be a vegetarian dish or two, interesting daily specials, and the Sunday roast beef cooked on a spit in the dining room – you can try some of their award winning beers: Cartmel Buttermere Bitter, Thoroughbred and Lakeland Gold. There will also be a guest beer. Guided Fell walks if you are feeling energetic. Beer festivals too. Seats at the front and the back of the pub among the flowers.

OPEN: 11.30–11
Real Ale. Restaurant.
Children welcome. Dogs in garden only.

COCKERMOUTH

The Swan Inn   Tel: 01900 822425

Kirkgate, Cockermouth, CA13 9PH
Jennings. Eric Starkie, licensee.

William Wordsworth, poet – (he of the daffodils) – was born in the Georgian
House at the end of the main street in 1770. The Swan Inn, in the cobbled
main square near the Kirkgate Centre, is a busy traditional pub – well kept
ales, plenty of whiskies and no food – the refreshment is purely liquid.
Jennings Best Bitter and Cocker Hoop ales.

OPEN: 11–3. 7–11. closed Tues morning.
Real Ale. No food
Children at landord's discretion. Dogs until 9 o'clock, (bedtime then!)

DENT

Sun Inn   Tel: 01539 625208

Main Street, Dent, Sedbergh, Cumbria LA10 5QL (village off A683).
Own Brew. Martin Stafford, licensee.

A charming, typical Dales village inn within the Yorkshire Dales National
Park. The cobbled streets of Dent are lined with cottages, some of which
date back to the 15th century. There is the added attraction of the Dent
Brewery not far away, which provides the Sun with its own beer – Bitter,
Ramsbottom, T'Owd Tup and a strong ale called "Kamakazi". Inside the pub
are lots of beams, comfortable furnishings and home-cooked bar food. This
includes the stalwarts, also pasties, chicken curry, chilli, steak & kidney pie,
Cumberland sausage, salads and a changing variety of puds. Seats outside
in summer.

OPEN: 11–11 (11–3. 7–11 winter).
Real Ale.
Children welcome until 9 pm. Dogs on leads.
Bedrooms.

ELTERWATER

Britannia Inn   Tel: 01539 437210

Ambleside, Cumbria, LA22 9HP
Free House. Judith Fry, licensee.

Opposite the village green and in the very heart of the Lake District, the Britannia Inn is ideally situated to sustain you whilst you admire the magnificence of the surrounding countryside, or recover from walking the peaks and fells. Small friendly bars with beams and log fires. There is a wide-ranging menu with the usual favourites: soups, filled baps, baked potatoes, ploughmans, some unusual alternatives and daily specials. Jennings Bitter, Cumberland Ale and Boddingtons Bitter plus guest ales. Lots of garden chairs and tables on the terrace in front of the pub.

OPEN: 11–11.
Real Ale. Restaurant.
Children & Dogs welcome.
Nine guest bedrooms, plus four in annex.

ESKDALE GREEN

Bower House Inn   Tel: 0194 6723244

Eskdale, Holmrook, Cumbria CA19 1TD (on Santon Bridge Road)
Free House. Derek Connor, licensee.

Old, rambling, comfortable, friendly; all a traditional country inn should be, complete with cosy log fires, good ales and imaginative food. Usual bar snacks plus daily specials which could be: pork in cider, fillet of beef in red wine sauce, wild duck or guinea fowl, locally smoked mackerel and trout, good choice of cheeses and a range of puddings. Hartleys XB, Courage Directors, Theakstons Best, Boddingtons and various guest beers. Seats outside in the garden. No need to tell you that there are lots of wonderful walks.

OPEN: 11–11.
Real Ale. Restaurant.
Children at lunchtime and early eve. No dogs.
Wheelchair access.

GRASMERE

Dove & Olive Branch Tel: 015394 35592

Wordsworth Hotel, Grasmere, Cumbria
Free House. R M Lees, manager.

The Dove and Olive Branch is an "in-house pub", attached to the very elegant, smart, Wordsworth Hotel. In the centre of Grasmere, and next to the churchyard where the poet William Wordsworth is buried, the Dove is the drinking place for all appreciative locals and visitors. Tasty bar snacks, lots of filled baguettes, ploughmans, savoury baked potatoes and daily specials. Tetley Bitter and Boddingtons from the cask and Mitchells Ales, plus an occasional guest beer. There are seats and tables on the veranda, from where you can watch the world go by.

OPEN: 11–3. 6–11.
Real Ale.
Children welcome, but no infants. No dogs.

HAWKSHEAD

Drunken Duck Tel: 015394 36347

Barngates, Ambleside, Cumbria LA22 0NG (off B5286 Hawkshead-Ambleside).
Free House. Stephanie Barton, licensee.

At a crossroads, set in its own 60 acres and the magnificent scenery of the Lake District, The Drunken Duck has been a haven for the traveller for over 400 years. How the Barn Gates Inn became the Drunken Duck is worth a journey for the telling alone. Cosy, beamed rooms with good winter fires, good ales and a daily changing menu. Food includes sandwiches, many home-made patés, smoked trout (very local), Cumberland sausage casserole, game pie, pastas and puddings of the jam rolypoly, spotted-dick genre. Jennings Best Bitter, Boddingtons, Mitchells Lancaster Bomber, Theakstons Old Peculiar, Yates and other guest beers. Over 60 malt whiskies. A pretty pub, with a veranda at the front on which there are seats and opulent hanging baskets in summer.

OPEN: 11.30–3. 6–11.
Real Ale. Children in eating area. Dogs on leads.
Bedrooms

INGS

Watermill Inn   Tel: 01539 821309

Ings, Nr. Stavely, Kendal, Cumbria LA8 9PY (E of Windermere)
Free House. Alan & Brian Coulthwaite, licensees.

Originally a wood mill which made shuttles and bobbins for the Lancashire
cotton mills, the watermill is now a family-run, Lakeland inn only two miles
from Windermere. Comfortable, friendly bars with log fires, and in them an
interesting use of old wooden church fittings to create a "gothicky" bar
counter. With no juke box or machines, "the art of conversation in being re-
born". All bar favourites and a constantly changing chef's special on the
blackboard i.e. vegetable and almond ravioli in an asparagus sauce, Italian
syle meatballs in a basil sauce, leeks au gratin, peppered pork with rice and
other dishes. Up to 15 real ales on hand pump, among them Moorhouses
Black Cat and Pendle Witches Brew, Greenwoods Hop Pocket, Jennings
Cumberland and the rest. Also a traditional cider, plus continental and
English bottled beers. The River Gowan, which used to power the old mill,
runs through the grounds.

OPEN: 12–2.30 (3 Sun). 6–11. (6–10.30 Sun)
Real Ale.
Children in lounge. Dogs on leads
Bedrooms.

KENDAL

Black Swan   Tel: 015397 24278

8 Allhallows Lane, Kendal, LA9 4JH
Matthew Brown & Bass. William Croskell, licensee.

A mere 50 yards from the centre of Kendal, with its narrow winding streets,
the 18th century Black Swan is a favourite meeting place. A good range of
traditional bar food, snacks and more substantial hot dishes such as Irish
Stew are available at lunchtime only; evening meals by arrangment. Draught
Bass, and at the moment Theakstons Best Bitter and Stones Best Bitter.
Seats in the garden.

OPEN: 11–3. 6–11. (11–11 summer Sats)
Real Ale
Children welcome. No dogs.
Bedrooms. Car park.

KIRKBY LONSDALE

Snooty Fox   Tel: 0152 4271308

Main Street, Kirkby Lonsdale, Cumbria LA6 2AH
Free House. Jack Shone, licensee.

An imposing, listed, white-painted Jacobean town inn, in what is known as the "capital" of the lovely Lune Valley. Two traditional bars, hung about with lots of interesting objets d'art; birds and animals – stuffed and mounted – uniforms, bugles, swords and china, and an attractive dining room. All the dishes are freshly prepared home-made soups, sandwiches, baked potatoes with various fillings, steak & kidney pie, poached salmon, salads and lunchtime daily specials. Sunday roast too, for which you need to book. Hartleys XB, Theakstons Best and Timothy Taylors Landlord on hand pump. Tables on the terrace and in the garden. Walks along the River Lune from the medieval Devil's bridge.

OPEN: 11–11. Meals & snacks all day.
Real Ale.
Children in eating area. Dogs in bar only.
Bedrooms.

LANGDALE

Old Dungeon Ghyll   Tel: 015394 37272

Gt.Langdale, Ambleside, Cumbria LA22 9JY
Free House. Neil Walmsley, licensee.

This is one place where you can be sure of peace and quiet, inside and out. At the foot of the Langdale Pikes, the road from Chapel Style on the Great Langdale beck, comes to an abrupt end at the Old Dungeon Ghyll Hotel. Here it really is "on with your boots" to climb the steep path that leads you to the spectacular Dungeon Ghyll waterfall which drops into an abyss 100 feet below. Back at the hotel the Hikers Bar has refreshing beer and good food. Home-cooked meals and snacks – soups, sandwiches, Cumberland sausages, chicken dishes, local trout, steaks, etc. A four-course dinner is served in the no-smoking restaurant. Jennings Cumberland, Theakstons XB, Old Peculiar and Yates Bitter plus some guest beers. The pub is opposite a National Trust campsite, which can get very jolly and busy at weekends.

OPEN: 11–11.
Real Ale. Evening restaurant.

Children welcome. Dogs on leads.
Bedrooms.
Occasional live music.

LITTLE LANGDALE

Three Shires Inn   Tel: 015394 37215

Little Langdale, Ambleside, Cumbria LA22 9NZ
Free House. Ian Stephenson, licensee.

A few miles west of Ambleside in the pretty Little Langdale valley. This 19th century slate inn was built near the meeting point of the three shires of Cumberland, Westmorland and Lancashire. Somewhere to rest before climbing the high passes of Wrynose and Hardknott en route to Ravenglass. A very attractive building in a wonderful setting. There are seats under the veranda at the front of the hotel which is hung with colourful hanging baskets in summer. Inside there is a slate floored, beamed bar where you can enjoy either a bar snack or more substantial dishes: home cured marinated salmon in a sweet mustard and dill sauce, chicken liver paté flamed in brandy and served with a tomato salad, spinach filled cannelloni, French onion soup and daily specials, if you are still hungry you could have the pie of the day, creamy chicken tikka or a locally made Cumberland sausage. A full menu is served in the restaurant. All dishes are cooked to order from fresh ingredients. Webster Yorkshire Bitter, Ruddles County, Theakstons XB, Morlands Old Speckled Hen and Black Sheep Bitter ales: also an extensive wine list. Tables in the stream-side garden. Lots of walks.

OPEN: 11–11.
Real Ale. Restaurant.
Children until 9pm. No dogs.
En-suite bedrooms.

SAWREY (Nr.)

Tower Bank Arms   Tel: 015394 36334

Nr. Sawrey, Hawkshead, Ambleside, LA22 0LF}
Free House, Philip Broadley, licensee.

At least you now know there is a quiet, desirable refuge when you have made the long journey around the lake from Grasmere to see Beatrice Potter's Hill Top Farm, now run by the National Trust, only to find it closed.

THE QUIET PINT

You will note that this is said through clenched teeth. However, the countryside is wonderful, and any disappointment is soon forgotten at the Tower Bank Arms. Here in the beamed bar with its winter log fire you will be able to refuel before the journey back. Traditional bar food: home-made soup, filled rolls, ploughmans, there will be a pie of the day, salads, something for the vegetarian and a pudding or two. More substantial dishes are available during the evening. Theakstons ales, a guest beer, Belgian fruit beers and a good selection of malt whiskies. There are seats outside and good walks nearby.

OPEN: 11–3. 5.30–11. (6–11 winter)
Real Ale. Restaurant. N.B. Tapes played in restaurant.
Children lunchtime only. Dogs on leads.
Bedrooms.

SEATHWAITE

Newfield Inn   Tel: 01229 716208

Duddon Valley, Broughton in Furness, Cumbria LA20 6ED
Free House. Chris Burgess, licensee.

In a small hamlet in the Duddon Valley, this old lakeland pub is a popular stopping place for fell walkers. There is an interesting slate floor in the main bar, showing different levels of volcanic activity, and legend has it that the old beams in the pub came from ships of the Spanish Armada. Homely bar food: soups, sandwiches, Cumberland sausages, home-cooked gammon and steaks, plus a vegetarian dish or two. There is a more extensive evening menu. Theakstons ales, and during the summer, guest ales, i.e. Marstons Pedigree, Abbot Ale and Charles Wells Fargo. Interesting selection of malt whiskies and Polish vodkas. Tables in the garden from where you can admire the dramatic scenery.

OPEN: 11–3. 6–11 (11–11 Sat).
Real Ale. Restaurant.
Children welcome if well behaved. Dogs on leads.
Wheelchair access to the pub. Self-catering flats available.
Occasional folk music.

TALLENTIRE

The Bush Inn   Tel: 01900 823707

Tallentire, Nr. Cockermouth, Cumbria CA13 0PT
Free House. Mr & Mrs Alan Wilkie, licensees.

In attractive countryside three miles north-west of Cockermouth, the small
village of Tallentire has a pub which wears two hats. Not only is the 17th
century Bush the local pub, it is also the local post office, and Mr Wilkie is
the sub-postmaster. And that is the best, and most novel excuse anyone can
think of for going to the pub – "just off to buy a stamp!" It is also by Royal
Appointment once removed – a member of Prince Charles' staff calls in for
a welcome break when journeying to and from Scotland. A very relaxing and
welcoming pub serving an interesting variety of home-cooked food including
several vegetarian dishes. Quality and value are of high order, says our
informant. Theakstons XB, Youngers Scotch Bitter, Gillespies Stout,
McEwans lager and a guest beer.

OPEN: 12–3. 7–11
Real Ale
Children Welcome. Dogs on leads.

TROUTBECK

The Mortal Man   Tel: 015394 33193

Upper Road, Troutbeck, Cumbria
Free House. Christopher Poulson, licensee.

High above Lake Windermere, the village of Troutbeck scatters along the
fellside near the beck that tumbles into the Lake below. Inside this
welcoming 17th century hotel there's a bar with beams and log fire where
you will find all you'll need to sustain you on your journey. You'll find: home-
made soups, paté, home cooked ham, poached salmon, beef in ale pie,
salads, steaks, a vegetarian dish and home-made puddings. There is also
a set menu in the no-smoking restaurant. Theakstons Best Bitter and
Youngers Scotch beers. Seats in the garden with views of the valley. Lots of
walks nearby.

OPEN: 12–2.30.5.30–11
Real Ale. Restaurant.
Children until 9pm. Dogs on leads.
Bedrooms.

WASDALE HEAD

Wasdale Head Inn   Tel: 0194 67 26229

Gosforth, Seascale, Cumbria CA20 1EX (NE of Lake)
Free House. Stephen & Pheona Hosking, licensees.

This is one of the more remote taverns of the Lake District, situated at the head of the dramatic Wast Water – the deepest lake in England. Understandably popular with travellers and climbers alike, as Wasdale Head is approximately 8 miles from the nearest habitation. Someone described the area as a collection of sheep pastures and an inn. This particular inn is a wonderfully sturdy, handsome, three-storey building with a good selection range of well-prepared bar food which ranges from home-made soups and Fisherman's crumble to vegetable curry. There is also an evening restaurant. Well-kept ales: Theakstons XB, Jennings Cumberland and Yates Bitter on hand pump, plus a summer guest beer. Dramatic scenery. No need to say there are wonderful walks round here because that is what you are here for anyway.

OPEN: 11–11 (closed mid-Nov–Dec 28, mid Jan–mid Feb).
Real Ale. Restaurant.
Children in own room. No dogs.
Bedrooms (10). and self catering cottages.

WINSTER

Brown Horse   Tel: 0153 9443443

Winster, Nr. Bowness-on-Windermere, Cumbria LA23 3WR (S of Windermere).
Free House. Rudolph Schaffer, licensee.

Not quite so many of the big boots and hairy socks brigade here, but that's not to say you wouldn't be welcome for a pint in this appealing pub if you were so attired, but you will find the food on offer has gone up a few notches – beyond the merely sustaining. It has a reasonably priced and creative menu, and such is the popularity of the pub, that you need to book to be sure of a table. Pork and chicken liver house paté, home-made soups, various pasta dishes, seafood pancakes, some German specialities, fish and steaks. Good puds too. Sandwiches are available if they are not too busy. Beers are Jennings Bitter and Marstons Pedigree all guests, and change periodically. Bittburger Pils on draught, Carlsberg Hof, Murphys Stout. Good short wine list.

OPEN: 12–3. 6–11.
Real Ale.
Children welcome. Dogs on leads if pub not too busy.
Wheelchair access

D
DERBYSHIRE & STAFFORDSHIRE

ALSTONEFIELD

The George   Tel: 01335 310205

Alstonefield, Ashbourne, Derbyshire, DE6 2FX
Burtonwood. Richard & Sue Grandjean, licensees.

Situated in the glorious Peak District, between Ashbourne and Buxton, Alstonefield is a small village of about 250 inhabitants and The George, a late 17th century building still with its beams and open fires – "not tarted up at all" – is just as a village pub should be. Reputed to have the smallest bar in either Derbyshire or Staffordshire, it has an amazing turnover, so size isn't everything. There is a good selection of bar food: home-made soup, five different ploughmans, five or six different fillings for the sandwiches, meat and potato pie, lasagne, asparagus flan and much more, plus about eight home-made puds. Burtonwoods range of ales. The children have a separate room and there are seats in the garden.

OPEN: 11–2.30. 6–11.
Real Ale
Children Welcome. No Dogs.
Wheelchair access.

BEELEY

Devonshire Arms   Tel: 01629 733259

Beeley, Nr Matlock, Derbyshire DE4 2NR
Free House. J A Grosvenor, licensee.

The village of Beeley is situated at the southern end of Chatsworth Park. The Devonshire Arms was originally three separate cottages. They were converted in 1726 and during the early 18th century became a prosperous coaching inn on the road between Bakewell and Matlock. Now a popular, charming, well-kept village inn, catering for locals and visitors to the lovely

Derbyshire Peak District. There is an interesting bar menu, ranging from sandwiches, ploughmans and vegetarian dishes plus salads to mushrooms in a tarragon, mustard and sour cream sauce, trout with lemon and herb stuffing, venison in a plum sauce, gammon and pineapple and breast of chicken in a stilton sauce. Dishes of the day on the blackboard; also a wide range of home-made puds. On Sunday mornings they serve a "Victorian breakfast" from 10.00 until 12.00 noon, for which you must book. Theakstons Best, Old Peculiar, Boddingtons, Black Sheep and a guest beer. An outstanding area for walking and cycling. Also very near Chatsworth House.

OPEN: 11–3. 6–11 (11–3; 7–10.30 Sun).
Real Ale. Restaurant.
Children welcome, upstairs family room. No dogs.

BRASSINGTON

Ye Olde Gate   Tel: 01629 540448

Well Street, Brassington, Derbys DE4 4HJ (NE of Ashbourne)
Marstons. Paul Burlinson, tenant.

An unchanging, old country pub dating back to 1616. The panelled dining room was used as a temporary hospital during the Civil War, and to add to the atmosphere they have a resident ghost. A mere stripling – dating back to the Victorian era. In spite of all the "happenings" there is a very jolly ambience in the beamed bars. Bar food changes by the day, but baguettes with varied and interesting fillings are available at lunchtime as well as home-made curries, cajun chicken, sea-food dishes, roasts, steaks and good puds available. No chips with anything! No-smoking dining room. Marstons Pedigree, Owd Roger at Christmas and a guest, plus lots of malt whiskies. Seats in the sheltered garden.

OPEN: 12–2.30 (3 Sat). 6–11.
Real Ale. Summer barbecue.
Children over 10 in dining room. Dogs on leads.
Wheelchair access.

BRETTON

Barrel Tel: 01433 630856

Bretton, Nr Eyam, Sheffield S30 1QD (between Eyam & Hathersage)
Free House. Derek Smith, licensee.

A totally unspoilt historic inn, 1300 feet above sea level, with the reputation of being the highest pub in Derbyshire, and having views, (on a good day), over five counties. You don't have to be Einstein to work out that at that height it can be a bit cold in winter, so you need to know there are good log fires in this pub. Also reasonably priced bar food. There could be soups, sandwiches with various fillings, double decker sandwiches, filled baps, salads, chicken ham and mushroom pie, all freshly prepared to order. Bass and Boddingtons Ales, and a choice of whiskies. Seats outside; but be warned – at this high altitude it can feel very chilly.

OPEN: 12–3. 6.30–11. (12–11 Summer Sats.)
Real Ale.
Children welcome. Dogs on leads.

BURTON ON TRENT

Burton Bridge Inn Tel: 01283 536596

24 Bridge Street, Burton-on-Trent, Staffs DE14 1SY
Own Brew. Kevin McDonald, tenant.

Burton Bridge Brewery tap. The beer is brewed on site – Tuesday is viewing day but you must book your place. Lots of bits and pieces relating to brewery – notices, awards etc. Quite a range of bar snacks: filled cobs and filled oatcakes, Yorkshire puddings with faggots and peas, roasts and hot bacon and egg rolls. A skittle alley, which seems to be booked months ahead, is available for private parties. Burton Bridge Bitter, XL Bitter, Porter and Festival plus seasonal varieties. Selection of malt whiskies and fruit wines.

OPEN: 11.30–2.15. 5.30–11. (Sun: 12–2. 7–10.30)
Real Ale. No food Sunday.
Children over 10 in eating area. Dogs on leads.

CHESTERFIELD

The Derby Tup
Tel:01246 454316

387, Sheffield Road, Wittington Moor S41 8LS
Free House. Peter Haynes, licensee.

It has only been the Derby Tup for about 14 years; before that the Brunswick Hotel, although it was never really a hotel – just a pub. What you have now is an unspoilt town pub with three rooms, open fireplaces and better than average bar food. The blackboard menu includes a full range of sandwiches, ploughmans, omelettes, pasta, salads and some vegetarian dishes, as well as beef in red wine or pork in a mushroom and sherry sauce. Kelham Island Fat Cat, Marstons Pedigree, Theakstones XB and Old Peculier, Tetleys and five guest beers. No garden.

OPEN: 11.30–3. 5–11 (11–11 Fri & Sat. 12–4. 7–10.30 Sun.)
Real Ale
Children welcome. Dogs on leads.
Wheelchair access.

DERBY

The Flower Pot
Tel: 01332 204955

25 King Street, Derby DE1 3DZ
Free House. Michael John Evans, licensee.

Close to the centre of Derby and within walking distance of the Cathedral and shopping centre, the Flower Pot, built in the early eighteenth century as a private house, was first licensed in about 1750. Not only does it provide refreshment for the inner man, it also offers the opportunity to improve the mind. It has a small library of books – mostly donated by the customers – with which you can while away the time, or even take home to read. There is quite a choice of bar food – sandwich platters served with salad and spicy potatoes, filled jacket potatoes, home-made soup, lots of meat or fish dishes, a selection of vegetarian meals, and some bar snacks like chip butties and cheese burgers. Fruit crumble or bread and butter pudding are among the puds. Sunday lunches too. Timothy Taylors Landlord, Bass and Marstons Pedigree are the regular ales; there are also guest beers and quite a selection of malt whiskies. Small walled garden at the back of the pub, where there is also a children's play area.

OPEN: 11–11.
Real Ale.
Children welcome. Dogs on leads.

DERBY

Brunswick   Tel: 01332 290677

1 Railway Terrace, Derby
Free House. Trevor Harris, licensee.

Built to accomodate the railway workers, this pub is now a magnet for those appreciating a comfortable, busy, friendly tavern which also offers a full range of ales – including its own brew. Closed in 1974, it was refurbished and re-opened on 3rd October 1987, an annual beer festival is held to celebrate their re-birthday. Fourteen ales on hand pump and guests from the cask. The Brunswick own brew includes: First Brew, Railway Porter, Old Accidental and Owd Abusive. One roomy serving bar and a no-smoking room with an open fire. Traditional bar food: soup, filled rolls, beef and onion pie and other hot dishes. Seats outside on the terrace behind the pub.

OPEN: 11–11.
Real Ale. Lunchtime meals/snacks. Filled rolls only Sun. Restaurant closed Sun.
Children in family parlour. Dogs on leads.
Jazz Thurs eves. Folk Club.

DERBY

The Smithfield   Tel: 01332 370429

Meadow Road Derby, DE1 2BH
Free House.(Headless Pub Company), Matthew Radborne, manager.

Originally the Cattle Market Hotel, the pub was built to serve the old Derby cattle market, which has long since gone. The site is now occupied by the Derby Evening Telegraph and the bus station. Close to the city centre and on the banks of the river Derwent the Smithfield offers a warm welcome, fine ales and a good selection of traditional bar food. Ten ales on handpump with Draught Bass and Marstons Pedigree the regulars. Food is served all week. Sunday lunches are a speciality. Seats in the large garden by the river and on the terrace. Large car park,

OPEN: 11–11 (12–10.30 Sun)
Real Ale.
Children welcome. Dogs on leads.

DERBY

Ye Olde Dolphin Inn   Tel: 01332 349115

6/7 Queen Street, Derby. DE1 3DL
Bass. D. Willis, manager.

Ye Olde Dolphin dates back to 1540 and has been a drinking and eating house throughout most of its history, although a doctor's surgery took some space – nothing sinister in that, we hope. A traditional period building with beamed interiors, comfortable bars and welcoming fires. Situated near the cathedral, it is popular with visitors and locals alike. The pub aims to provide the best traditional pub food with the addition of some continental specialities. Draught Bass, Worthingtons Bitter, Highgate Mild and Recession Ale, 2nd Brew. There is a small, paved rear garden.

OPEN: 10.30–11.
Real Ale. Restaurant.
No children. Dogs on leads.

EYAM

Miners Arms   Tel: 01433 630853

Water Lane, Eyam, Derbyshire S30 1RG
Free House. Nicholas & Ruth Cook, licensees.

Built in 1630 before the village was struck by the plague, the original inn's stones can be seen over the lintel. The pub also boasts a couple of ghosts, thought to be two unfortunate girls who perished in a fire on the same site before the inn was built. There are three unghostly, quiet rooms in the pub and a very good choice of home-made dishes, a lot of them prepared from local seasonal produce. Bar lunches, which change daily, might include home-made soups, crispy roast duck, Cumberland sausages in onion gravy, haddock mornay, quiche, ploughmans, sandwiches and a selection of home-made puds. There is also an evening à la carte menu when the selection of dishes goes up a notch. No bar snacks on Sunday, but there is a traditional roast. Tetleys and Stones Ales.

OPEN: 12–3. 7–11.
Real Ale. Evening Restaurant No food Sun or Mon except Sun lunch in restaurant.
Children welcome. No Dogs.

HASSOP

Eyre Arms   Tel: 01629 640390

Hassop, Nr Bakewell, Derbys DE45 1NS
Free House. Nick & Lynne Smith, licensees

A fifteenth century village pub serving popular good wholesome food and well kept ales. Spacious public bar. Tables are laid in the roomy lounge bar for dinner in the evenings. Extensive menu of traditional English fare. Morlands Old Speckled Hen, John Smiths Pedigree ales.

OPEN: 11–11.
Real Ale.
Children at lunchtime only. Dogs on leads & well behaved.

KIRKIRETON

Barley Mow   Tel: 01335 370306

Main Street, Kirkireton, Ashbourne, Derbyshire DE6 3JP
Free House. Mary Short, licensee.

On the edge of the Peak District, the imposing 17th century Barley Mow, which was built at the top of the village street, has been catering for villagers and visitors for nearly 200 years. There is an unspoilt interior with open fires and a small bar. Only filled rolls are available at lunchtime. Evening meals are served, but only for residents. Well kept beers from the cask: Hook Norton Best, Old Hooky and Marstons Pedigree. These can do a quick change with Adnams, Courage Directors, Greene King and Wadworths. Seats in the garden and at the front of the pub.

OPEN: 12–2. 7–11.
Real Ale. Rolls at lunchtime.
Children welcome by arrangement. Dogs on leads.
Bedrooms (5 en suite)

LICHFIELD

Queens Head   Tel: 01543 410932

Queen Street, Lichfield, Staffs WS13 6QD
Marstons. John P Ketley & Sue Midgley, tenants

"The art of conversation is not dead at the Queens Head" is the slogan thought up by the landlord when he took over two years ago. Deciding he wanted a "talking" pub, the wiring for the muzac was somewhat trimmed back! The pub is Marston's first real ale house and John and Sue are doing all they can to make it a resounding success. Now known as the "Ale and Cheese House" there are over 40 different cheeses on offer, also patés, breads, pickles and tracklements. No, we didn't know what it meant either! Apparently it is a collective noun for a number of pickles and relishes. Marstons Pedigree, Timothy Taylors Landlord and something from Adnams. Two regularly changing guests.

OPEN: 11–11, (12–3.7–10.30 Sun)
Real Ale
Children welcome. Dogs on leads.

LITTLE LONGSTONE

Packhorse   Tel: 01629 640471

Little Longstone, Nr Bakewell, Derbys DE45 1NN (Nr Monsal Dale).
Marstons. Lynne & Mark Lythgoe, tenants.

Here we have a small, two-roomed, old-fashioned 16th century pub, popular with locals and those energetic walkers on the Monsal Trail. Simply furnished comfortable bars with a very good choice of bar food: hot beef and pork rolls, garlic and stilton mushrooms, lamb in stilton sauce, steak & kidney pies and steaks. Good puds too. Marstons Ales. Seats in the little garden.

OPEN: 11–3. 5–11 (6 –11 Sat).
Real Ale. Restaurant.
Well behaved children lunchtime and early eves. Dogs on leads.
Live music alternate Wed eves.

MILLTHORPE

Royal Oak   Tel: 0114 289087

Millthorpe, Holmesfield, Derbyshire. S18 DW5
Free House, R.H & E. Wills, licensees.

This is an attractive, friendly, 17th century roadside pub. Stone walls, beams and good fires in the bar . As our informant said "a real pub, serving real food, and the best kept beer I have tasted." Well, I don't think you can do much better than that! As well as the usual bar snacks, there could be: fresh salmon fish cakes, fishermans pie, beef in red wine and some vegetarian dishes. Bread and butter pudding and treacle tart to follow. Real, freshly percolated coffee too. Wards Thorne Best Bitter, Carlsberg Export and a wide range of malt whiskies. There is a very pleasant garden and seats on the terrace. You are in good walking country here.

OPEN: 11.30–2.30. 5.30–11.30. Closed for lunch Monday.
Real Ale.
Children in garden. Dogs, not at meal times.

MONSAL HEAD

Monsal Head Hotel   Tel: 01629 640250

Monsal Head, Bakewell, Derbyshire. DE45 1NL.
Free House. Nicholas Smith, licensee.

There are panoramic views of the Dales from this hotel high above the valley of the River Wye. Comfortable, popular bars and a no-smoking restaurant. Reliable bar food includes home-made soups, steak & kidney pie, gammon and eggs, garlic mushrooms and also a children's menu. Sunday roast. Ruddles Best and County, Courage Directors, Morlands Old Speckled Hen, John Smiths and Theakstons Old Peculiar on hand pump.

OPEN: 11–11.
Real Ale. Restaurant.
Children not after 7 in bar. Dogs on leads.

OCKBROOK

White Swan   Tel: 01332 662088

Church Street, Ockbrook, Derby.
Ansells Brewery. June & Alan Newton, tenant.

Set in the conservation area of a delightful Derbyshire village, the white painted 18th century White Swan – winner of Ansells Best Kept Pub Award – is a friendly mixture of young and old drinkers. It is a regular meeting place for the local car clubs. A large range of changing bar meals is offered daily, with traditional roasts on Sunday. Ansells and Marstons Pedigree Ales. There is an attractive rear garden which has won many gardening prizes over the past few years.

OPEN: 11.30–3. 7–11.
Real Ale.
Children welcome. Doubtful about dogs.

SCARTIN

The Boat Inn   Tel: 01629 823282

Scartin, Nr Cromford, Derbyshire DE4 3QF
Free House. Des and Vicky Cooper, licensees.

The village of Scartin, just south of Matlock in the magnificent Derbyshire Peak District, attracts visitors from far and near. A delightful walking area and walkers are very welcome in the pub (mind the carpets). Located off Cromford Square the Boat Inn has one comfortable, long bar, with a low beamed ceiling and exposed stone and brick walls. Bar food, at lunchtime and in the evening is listed on the blackboard and varies daily. Townes of Chesterfield ales, and other beers such as Bass and Mansfield.

OPEN: 11.30–2.30 (approx.) (11.30–11 Sat. 12–3.30 Sun).
Real Ale.
Children welcome, dogs on leads.

STANTON-BY-DALE

The Chequers   Tel: 01159 320946

Dale Road, Stanton-By-Dale, Derbyshire, DE7 4QF
Bass. J. Nicholson, lease.

A cottagey pub in an empty-ish bit of Derbyshire between the M1 and A 6096. Another pub with only one bar, but here you have a raised lounge area at the back giving you more room . Well known for its excellent lunches – all home-made – plus other bar snacks. A favourite is the home-cooked ham with cauliflower cheese. A vote of approval has been given by the Retirement home opposite. Several residents come across the road for lunch in their wheelchairs. They also have the occasional summer barbecue. No evening meals. Ales are restricted to the Bass range. Seats in the garden.

OPEN: 11–2.30. 7–11
Real Ale – Draught Bass.
No children inside pub. Dogs on leads.
Parking.

STERNDALE

The Quiet Woman   Tel: 01298 83211

Earl Sterndale, Nr Buxton, Derbyshire.
Marstons. Ken & Jen Mellor, tenants.

Rather a politically incorrect inn sign, but in spite of that, a wonderful example of a village local, surrounded by some of the prettiest countryside in the Peak District. Popular with walkers, there is always a warm welcome here. Sandwiches, pork pies, crusty bread and real Stilton cheese, plus good Marstons Ales. Seats outside in the large garden which has a picnic area and donkeys, geese, pigs, hens, ducks and turkeys – and no, none of them are lunch. But you can buy free range eggs. They have parking for three touring caravans, also a large park for caravettes and somewhere to pitch your tent.

OPEN: Moveable hours.
Real Ale.
Children welcome. No dogs.

TUTBURY

Ye Olde Dog and Partridge Inn   Tel: 01283 813030

High Street, Tutbury, nr Burton-on-Trent, Staffs DE13 9LS
Free House. Mrs Yvette Martindale, licensee.

"Excellent food in lavish quantities", which is a pretty good recommendation for a pub. Having looked after the travelling public for the last four hundred years, they've had a lot of practice in "doing the right thing." Just an inn all those years ago, this handsome half-timbered building was extended during the 18th century to cater for passengers on the London – Liverpool route. The culinary attraction here is the carvery, the roast of the day is hugely popular. Bar food is limited to home-made soup, sandwiches or ploughmans to go with the Marstons Pedigree and the guest beer. Seats in the attractive garden.

OPEN: 11–3. 6–11.
Real Ale.
Children welcome. No dogs.

WARDLOW

Three Stags Heads
Tel: 01298 872268

Wardlow Mires, Tideswell, Derbys SK17 8RW
Free House. Geoff & Pat Fuller, licensees.

Just the place for all those people with big boots, hairy socks and back packs. This charming, 17th century cottagey pub has sensible flagstone floors that will allow you in with your muddy boots. Sustaining bar food ranges from home-made soups to fillet steaks with garlic butter. Home-cooked food on home-made plates – there is a pottery in the barn. The ales are selected from the smaller local breweries and could include Kelham Island Pale Rider, Springhead Bitter and Hoskins and Oldfields Navigation among others. Lots of continental and British bottled beers.

OPEN: 12–3. 7–11. (12–11 Sat)
Real Ale. Restaurant.
Children until 8.30. Dogs on leads.
Live music Sat eve / Sun lunch.

WHALEY BRIDGE

Shepherds Arms
Tel:01663 732384

7, Old Road, Whaley Bridge Derby/Shrophire border. SK12 7HR
Marstons. Derek Abbott, tenant.

Dedicated to the keen drinker – with the added attraction to us of a landlord adamant that his pub should remain music free. This town pub, dating back to the 16th century is a traditional local. Only one bar – with a flagstone floor, beams and a good fire in winter. No food – just crisps and a nut. Marstons range of ales. Seats (and children on Sundays) in the large beer garden.

OPEN: 11.30–3. 7–11 (12–3.7–10.30 Sun)
Real Ale.
Children Sunday lunchtime in the beer garden only. Dogs on leads.

WHITMORE

Mainwaring Arms   Tel: 01782 680224

Whitmore Road, Whitemore, Nr. Newcastle-under-Lyme, Staffs. ST5 6HR.
Free House. Simon Hastings, licensee.

An attractive village with a creeper covered pub which is an ideal place for people watching, according to our researcher. Popular with all cross sections of the community – if you're clever you can try and spot the heir to the estate, who will then explain the history of the photographs in the snug. A single bar and three interconnected, comfortable rooms, each with log fires in winter. Good value sandwiches, and a reliable blackboard menu. Draught Bass, Boddingtons and Marstons Pedigree. Seats on the terrace.

OPEN: 12–3. 5.30–11. (12–11 Fri & Sat. 12–3. 7–10.30 Sun.)
Real Ale.
Children in eating areas. No dogs lunchtimes.

WOOLLEY MOOR

White Horse   Tel: 01246 590319

White Horse Lane, Woolley Moor, Derbyshire DE5 6FG
Free House. Bill & Jill Taylor, licensees.

There just may be classical music playing in the restaurant but there are plenty of opportunities to get away from it if you want to. In winter you can tuck yourself into a corner of one of the bars and in summer spread yourself out in the big garden. The pub has a printed menu with the usual selection of traditional bar food and quite a number of daily blackboard specials. Much of the food is from very local sources: butcher, baker and an enthusiastic vegetable grower. Among the most popular dishes are steak and kidney pie, lamb Isabella and fresh salmon, prawns and courgettes au gratin. In winter there are special food nights; beer festivals are held throughout the year. Draught Bass, Jennings Mild and three guest beers – one weak, one medium and one strong – these change weekly. Excellent walks nearby.

OPEN: 11.30–2.30 (3.30 Sat & Sun). 6–11.(5–10.30. Sat & Sun)
Real Ale. Restaurant.
Children in eating area or restaurant. Dogs in public bar.

The Daily Telegraph
"Q" Publications
The Quiet Pint Cover Painting Competition

There were 107 entries for the competition to find a cover picture for this, the 1997 edition of The Quiet Pint. It had to be a watercolour of a pub that would blend happily with the design of the cover, with Messrs Daler Rowney, Winsor & Newton and Royal Sovereign enthusiastically offering generous prizes.

Choosing the the top three paintings was no easy task. The judges – Vicky Unwin, The Daily Telegraph's Books and Publications Manager, Laura Gascoigne, Editor of Artists and Illustrators Magazine, Derek and Josephine Dempster, Publishers of The Quiet Pint – were faced with a lot of talented contributions.

First Prize went to Alan Palmer for his painting of The White Swan at Richmond, because it answered the requirements of the cover best of all. Second prize went to A.H.Marshall's very colourful picture of The Royal Fountain, Cleobury Mortimer, Nr. Kidderminster, and third prize to Robert Gibson for a striking painting of The Fox and Hounds in Chelsea.

There will be another competition to find a cover for the 1998 edition of The Quiet Pint next year. Details will be announced nearer the time in The Daily Telegraph.

First Prize from Daler Rowney for Alan Palmer's White Swan, Richmond

WADWORTH 6X

a day in the life . . . .

Wadworth & Co. is a family run brewery in Devizes, Wiltshire. It was set up in 1875 by Henry Alfred Wadworth then aged just 22 and already having accumulated some six years' brewing experience. Wadworth was a man who lived life to the full, from regular ballooning exploits to completing the first ever cycle ride from London to Bath (two and a half days on a bone-shaking iron tyred bicycle).

Today, descendants of his brewing partner, JS Bartholomew, run this classic brewery. Wadworth 6X and 6X Export are brewed in an impressive original Victorian brick brewhouse - The Northgate Brewery, which has been in operation since 1885. However, Northgate may not have survived after 1945 - having fallen into disrepair

during the war, a famous London architect was invited to make his recommendations on its renovation. Resplendent in long black coat, trilby, spats and white gloves, his brief inspection resulted in the haughty pronouncement that; "You might as well tear it down and start again".

Shocked, Wadworth pai his fee and hurriedly saw hir off to the train station Thankfully, Northgate ha survived despite the grea man's gloomy prognosis!

It is a brewery rich i tradition that is still on displa every working day. Shir horses have been used for ove

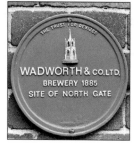

a century and ale continues t be delivered to Wadwort houses, situated within a tw mile radius of the brewery using a team of four - Harry Henry, Prince and Waggone Each weighs just under a to with an average height o eighteen hands. They work a two pair drays, each pullin approximately three tons.

The picture show Gordon Snook, head horsema and Barry Petherick, secon horseman with Waggoner an Prince.

Wadworth & Co. is one of the few brewers still with a cooper - one of brewing's most evocative skills and first mentioned in England in the

array of tools and collection of beer pump clips - not to mention visiting photographers eager to capture his skills on film....

Sign writing is another

ale of 4.3% ABV. With a unique full-bodied taste and rich malty flavour, finely balanced by the addition of whole hops, it takes its name from the ancient habit

etter Books of the City of ondon in 1298. When a half

aade cask comes out of the team bell, Alastair Simms nly has sixty-five seconds to nock down the truss hoops ncircling the wooden staves nd bend the barrel into shape. e works surrounded by an

skill on show daily at Wadworth. A team of five craftsmen custom produce signs and internal fixtures for pubs throughout the year.

A further unique aspect of Wadworth is the presence of a working open copper - more modern breweries only use stainless steel.

6X is a connoisseur cask

of branding casks with X's to indicate strength. 6X is available on draught and in 500ml cans, while 6X Export (5% ABV) is available in 500ml bottles.

See the nomination forms at the rear of the Quiet Pint to see how you could win one of ten cases of 6X Export.

Second Prize from Winsor & Newton for A. H. Marshall's Royal Fountain,
Cleobury Mortimer, Nr Kidderminster.

Third Prize from Royal Sovereign for Robert Gibson's Fox & Hounds, Chelsea

D

DEVON

BARNSTAPLE

Corner House   Tel: 01271 43528

108 Boutport Street, Barnstaple, N. Devon
Free House. Christine Billet, manager.

Built on the site of the old East Gate, The Corner House is a traditional town
alehouse. A drinking man's pub with an unspoilt interior. Popular with local
office workers, particularly at lunchtimes Friday. Sustaining simple bar
snacks – sandwiches and filled rolls to go with the M & B Brew X1 and the
weekly changing guest beer.

OPEN: 11–3. 5–11.(11–11 Fri & Sat. 11–3. 7–10.30 Mon)
Real Ale.
Dogs on leads.

BARNSTAPLE

Rolle Quay   Tel: 01271 45182

Rolle's Quay, Barnstaple, N. Devon
Free House. John & Mary Lawton, licensees.

Granted a charter in 930 AD Barnstaple claims to be one of the oldest
boroughs in England; it was only one of four Devon boroughs mentioned in
the Doomsday Book. Overlooking the river Taw, this friendly, welcoming pub
consists of three separate buildings. Such a long local history is bound to
attract a few ghosts and one has taken up residence at Rolle Quay; there are
regular hauntings by a spirit who, according to the landlord "has a wry sense
of humour". Two comfortable bars serve a good range of real ales. All the
food on the reasonably priced bar menu is home-made – the daughter of the
house does the cooking. Ushers Best Bitter, Cotleigh Barn Owl and two
other changing guest beers. Seats in the garden.

OPEN: 11–11 (12–10.30 Sun)
Real Ale.
Children welcome. Dogs on leads.
Wheelchair access.

BOVEY TRACEY

Cromwell Arms Hotel   Tel: 01626 833473

Town Centre, Bovey Tracey, Devon TQ13 9AE
Free House. John & Dorothy Tribble, licensee.

Pronounced "Buvvy" for those of us who are uninitiated, this delightful small town is on the edge of Dartmoor. At the centre of which you'll find the Cromwell Arms – an attractive old building, inside which are two comfortable bars and a dining room with distant views of Dartmoor. Busy and popular, they serve a tradional English menu with daily specials. Tetleys, Wadworths 6X and St Austells Hicks Special Draught. Seats on the small terrace.

OPEN: 11–3. 5.30–11.20 (12–3; 7–10.30 Sun)
Real Ale. Restaurant.
Children in restaurant only. Dogs on leads.

BRANSCOMBE

Fountains Head   Tel: 01297 680359

Branscombe, Nr Seaton, Devon EX12 3BG
Free House. Mrs Catherine Luxton, licensee.

Mrs Luxton's husband runs his own brewery a mile away, so there is never any fear of this pub running dry. Two bars: both of them cosy with log fires in winter. The snug is panelled; the other used to house the village smithy. There is also a small no-smoking room for children. Fishy things on the bar menu such as cockles, mussels and crab sandwiches; home-made lasagne, cottage pie, salads, and occasionally fried sardines and salmon steaks with fresh herbs as daily specials. Fish and chip night Fridays. Speciality food nights at other times. Own brewed beers include Branoc, Jolly Geff, Olde Stoker in the winter and Summa' That during the summer. Farm cider. Seats outside on the terrace.

OPEN: 11.30–2.30. 6.30–11 (11.30–2; 7–11 winter).
Real Ale.
Children in own room lunchtimes; over 10, in eating area eves. Dogs on leads.

BRANSCOMBE

Masons Arms   Tel: 01297 680300

Branscombe, Nr Seaton, Devon EX12 3DJ
Free House. Veronique Pontoizeau, manager.

What a lucky community to have two pubs offering so much. At the lower end of the village, which is scattered over the slopes of a steep green bowl, the Mason's Arms – with its thatched hats over the doors and thatched umbrellas over the tables – can't be missed. The rambling beamed bar has a roaring log fire, with a spit that is used every day for roasting beef, lamb, pork, sometimes goose and occasionally, a whole shark. The menu now includes dishes from Italy, France, South America and the Caribbean. Bar food includes soups, sandwiches, ploughmans, Caribbean Chicken, Chicken Piri Piri, steak & kidney pudding, grilled fish, mullet, sea bass, plaice or whatever is available. There is a bar specials board which includes vegetarian dishes and this changes every day. Sundays: sandwiches, ploughmans and a roast only. Part of the restaurant is no-smoking, and there is a no-smoking bar in place of the top dining room. Always five real ales: Otter Bitter, Bass and Dartmoor, plus two guest beers. Eighty wines on the list, eighteen by the glass. Twenty whiskies; a beer festival in August and a whisky festival in December. Last but not least, two draught ciders and in summer a local farmhouse cider.

OPEN: 11–3. 5.30–11. (11–2.30. 6–11 winter)
Real Ale.
Well behaved children may be allowed, away from bar. Dogs on leads.
Live jazz and other music Fridays.
Wheelchair access.

BROADCLYST

Red Lion   Tel: 01392 461271

Broadclyst, Nr Exeter Devon EX5 3EL
Free House. Stephen & Susan Smith, licensees.

On what must have been the country road to Exeter, The Red Lion is in an idyllic situation; on the green, near the church in a quiet village largely owned by the National Trust. Well beamed, with an open fire in winter, this is a very popular comfortable old inn – on the recommended list when you visit the National Trust's Killerton House nearby. They offer a good tradional bar snack menu and interesting specials: Tanglefoot rabbit braised in a whisky and cream sauce or whole red mullet, oven baked in an orange and ginger sauce. Bass, Eldridge Pope Royal Oak, Worthingtons Best, Wadworths 6X and a changing guest, currently Morlands Old Speckled Hen. Good range of house wines by the glass. Seats at the front of the pub, and in the garden.

OPEN: 11–3. 5.30–11
Real Ale. Restaurant, not Sun eve.
Children in own room. Dogs on leads.

BURRINGTON

Portsmouth Arms   Tel: 01769 560397

Burrington, Nr. Umberleigh, N. Devon EX37 9ND
Free House. Mrs Maureen Casey, licensee.

Burrington is a charming Devon village, in wooded countryside overlooking the Taw valley. We are in "Tarka the Otter" country here. The Portsmouth Arms, on the Exeter to Barnstaple road backs onto "Tarka-land." Over 300 years old, this is another haunted Devon pub. Thought to be haunted by just one female ghost, a visiting psychic maintains there are actually two of them haunting the dining room. So if the plates move, it isn't the strong ale it is more of an ethereal spirit. As the dining room is decorated in medieval style –suits of armour and other period pieces – maybe it is a case of them thinking they are back home. Two bars, beamed, with big log fires. Home-made bar food: soups, well filled sandwiches, local trout and salmon and roast lunches. All the vegetables are grown locally. Ushers Best Bitter, Draught Guinness, Tetleys Best, Portsmouth Arms Bitter and Milligans Mist. A local Dry and Sweet Cider. You can sit in the garden and enjoy the views of the glorious Taw valley.

OPEN: 11.30–2.30. 6.30–11
Real Ale.
Children welcome. Dogs on leads.
Extensive fishing on the River Taw.
Bedrooms.

CHURCHSTOW

Church House   Tel: 01548 852237

Churchstow, Nr Kingsbridge, Devon
Free House. Nick & Vera Nicholson, licensees.

A fine 13th century village pub with a long welcoming bar, stone walls, low oak beams and a great stone fireplace complete with a bread oven. There is the usual choice of reliable bar food; home-made soup of the day, sandwiches, ploughmans, whitebait, garlic mushrooms, a choice of fish dishes, devilled chicken, beef and onion pie, fresh pasta and steaks are among the dishes on offer; daily specials on the blackboard. The carvery Wednesday to Saturday evening and Sunday lunchtime is so popular you are advised to book well in advance. The restaurant is no-smoking. Bass, Marstons Pedigree and a guest beer.There is a conservatory for days that are less than warm, and seats outside in summer.

OPEN: 11–2.30. 6–11. Closed first Mon in Feb.
Real Ale. Restaurant (not Sun eves)
Children welcome. Dogs on leads.
Wheelchair access.

COLYTON

Kingfisher   Tel: 01297 552476

Dolphin Street, Colyton, Devon EX13 6NA
Free House. Graeme & Cherry Sutherland, licensees.

In the 16th century Colyton was a prosperous wool town owned by the Marquis of Exeter who carelessly lost his head and his land when he had a little argument with Henry VIII. The locals clubbed together to buy the manor by a deed of Feoffment, and sixteen Feoffees direct the town to this day. The Kingfisher is a friendly pub with a comfortable bar and an upstairs family and games room. Bar food and daily specials, home-made cheesecakes and fruit pies. Badger Best, Tanglefoot, Charles Wells Bombardier and several guest beers on hand pump. Farm ciders. Seats on the terrace overlooking the garden.

OPEN: 11.30–2.30. 6–11.
Real Ale.
Children in eating area. Dogs on leads.

DARTINGTON

Cott Inn   Tel: 01803 863777

Dartington, Nr Totnes, Devon TQ9 6HE
Free House. David & Susan Grey, licensees.

Licensed since 1320, this thatched pub is reputed to be the second oldest in the country. Plenty of beams, flagstone floors, big fireplaces and lots of room. One area is non-smoking. There is an excellent hot and cold buffet at lunchtime with a choice of salads, cold meats, Dart salmon, quiches, etc. The menu changes daily; in the evening the menu is more extensive and could include lamb casserole with rosemary and orange dumplings, Torbay sole stuffed with crab, rib steak with mushrooms and red wine sauce and home-made puds. West Country cheeses. Bass, Butcombe Bitter and Cotts Wallop. Farm ciders, and an extensive wine list, some by the glass. The pub has its own cricket team, so if you are feeling energetic, fixtures can be arranged. The flowery courtyard is pleasant to sit in during the summer. Dartington Hall, the largest medieval house in the west of England, is close by and worth a visit.

OPEN: 11–2.30. 5.30–11.
Real Ale. Restaurant.
Children in restaurant. Dogs on leads.
Bedrooms.
Wheelchair access tricky but can be arranged.

DODDISCOMBSLEIGH

Nobody Inn   Tel: 01647 252394

Doddiscombsleigh, Nr Exeter, Devon EX6 7PS
Free House. Nick Borst-Smith, licensee.

At first glance, it's more of a village house than an inn, with a proper front garden and gate. The inn sign is nearly hidden by foliage along with a notice saying "Unsuitable for Motor Vehicles". Ignore it. With map in hand, navigate the deep Devon lanes to reach the Nobody Inn with its striking beamed bar, antiques and open fires. There is a tremendous wine list, 250 different malt whiskies and varied, well thought-out bar food and changing blackboard menu. " Specials" could include locally caught trout, venison casserole, fillet of salmon om smoked salmon pasta with an asparagus sauce and from the bar menu, the untimate toasted sandwich – ham, cheese, tomato, onion herbs and sweet pickle in brown bread. But that's not all: here you find a cheese-lover's paradise, usually about 40, many from the county. Not difficult to find a good wine to go with the cheese as between 700–800 are in the pub cellar; about 20 by the glass. Nobody's Beer (brewed by Branscombes), P.G. Steam Best Bitter from the RCH Brewery in Somerset, Bass and other guest beers on hand pump or from the cask. Farm ciders. Seats on the terrace from where you can look at the view and appreciate the peace and quiet.

OPEN: 12–2.30. 6–11 (7–11 winter).
Real Ale. Restaurant evenings only (not Sun)
No children under 14, and only in restaurant. No dogs.
Bedrooms.

DREWSTEIGNTON

Drewe Arms   Tel: 01647 281224

The Square, Drewsteignton, Devon
Whitbread. C. F Sparks, tenant.

We were taking a chance including this wonderful old thatched pub, as its future was uncertain, but there is a new tenant now so things should get back to normal. The social life of the village revolves around the Drewe Arms; spiritual matters are taken care of by the church next door. Virtually unchanged since the 19th century, the ales and draught ciders are kept on racks in the tap room. Now there is a small restaurant. They are also doing bed and breakfast so things are really looking up. The " Save the Drewe Committee" obviously did its stuff. Life at the Drewe Arms goes on. An unspoilt ale house should have a preservation order put on it and be supported by everyone.

OPEN: 11.30–3. 6–11. (11.30–11 Sat).
Real Ale. Restaurant.
Children welcome. Dogs on leads.
Bed and breakfast.

EAST DOWN

Pyne Arms   Tel: 01271 850207

East Down, Nr Barnstaple, N Devon EX31 4LX
Free House. Jurgen & Elizabeth Kempf, licensees.

It has a spacious, low-beamed bar with a wood-burning stove, horse harnesses and horse racing prints on the wall, a flagstone-floored games area with a juke box and a no-smoking gallery with tables and chairs. Good varied pub food – home-made soup, sandwiches, paté, ham and eggs, four different recipes for mussels, scampi provençale, lots of steaks etc; also a daily specials board which will include some vegetarian dishes. Selection of puddings. Worthington Best Bitter and Draught Bass. A selection of wines, some by the glass.

OPEN: 11–2.30. 6–11.
Real Ale.
No children. Dogs, maybe, you have to ask.

EXETER

Imperial   Tel: 01392 434050

New North Road, Exeter, EX4 4HF
Wetherspoons. Jonathan Randall & Wendy Gardner, managers.

This fairly new Wetherspoon outlet opened in February 1996. Originally The Imperial Hotel, it has quickly become a landmark. Next to St David's railway station, it is set in its own substantial grounds. Much of the original "grand" decor, as befitted the hotel's standing in Exeter society, still exists. Inside there are now three separate bars, one of which is in the old orangery. Originally built to house a collection of tropical plants, it had been allowed to deteriorate but is now fully restored, and from the windows there is a wonderful view across the city. Always six, reasonably priced, cask conditioned ales. A full menu is available throughout the day, seven days a week.

OPEN: 11–11
Real Ale
No children.No dogs.

EXETER

White Hart   Tel: 01392 79897

66, South Street, Exeter, Devon EX1 1EE
Davy's. Graham Stone, manager.

This old coaching inn practically at the centre of Exeter, is entered through a wisteria-covered loggia. The bars are abundantly beamed and filled with gleaming copper that reflects the glow of the fires in winter. Food in the Tap bar is generous traditional and includes: soups, sandwiches, filled baked potatoes, sausage and mash, steaks and daily specials. The wine bar – called Bottlescrue Bill's – has bare stone walls and sawdust on the floor. It serves much the same choice of food. This bar boasts it's own small garden with a huge vine, colourful geraniums and lots of roses in summer. There is also an "Express Menu" in the Hotel Bar. Here you can have cod and salmon fishcakes with a black bean dressing, casserole of pork Devon style with sweet cider, sage, fried apples and sage dumplings, vegetarian dishes and others. Davy's Old Wallop, Bass and John Smiths. Davy's wines, vintage port and Bucks Fizz in summer when you can also eat from a barbecue in the courtyard.

OPEN: 11.30–3. 5–11.(11.30–11 Sat)
Real Ale. Three Restaurants. No food in the two smaller bars Sun.
Children welcome. No Dogs.
Bedrooms. Limited wheelchair access to certain areas.

HARBERTON

Church House Inn	Tel: 01803 863707

Harberton, Nr Totnes, Devon TQ9 7SF
Free House. Mrs Jennifer Wright, licensee.

Built around 1100 AD this listed building is full of oak panelling and is reputed to have the oldest oak screen in the country. It has a huge inglenook fireplace around which are oak pews of great antiquity. Food here is up to the mark and lunchtime specials include – fillet of plaice marinated in white wine, garlic and lemon, steak & kidney pie, home-made soups, locally made sausages, curries and grills. A choice of "little eats" rollmops, devilled whitebait, mushrooms in garlic butter and their own chicken liver paté etc., ploughmans and various sandwiches. There is also a daily specials board. Virtually all the vegetables are fresh, free range eggs from the village, local pork, lamb and the rabbits have a Devon accent too. Bass and Courage Best plus two weekly changing guest beers. Good selection of wines.

OPEN: 12–2.30. 6–11 (11.30–3 Sat)
Real Ale. Restaurant.
Children in family room & eating area. Dogs on leads.
Occasional jazz or folk. Morris dancers in summer.
Accomodation will be ready late 1996.
Wheelchair access to pub only.

HAYTOR VALE

Rock   Tel: 01364 661305

Haytor Vale, Nr Newton Abbot, Devon TQ13 9XP
Free House. Christopher Graves, licensee.

Only 200 years old, yet this old coaching inn has gained a ghost called
Belinda. Legend has it that Belinda was having an affair with the coachman
and was murdered by the coachman's wife on the stairs of the pub. Some
guests have seen her but not the landlord. It's a friendly local serving a small,
rural community. It has two panelled rooms, both with big log fires, a no-
smoking dining area and a restaurant. Good choice of bar food with all the
usuals: home-made soup, ploughmans etc., local rabbit in mustard sauce,
curries, poached Devon salmon, steaks and daily specials. Also home-made
puddings and a Sunday roast. It can get very busy. Dartmoor Best, Royal
Oak and Thomas Hardy on hand pump. Malt whiskies. A pretty garden and
an adjoining terrace are in high favour in summer. Being on the edge of the
Dartmoor National Park there are some wonderful walks.

OPEN: 11–3. 6–11 (11–11 Sat.)
Real Ale. (No snacks Sun or Bank Holidays)
Children in eating area of bar. No dogs.
Bedrooms. Wheelchair access.

HOLCOMBE ROGUS

Prince of Wales   Tel: 01823 672070

Holcombe Rogus, Wellington, Somerset TA21 0PN
Free House. Douglas Whiteley, licensee.

In the middle of the village, the pub was originally a row of 16th century
cottages which were knocked into one about 150 years ago. Three rooms,
a long main bar, a games room with pool and darts and a no-smoking snug.
Traditional bar food only: soup always available, ploughmans, sandwiches,
pizzas and they do a very popular "fry-up" – sausage, egg, chips and beans.
Cotleigh Tawney and Otter Bitter, all the other beers are guests. One or two
all the time, seven or eight on bank holidays. Outside, there are plenty of
seats in the large lawned walled garden.

OPEN: 11.30–3 6.30–11
Real Ale.
Children welcome. Dogs on leads.
Wheelchair access.

HOLBETON

Mildmay Colours   Tel: 01752 830248

Fore Street, Holbeton, Plymouth, Devon PL8 1NA
Own Brew. Andrew Patrick, licensee.

Originally The George, this friendly little pub was renamed in 1967 on the death of Lord Mildmay. The sign is painted in his racing colours. All the beers they brew here have horsey names, 50/1, Old Horsewhip, SP, and Colours Best. If there is a quiet moment, you can look over the brewery. Bar food includes ploughmans, beef in ale, Mexican dishes and daily specials on the large blackboard. They have a popular carvery on Friday and Saturday evening, also Sunday lunchtime. Plenty of tables outside at the front of the pub and in the garden at the back.

OPEN: 11–3. 6–11 (occasionally all day summer).
Real Ale. Carvery Restaurant closed Mon–Thurs.
Children welcome. Dogs on leads.
Bedrooms.

HOLNE

Church House   Tel: 01364 631208

Holne, Nr Ashburton, Devon TQ13 7SJ
Free House. N E & W J Bevan, lease.

This pub is on the edge of Dartmoor and the place to be after walking in the beautiful National Park. It has a pine-panelled bar, a comfortable, carpeted lounge – both with big log fires in winter – and a no-smoking restaurant. Lovely views over the moors from the front of the pub. Fresh, locally produced organic vegetables, some of them home-grown; fish from Brixham; carefully chosen local meat. Lunchtime snacks could include mushrooms in garlic butter, filled baked potatoes, various ploughmans, sandwiches, omelettes and vegetarian dishes. Daily specials – perhaps grilled local sole, Dartmoor rabbit pie, casseroled Devon lamb in cider and various home-made puddings, such as fruit crumble or trifle. Furgusons Dartmoor, Blackawton Bitter, Wadworths 6X and Palmers IPA. Guest beers vary. Farm cider and a good choice of house wines.

OPEN: 11.30–3. 6.30–11 (12–3, 6.30–10.30 winter Sun–Thurs).
Real Ale. Restaurant. No snacks evenings.
Well behaved children in eating area: none under 7 in eve. Dogs on leads.
Bedrooms.

IDDESLEIGH

Duke of York Tel: 01837 810253

Iddesleigh, Winkleigh, Devon EX19 8BG
Free House. Bill Pringle, licensee.

Very popular village pub, full of friendly regulars, some of whom can be found pulling their own pints when the landlord is busy elsewhere, a tradition in this long, low 14th century thatched pub dating back to before the arrival of the present landlord. The customers divide themselves into categories: those who tell the landlord later what they have had and then pay up, and those who pull pints for themselves and anyone else and put the money straight into the till. Too many locals around for the obvious in this day and age –those who just serve themselves and don't pay. Home-made bar food, sandwiches, soups, local sausages, fish and steaks. Locally made ice-creams. Wednesday evenings you can experience an "Oriental Adventure" and choose from a selection of dishes from India, Pakistan and South East Asia. As they say – some are hot, – some are not! Booking essential. Cotleigh Tawny, Adnams Broadside and Jollyboat Mainbrace Bitter from the cask. Farm ciders and guest beers. A pretty back garden to sit in.

OPEN: 11.30–3. 6.30–11. Real Ale. Restaurant. No food Mon in winter. The licensee would prefer the children on leads and the dogs loose if well behaved! Bedrooms. Limited wheelchair access.

LITTLEHEMPSTON

Tally Ho! Tel: 01803 862316

Littlehempston, Nr Totnes, Devon TQ9 6NF
Free House. Alan Hitchman & Dale Hitchman, licensees.

Thought to be the prettiest pub in Devon, dating back to the 14th century. It has a comfortable, low beamed room, filled with interesting objets d'art, fresh flowers, and pieces of antique furniture. Wide range of bar food: home-made soups, paté, vegetarian dishes, steaks and fish fresh from Brixham. A favourite choice at lunchtime is the fresh Brixham "fish and chips", Brixham fisherman's pie and roast duckling; also "Bonnie Prince Charles' Breakfast" – scrambled egg, smoked salmon, brown bread and butter and salad. In addition there are "daily specials" and a "veggy" board, which changes every day. Home-made puddings. Furgusons Dartmoor, Palmers Tally Ho! and Teignworthy Reel Ale on hand pump. There is a flower-filled courtyard for sitting in during the summer.

OPEN: 12–2.30. 6–11.
Real Ale.
Children in eating area. Dogs on leads.

LUSTLEIGH

Cleave   Tel: 016477 223

Lustleigh, Nr Newton Abbot, Devon
Heavitree. A Perring, tenant.

An attractive 15th century thatched inn at the centre of a picturesque village
nestling in the Dartmoor foothills. Lustleigh – with its thatched cottages
surrounding the village green and church – is considered one of the prettiest
villages in Devon. The Cleave, with its charming, low-ceilinged bar and huge
inglenook fireplace, is open every day for bar meals, lunchtime and evening.
Home-made soups, sandwiches, ploughmans, pasta dishes, salads, lots of
roasts and their own steak & kidney pie. Sunday roast lunches. Home-made
puddings too. Whitbread Pompey Royal, Bass, Boddingtons and Flowers
Original on hand pump. Farm ciders. Morning coffee.

OPEN: 11–3. 6–11 (11–11 Sat).
Real Ale.
Children in no-smoking family area. Dogs on leads.
Wheelchair access.

LYDFORD

Castle Inn & Hotel   Tel: 0182 282 242

Lydford, Nr Oakhampton, Devon EX20 4BH
Free House. Clive & Mo Walker, licensees.

You are not far away, here, from two of the most spectacular waterfalls in
Devon: the White Lady Waterfall which slides 100 ft down a rocky shute to
join the River Lydd in a wooded valley below, and the Devil's Cauldron –
along a twisting footpath – where the river crashes through a narrow gap,
down a vertical, mossy cliff. After that excitement, back to the Castle Inn –
a very pretty, pinkwashed Tudor building – for refreshment. Lots of room in
the low-beamed bars which are filled with antique settles and interesting bits
and pieces collected over the years, including some Lydford pennies dating
back to King Ethelred the Unready. A good choice of food: home-made
soups, Devon cheese platter, mussel chowder, Moroccan vegetable

casserole, Provençale chicken with olives, herbs and tomatoes, are among those on offer, plus home-made puddings. There is also an evening restaurant. Blackawton Bitter, Wadworths 6X, Fullers London Pride and up to three different guest beers a week on hand pump or from the barrel. Wines by the glass. Bucks Fizz in the summer. Seats on the terrace; also a pets corner for children. Part of the restaurant is no-smoking.

OPEN: 11.30–3. 6–11.
Real Ale. Restaurant.
Children in eating area bar (lunchtime only), Snug & Restaurant.Dogs on leads.
Bedrooms.
Wheelchair access to the hotel.

MILTONCOMBE

Who'd Have Thought It   Tel: 01822 853313

Miltoncombe, Plymouth, Devon PL20 6HP
Free House. Keith Yeo & Gary Rager, licensees.

Many years ago this pub applied for a licence to sell spirits. Locals were generally of the opinion that the odds were not in its favour. Much to everyone's surprise the licence was granted, eliciting the reaction "Well, who'd have thought it" – and the name stuck. This also explains the celebratory inn sign of a man waving a piece of paper surrounded by a crowd of locals. There is a panelled bar in this fine old pub, with polished tables and a big fireplace: two other rooms, one no-smoking, have half barrels (with cushions) for seats. Generous helpings of bar food: home-made soups, patés, chicken or vegetable curry, grilled trout, steaks. Daily specials on the blackboard. On Sundays there is less choice but always a roast. Blackawton Headstrong, Eldridge Pope Royal Oak, Golden Hill Exmoor Ale, Bass and Wadworths 6X on hand pump. Farm ciders. Tables outside on the terrace. There is also a pub ghost called Ed Bere, (how do they know his name?).

OPEN: 11.30–2.30 (3 Sat) 6.30–11
Real Ale. Restricted food Sun lunchtime.
No children. Dogs on leads.
Wheelchair access no problem.
Folk club Sun evenings.

NEWTON ST. CYRES

Beer Engine   Tel: 01392 851282

Newton St. Cyres, Exeter, Devon EX5 5AX
Own Brew. Peter Hawksley, licensee.

Built a hundred and fifty years ago when the trains first arrived, this old station pub now brews its own beer – all of it with a railway theme: Rail Ale, Piston Bitter, Sleeper (rather strong) and the new Return Ticket. You can see through to the Brewery from the Boiler Room Bar. The landlord would rather concentrate on just the ales but realises that you have to offer good pub food to make a living. Reasonably priced bar meals include cod and parsley pie, speciality sausages, lasagne, casseroles, seafood dishes, at least three vegetarian dishes and a vegetarian soup. Roast lunches every Sunday. Rumour has it there is a female ghost walking the pub but as the only people who have seen it are the chaps who have had quite a few beers – it could be a case of a vivid imagination! There are tables in the large sunny garden.

OPEN: 11–11 Mon–Sat. 12–10.30 Sun. If live music Fri/Sat. Cellar Bar open until midnight.
Real Ale. You can take home up to 20 litres of beer from the Brewery.
Children in eating area. Dogs on leads.
Rock & Blues Fri/Sat eve. Folk/Jazz Sun lunch.

POUNDSGATE

Tavistock   Tel: 01364 631251

Poundsgate, Newton Abbott, Devon TQ13 7NY
Ushers. Ken & Janice Comer; lease.

Legend has it that one night in 1638 the devil called at the Tavistock on his way to collect the soul of a gambler. He ordered a beer and as he drank steam rose from his lips. He paid with a gold piece and when he'd gone the gold turned to dry leaves. Let's hope nothing so dramatic happens when you stop at this hospitable old inn for refreshment. There are big log fires and flagstone floors in the bars and a family room in what was the stables. Home-made soups – some vegetarian, ploughmans, steak sandwiches, lots of fish dishes, steaks, curries, good selection of vegetarian main dishes, all day breakfasts, daily specials. Ushers Best and Founders, Courage Best. Farm cider. Mulled wine in winter. The pub has a lovely garden to sit in during the summer.

103

THE QUIET PINT

OPEN: 11–3. 6–11.
Real Ale.
Children in family room. Dogs on leads.
Wheelchair access not easy but they are willing to give all assistance.

RATTERY

Church House   Tel: 01364 642220

Rattery, South Brent, Devon TQ10 9LD
Free House. Mr B & Mrs J Evans, licensees.

A listed building dating back to about 1028 AD, it is said to be connected to the church by a tunnel, which indicates the monks knew when they were onto a good thing. Good range of bar food, soups of course, filled rolls, home-baked ham, smoked salmon, chicken, Algerian lamb and home-made puddings. Children's menu. Furgusons Dartmoor, Dartmoor Legend and guest beer on hand pump. Range of old malt whiskies. Farm cider. Wine. Lovely views of the wooded countryside from the pub.

OPEN: 11–2.30. 6–11.
Real Ale.
Children in eating areas. Dogs on leads.
Wheelchair access.

SHEEPWASH

Half Moon   Tel: 01409 231376

Sheepwash, Nr. Hatherleigh, N Devon EX21 5NE
Free House. Ben Inniss & Charles Inniss, licensees.

Very much a fishing pub, and totally geared up for it: a rod room, somewhere to dry yourself when you fall in, and a shop where you can buy all those bits and pieces you thought you had packed. Ten miles of glorious fishing on the River Torridge and plenty of room at the bar for the "one that got away" stories. Bar snacks at lunchtime are all you could wish: home-made soup, pasties, home-cured ham, salad, ploughmans. Dinner at night includes roasts, steaks and fresh fish. Courage Best and Directors, Marstons Pedigree, and one locally brewed ale as a guest on hand pump. Selection of malt whiskies. Impressive wine list.

OPEN: 11.30–2.30. 6–11.

Real Ale. Evening restaurant. Snacks lunchtimes.
Children lunchtime only. Dogs on leads.
14 Bedrooms en suite.
Wheelchair access.

SOUTHPOOL

Mill Brook   Tel: 01548 531581

Southpool, Kingsbridge, Devon TQ7 2RW
Free House. Jed Spedding and Liz Stirland, licensees.

Very popular with yachtsmen who can virtually sail straight in and order
drinks. This tiny pub is one of a few with variable opening times; they
depend on the state of the tide in the creek, which runs into the middle of
the pretty little village. It has a charming, comfortable bar with lots of fresh
flowers on the tables. Good, dependable bar food such as soup, filled
potatoes, cottage pie, smoked mackerel, fish pie and chilli. Daily specials
with Devon Apple Cider Cake to finish. Ruddles Best, Bass and Wadworths
6X plus a guest ale on hand pump. Farm ciders.

OPEN: 11–3. 5.30–11 (summer). 11.30–2.30. 6.30–11 (winter). May open
longer in summer.
Real Ale
Children in eating room. No dogs.

STICKLEPATH

Devonshire Inn   Tel: 01837 840626

Sticklepath, Oakhampton, Devon EX20 2NW
Free House. John & Ann Verner-Jeffreys, licensees.

There has been an inn here since 1640. The Devonshire has a low-beamed,
slate-floored bar with comfortable furnishings and a big log fire in winter. The
owners have made a big effort to create a very welcome "new" village inn,
and they are succeeding because the food they offer – including a roast
every Sunday – is reasonably priced and freshly cooked to order; they also
cater for small dinner parties on request. Real ales include St. Austells
Tinners, Bass and some guest beers. Also farm ciders.

OPEN: 11–3. 6.30–11. (11–11 Fri & Sat & Summer)
Real Ale.
Children welcome. Dogs on leads.

105

THE QUIET PINT

SWIMBRIDGE

The Jack Russell Tel: 01271 830366

Swimbridge, Nr Barnstaple, N. Devon
Free House. Mr & Mrs Johnson, licensee.

On the main Barnstaple to South Molton road, the name of this delightful village is thought to derive from a priest living at the time of Edward the confessor – Sawin of Birige. When you visit the pub, it is well worth seeing the inside of the church too; there is a handsome font, a medieval stone pulpit, a very fine screen and outside, a medieval spire. Even the pub is quite old. There has been a hostelry on the site since the beginning of the 18th century; this one got it's name from The Rev. Jack Russell who popularised the Jack Russell terrier. Good log fires in winter, and lots of home-made game dishes. Familiar, reliable bar food, grills and a Sunday carvery. Draught Bass. Wadworths 6X and local guest ales.

OPEN: 12–3. 5–11 (12–11 Thurs–Sat. 12–10.30 Sun.)
Real Ale. Restaurant.
No Children. Dogs on leads.

TOPSHAM

Bridge Inn Tel: 01392 873862

Bridge Hill, Topsham, EX3 0PQ
Free House. Mrs Phyllis Cheffers, licensee.

Four miles South East of Exeter, Topsham, was until the 16th century the main port for Exeter. A weir contructed downstream in the late 13th century prevented access to the city, and started a legal battle that went on for three centuries. However, when it was finally settled the River Exe had silted up, making it unnavigable. Built after all the legal squabbling, the Bridge, an 18th century Grade II building, has been in the same family for five generations. Traditional pub food only, but lots of different beers. Years ago they used to brew their own beer now they just keep trying different ones, but you could find: Draught Bass, Branscombe Vale Branoc, Exe Valley Devon Glory and about nine others.

OPEN: 12–2. 6–10.30. (11 Fri & Sat. 12–2. 7–10.30 Sun)
Real Ale.
Children welcome. No Dogs.
Wheelchair access.

TOTNES

Kingsbridge Inn   Tel: 01803 863324

9 Leechwell Street, Totnes, Devon TQ9 5SY
Free House. David Wright, licensee.

There is a new landlord at the Kingsbridge Inn, which dates back to the time of the Domesday Book and is situated in the oldest, highest part of this historic town. Pass through the low beamed rambling bar and you will find a room with an ancient spring bubbling into a stone trough. No printed menu, as everything is fresh and cooked in small quantities. The dishes are written up on three blackboards and are changed several times – apart from the lunchtime snack board – the only thing not home-made is the ice cream. Food includes fish from Brixham, filled French sticks, Devon cheese platter with home-made pickle, rabbit pie, fishermans pie Florentine, Pork Normand, creamy leek and Stilton bake, filled pancakes and you can always get a sandwich. There is a more elaborate evening menu. The " Mexican Specials Board" is a new addition and is "on trial". Home-made puds too. Furgusons Dartmoor, Bass, Courage Best and Theakstons Old Peculiar and a guest beer on hand pump. Farm ciders. In winter, mulled wine. The ghost here is Mary Brown, a maidservant murdered by the landlord 300 years ago and buried in one of the walls. The previous landlady, Mrs Triggs, and her daughter, both saw her in daytime and at night. They chatted to her and said she was friendly but mischievious – can't say I blame her!

OPEN: 11.30–2.30. 5.30–11.
Real Ale.
Children in eating area. Dogs on leads.
Local groups Wed evenings.

WIDECOMBE-IN-THE-MOOR

Rugglestone Inn   Tel: 01364 621327

Widecombe-in-the-Moor, S. Devon TQ13 7TF
Free House. Lorrie & Moira Ensor, licensees.

There is an elaborate carved sign of Uncle Tom Cobbleigh on the village green, commemorating Widecombe fair, the song that made the village famous. Widecombe fair is still held on the second Tuesday in September in this delightful village high on Dartmoor. Just south of the village this quiet old country inn is a popular stopping off place for walkers and anyone else enjoying the surrounding countryside. Stone floors – just the thing for all those walking boots – and open fires. Two local girls, who run their own small bakery, bake for the pub. Traditional pasties and pot meals. The pub deliberately excludes children and chips! Draught Bass, Flowers IPA and Butcombe Bitter. Seats in the large garden. Plenty of dogs come here; there are three in the pub – two Jack Russells and a retriever.

OPEN: 11.30–2.30.(11–3 Sat). 7–11 (6–11 Summer)
Real Ale.
No children. Dogs on leads.

WONSON

Northmore Arms   Tel: 01647 231428

Wonson, Nr. Throwleigh, Devon BX20 2JA
Free House. Maureen Miles, licensee.

This pub is on Dartmoor, slightly south west of Drewsteignton and not far from the castle remains at Gidleigh. It's an area rich in prehistoric stone circles. The Northmore is another, "find the pub with a good map place." Drive down the narrow lanes, or better still walk. As you see, the pub is open all day so you can take your time. Beams and good fires inside and traditional simple bar food of the sandwich or roast lunch sort. Changing ales, some of them from local breweries. There is a garden to sit in from where you can appreciate the peace of the countryside.

OPEN: 11–11
Real Ale
Children welcome. Dogs on leads.

WOODBURY SALTERTON

Diggers Rest   Tel: 01395 232375

Woodbury Salterton, Nr Exeter, Devon EX5 1PQ
Free House. Sally Pratt, licensee.

Naturally, one of our antipodean cousins changed the name from the Salterton Arms to the Diggers Rest 21 years ago and I bet it is the only one in the country. All sounds very jolly with a summer skittle alley and a games room. It has a good-sized, comfortable, heavily beamed bar. Bar food includes filled pancakes, steak & kidney pie, liver & bacon, home- cooked gammon, curries, sandwiches and soups. There are daily specials. Always

fresh vegetables and home-made puddings. No kangaroo steaks here!
Furgusons Dartmoor, Tetleys and Bass on hand pump. Local farm ciders.
You get some splendid views over the local countryside from the terrace of
this thatched village pub.

OPEN: 11–2.30. 6.30–11.
Real Ale.
Well behaved children in family area. Dogs on leads.

WE'RE NOT AGAINST ALL MUSIC

We are not against all music in pubs. Live music is totally acceptable
and the pub piano is part of that tradition. Moreover, publicans nearly
always announce an event giving those who want to avoid it a chance
to drink elsewhere. What most QUIET PINT readers object to is having
to compete against a constant barrage of background music to hear
or be heard.

First glimpsed deep in the heart of Dorset, these three glorious Badger varieties can now be found countrywide.

D
DORSET

ASKERSWELL

Spyway Inn   Tel: 01308 485250

Askerswell, Nr Bridport, Dorset
Free House. Don & Jackie Roderick, licensees.

Down a country lane, deep in glorious countryside near the busy market
town of Dorchester – Thomas Hardy's home for many years and the setting
for his novel, "The Mayor of Casterbridge" – is this rambling, beamed old
pub, with scrubbed pine tables and settles, crammed with decorative rural
artefacts. Familiar pub food with daily-changing specials: rabbit or steak and
onion pies, mushroom leek and courgette bake, home-cooked ham, steaks
and lots of salads. Ushers Best, Ruddles County and Adnams Southwold
Bitter. Wines by the glass, country wines and a large selection of malt
whiskies. A pretty garden to sit in and admire the view. There is a good walk
to Eggardon Hill, 827 feet high, with an Iron Age hill fort and Bronze Age
barrows at the summit.

OPEN: 10.30–2.30 (10.30–3.00 Sat). 6–11.
Real Ale.
No children. No dogs.

BOURNEMOUTH

Goat & Tricycle   Tel: 01202 314220

27–29 West Hill Road, Bournemouth, Dorset BH2 5PF
Wadworths. Mr & Mrs D Hill, managers.

Close to the town centre, and without a juke box, pub games or a dart
board, this well run inn is a quiet oasis in what is a bleak area for "quiet "
pubs. Two bars, big winter log fires and a welcoming host. Our reporter says
a keen sense of humour is essential, though it is a joy to be insulted with
such abandon and good taste by the landlord! An appealing menu of home-
cooked favourites: soups, prawn and cheese garlic bread, sausages, a

sausage platter, half a pint of shell on prawns, cheese on toast with curry pickle, joint of lamb with rosemary and garlic, daily specials and "school" puds: jam roly-poly, treacle pudding and bread & butter pudding. Wadworths ales, six guest bitters and Gales local fruit wines. Seats in an enclosed flowery courtyard.

OPEN: 12–3. 5.30–11.
Real Ale.
Maybe dogs, you have to ask.

BOURNEMOUTH

Moon in the Square   Tel: 01202 314940

4–8 Exeter Road, Bournemouth BH2 5AD
Wetherspoons. Russell & Julie Downing, temporary managers.

Another very large Wetherspoons' pub. This one was a Forte coffee house until someone forgot to turn off the coffee. Burnt to a crisp. Rebuilt two years ago, it is now a thriving town-centre pub. On two floors, the top floor is non-smoking. As with all these outlets there will be five or six real ales, and a big selection of guest beers from the smaller breweries. One of the beers will be considerably cheaper than elsewhere. Consistently reliable bar food. A big plus among town centre pubs in that there is an outside drinking area.

OPEN: 10.30–11. (12–10.30 Sun)
Real Ale
No children. No Dogs.

BRIDPORT, West Bay

The Bridport Arms Hotel   Tel: 01308 422994

West Bay, Bridport, Dorset DT6 4EN
Palmers Brewery. John & Carla Jacobs, licensees.

On the edge of the beach at West Bay, the harbour area of Bridport, you'll find the Bridport Arms. A big, low beamed 16th century thatched building, with flagstone floors, two bars – one quite small – and a restaurant. As you might expect right by the seaside, there are lots of fish dishes on the bar menu also home-made lasagne, cottage pie and salads; a full restaurant menu too where you'll find dishes such as chicken with a peppercorn and lemon sauce. Palmers ales, and a varied wine list.

OPEN: 11–2.30. 6–11. (Sun 12–10.30. May to Mid Oct 11–11)
Real Ale. Restaurant.
No children. Dogs on leads.

CORFE CASTLE

Fox Inn   Tel: 01929 480449

West Street, Corfe Castle, Dorset BH20 5HD
Free House. Miss A Brown & Graham White, licensees.

Views of the castle ruins from the attractive and sheltered sunny garden,
makes this old village pub particularly appealing during the summer, real
fires keep you warm in winter. Cromwell destroyed the castle in 1646, and
much of the stone was used to build many of the surrounding houses in the
17th century. Medieval remains have been found within the pub, and these
have blended well with the changes made over the years. Traditional bar
food from the varied menu plus daily specials, some vegetarian dishes
always available. Sunday roasts in winter. Gibbs Mew, Bishops Tipple,
Eldridge Popes Thomas Hardy, Royal Oak, Ansells and Tetleys Bitter. Look
for the old well found during restoration work inside the pub. Good walking
country.

OPEN: 11 –3. 6–11. (11–2.30. 6.30–11 winter)
Real Ale.
Children in the garden only. Dogs on leads.

CORSCOMBE

Fox Inn   Tel: 01935 891330

Corscombe, Dorset, DT2 0NS (off A356 S. of Crewkerne towards
Dorchester, take the left turn to Corscombe & Halstock, NOT the one just
to Corscombe. Pub at bottom of hill)
Free House. Martin & Susie Lee, licensees.

Another one of those pubs that can be difficult to find; just think of it as good
practice at map reading. Don't give up. It is well worth it. On the road,
painted white with a thatched roof, thatched hats over the doors, climbing
roses, hanging baskets and a general air of well-being. This is just the sort
of pub we would all like as our local. Food is all you could wish for too: fish
soup, (mussels, prawns and whitefish), either as a starter or main course,
vegetable soup of the day, garlic mushrooms, sardines grilled with garlic
butter, devilled crab meat, Fox's favourite (chicken in cream sauce), stuffed

pancakes, seafood risotto with clams, scallops, monkfish and brill served with an endive sauce, venison casserole with thyme and red wine, sirloin steak with different sauces, puddings on the blackboard. Lots more. All fresh vegetables, and all freshly cooked. Definitely no microwave or chips here. Wide selection of wines. Exmoor Ale, Fullers London Pride and a Smiles beer. They also make their own damson vodka, sloe gin and elderflower cordial. Tables outside and by the stream; there is also a conservatory full of flowers and a large oak table to seat 22.

OPEN: 12–2.45. 7–11-ish.
Real Ale. Restaurant.
Well behaved children. No dogs.
Bedrooms will be ready early 1997.

CRANBORNE

Sheaf of Arrows   Tel: 01725 517456

4, The Square, Cranborne, Dorset BH21 5PR
Free House. John & Kate Tuppen, licensees.

If you want to see how beer is brewed, you can from the viewing gallery in the converted stables behind the Sheaf of Arrows, where the owners have installed their own micro-brewery. One of the ales has naturally been named "Quiver". Two traditional bars, a public and lounge bar plus a function room/ skittle alley. Full menu, bar snacks and specials which could be Italian tomato soup with garlic croutons, smoked mackerel, Dorset fish pie, beef lasagne, Spanish pork with olives, vegetarian cottage pie, and home-made puds. Daily specials are on the blackboard. All their own beers. Seats in the garden, outside bars too.

OPEN: 11.30–3. 6–11. (12–3. 7–10.30. Sun)
Real Ale
No Dogs.
Three en-suite bedrooms.

HINTON St MARY

White Horse   Tel: 01258 472723

Hinton St Mary, Sturminster Newton, Dorset DT10 1NA
Free House. Chris Thomas, licensee.

North of Sturminster Newton, off the B3092, in glorious Dorset countryside, this early 19th century pub is a pub with a difference –it leans towards the oriental. The chef is Scottish, but lived for some time in Hong Kong, so her cooking tends towards stir-fry dishes. Thailand lamb is a speciality. However, the seven page menu means you should find something to your liking. Two bars: a public and restaurant bar, which is a little like a cocktail bar. No regular beers – they are constantly changing. You can sit outside in the flowery garden and enjoy some lovely views.

OPEN: 11.30–2.30. 6.15–11.
Real Ale
Children welcome. Dogs in public bar only.

KINGSTON

Scott Arms   Tel: 01929 480270

8 West Street, Kingston, Nr Corfe Castle, BH20 5LH
Greenalls. Simon Trevis, manager.

Kingston is a typical Purbeck village, built of local stone. The Scott Arms, with the handsome inn sign and Virginian creeper covered walls, is easy to spot. When I tell you that they can accomodate about 190 people inside and 280 outside, you know this is quite a sizeable, rambling old place. Well thought out bar menu: home-made soup, ploughmans, mushrooms in garlic, baked crab, curries, a vegetarian dish, steak and kidney pie, venison in a port sauce, seasonal salads, daily specials and a choice of puds. Greenalls range of ales, guests constantly changing, but always Ringwoods Best. "Best view in Dorset," said the landlord, "overlooking Corfe Castle and the Purbeck Hills – and we've got our very own ghost." Not only are there seats in the large garden but also the Mayor of Casterbridge's tombstone. Good walks nearby.

OPEN: 11–2.30. 6–11 (12–3. 7–10.30 Sun)
Real Ale
Children welcome, not in little bar. Dogs welcome but not on the carpeted bit or the dining area.

MARSHWOOD

Bottle Inn   Tel: 01297 678254

Marshwood, Nr Bridport, Dorset DT6 5QJ
Free House, Frances Vincent, tenant.

In very good walking country with glorious views around Lamberts Castle –
about 400 yards up the road. On the edge of the village of Marshwood, this
15th century thatched pub is in an enviable position. From the back you look
over the Axe valley and from the front over the Vale of Marshwood. Two bars
with an inglenook fireplace and the original old Dorset oven and bacon
smoker. A varied menu from which you can pick and choose to create your
own substantial meal. "I have a good reputation for my Sunday lunches,"
says the landlady, "also cook my own ham .....I'm well known for my hams;
we don't have any of that plastic stuff up here. I've also got some very
friendly farmers who grow extra veggies and bring them to me." What more
could you ask for. Wadworths 6X, Otter ale, two keg ales: Toby and Tetley
– Strongbow Cider and Draught Guinness. There is a play area for children
in the garden.

OPEN: 12–3. 6–11
Real Ale
Children welcome. Dogs on leads.

MILTON ABBAS

Hambro Arms   Tel: 01258 880233

Milton Abbas, Nr Blandford Forum, Dorset DT11 0BP
Greenalls. Ken & Brenda Baines, tenants.

The new Milton Abbas, with its white thatched cottages, was built in the
1770s, replacing the earlier village, which was destroyed by the Earl of
Dorchester as he felt it spoilt the view from his mansion. The "new" village
is quite idyllic. In the summer you can sit in front of the Hambro Arms, and
admire its charming 18th century buildings. In winter, tuck yourself beside
the blazing log fires. Standard bar snacks, and a selection of hot dishes plus
the daily specials on the blackboard which include a selection of fresh fish.
There is a popular Sunday lunchtime carvery. Boddingtons and Flowers
Original ales. Seats outside on the terrace.

OPEN: 11–2.30. 6.30–11.
Real Ale.
No children. No dogs.

PLUSH

Brace of Pheasants   Tel: 01300 348357

Plush, Dorchester, Dorset DT2 7RQ
Free House. Jane & Geoffrey Knights, licensees.

Years ago, an attractive group of 16th century thatched buildings were combined to create the Brace of Pheasants, which is set in a peaceful hamlet in the Piddle Valley, not far from Piddletrenthide, with its own bubbling brook. A brace of stuffed pheasants welcomes you into the pub, where their cousins feature on the menu (when in season). Inside, all is as it should be; beamed, traditionally furnished, and with big log fires in winter. Good popular bar food with imaginative "extras": hot crab savoury, patés, soft herring roes with garlic butter, steak & kidney pies and fish pies. Evening menus go up a gear. Children's menu. Both the restaurant and family room are non-smoking. Smiles Best, Flowers Original, Wadworths 6X and between two and four guest ales always available. Seats, and a children's play area in the garden. Lovely walks.

OPEN: 11.30–2.30 (12–2.30 winter); 7–11.
Real Ale. Restaurant.
Children in family room. Dogs on leads.

PUNCKNOWLE

Crown Inn   Tel: 01308 897711

Church Street, Puncknowle, Nr Dorchester, DT2 9BN
Palmers. Mike Lawless, tenant.

Not far from Chesil Beach – that long strip of banked shingle fringing the Dorset coast – the Crown is a spacious, well run 16th century thatched Inn. Not only is it free of musak, it has no juke box, one armed bandits or cigarette machines. Wide and imaginative choice of well prepared food: home-made soup, freshly made sandwiches, ploughmans, salads, filled jacket potatoes, chicken chilli with French bread, fish and chips, as well as home-cooked steak and kidney pie cooked in Palmers Tally Ho! ale, pork, almond and mushroom casserole or rabbit and venison casserole, both cooked in white wine; grills and more besides. Children's portions and a traditional Sunday lunch. Palmers BB, IPA, Tally Ho! and 200 (the anniversary ale), and a selection of country wines. Seats in the big garden where they sometime erect a marquee for large functions. Outside bars. Delightful area with lots of walks.

THE QUIET PINT

OPEN: 11–2.30. 7–11.
Real Ale
Children welcome. Dogs on leads and to stay.
Bedrooms.

SEMLEY

Benett Arms   Tel: 01747 830221

Semley, Shaftesbury, Dorset SP7 9AS
Gibbs Mew. Joe Duthie, tenant.

You can't miss the Benett Arms when you come into Semley village on the
Wiltshire/Dorset border; it's three storeys high – unusual for this part of the
country – and opposite the village green. Just one bar, pleasantly furnished
with a good fire in winter. Bar food includes the well tried favourites: soups,
ploughmans and various sandwiches, plus omelettes, Wiltshire ham served
with either salad or chips, scampi royale, avocado and seafood salad,
venison pie, grills, steaks, occasionally bouillabaisse: also interesting daily
specials from the blackboard. Home-made puddings. Gibbs Mew ales:
Salisbury Best, Deacon and Bishops Tipple. Good extensive wine list. Inch's
ciders. Seats in the small garden.

OPEN: 11–3. 6–11.
Real Ale.
Children in upper bar. Dogs on leads.
Wheelchair access.

SHAFTESBURY

Ship Inn   Tel: 01747 853219

Bleke Street, Shaftesbury, Dorset SP7 8JZ
Badger. Gregg Noble & Sarah Bright, tenants.

The town of "Shaston" in Thomas Hardy's novels was modelled on the
historic town of Shaftesbury. Built on the edge of a 700ft high plateau, the
cottages lining the extraordinarily steep, cobbled Gold Hill, feature in many
tourist brochures and advertisements. The town has some very handsome
buildings, including the 17th century Ship Inn, which has an interesting,
simply furnished, panelled interior reflecting its age. The young gravitate
towards the public bar and the pool table over the weekend. Bar food
includes the pub stalwarts: home-made soup, sandwiches, paté, lasagne

and daily specials which sometimes lean towards the continental. Badger Best and Tanglefoot ales. Farm ciders. The Ship has an outdoor boules pitch and there are seats on the terrace.

OPEN: 11–3. 5–11 (all day Thurs–Sun)
Real Ale.
Children in eating areas. Dogs on leads.

SHAFTESBURY

Ye Olde Two Brewers   Tel: 01747 854211

24 St. James Street, Shaftesbury SP7 8HE
Free House. Richard & Maggie Pearce, licensees.

Just so you know where to aim for when you're at the top of the very steep – the word perpendicular comes to mind – Gold Hill, some bright spark had the pub's name painted on the roof. Under the roof you'll find a large, open plan, comfortable, carpeted bar with several differant drinking areas. All the food is freshly produced and there's something for everyone on the menu: soup, whitebait or crispy coated mushrooms, omelettes with various fillings, sandwiches, ploughmans, toasties, fish dishes, filled jacket potatoes, chilli con carne, lasagne, steaks, mixed grill and a vegetarian dish. Puds too. Well kept Wadworths 6X and Courage Directors are the permanent beers and there are quite a number of frequent guests. Wonderful views from the garden.

OPEN: 11–3. 6–11. (12–3. 7–10.30 Sun)
Real Ale
Children welcome. No dogs.

SHAVE CROSS

Shave Cross Inn   Tel: 01308 868358

Marshwood Vale, Shave Cross, Dorset DT6 6HW
Free House. Bill & Ruth Slade, licensees.

A 14th century hairdresser set up here so that pilgrims wending their way to the shrine at Whitchurch could have a trim before arriving. If you feel so inclined, you can still walk the route (without the haircut). The path is opposite the pub. The thatched pub is typical of the era, with beams, flagstoned floors, inglenook fireplaces and traditional furnishings. Bar menu varies from snacks to hot dishes with specials on the blackboard, among them could be lasagne, chicken ham and mushroom pie, Tiger prawns in filo pastry, char-grilled sardines or swordfish and gooseberry crumble with local ice-cream to finish. There's a children's menu and play area. Bass, Badger Best and Eldridge Pope Royal Oak. Sunny, sheltered garden.

OPEN: 12–2.30 (12–3 Sat). 7–11.
Real Ale. Closed Mon except Bank Holiday.
Children in lounge. Dogs in garden only.

SIXPENNY HANDLEY

Roebuck   Tel: 01725 552002

22 High Street, Sixpenny Handley, Nr Salisbury, Dorset SP5 5NR
Free House. Roger Greenhaugh, licensee.

Another address designed to confuse. Quite near the Dorset border, but definitely inside it – really nothing to do with Wiltshire, except to have the letters sorted. The signposts on the road from Blandford Forum to Salisbury point to '6d Handley'. The original Roebuck burnt down in 1920. The new one has one very comfortable bar with a good fire in winter. Better than average bar menus are listed on the blackboard. Good home-made soups and paté, sandwiches, quiche, salmon, chicken or steaks in good sauces. Ringwood Best Bitter, Fortyniner and varying guest beers. Well chosen wine list, several by the glass." Hardly an horticultural experience" says the landlord of the garden, "but there is grass and seats, and it is quiet."

OPEN: 11.30–2.30-ish. 6.30–11. (12–3. 7–11 Sun) Closed Mon. lunchtimes.
Real Ale
Children welcome. Dogs in garden only.

TRENT

Rose and Crown   Tel: 01935 850776

Trent, Nr Sherborne, Dorset DT9 4SL
Free House. Charles Marion-Crawford, licensee.

This very attractive pub really does have a sign outside saying "Dogs welcome, children on leads". Quite right too. A traditional 15th century village pub with an 18th century addition. Roses around the door, one big bar with smaller rooms off, flagstone floors, three open fires and a dining/conservatory at the back. A good choice of well cooked bar food, full menu and daily specials. Shepherd Neame Spitfire, Butcombe Bitter and two varying guest ales. Lovely views from the large garden. Swings and slides in the hope that children will stay in the garden.

OPEN: 12–2.30. 7–11. (12–3. 7–10.30 Sun)
Real Ale. Conservatory/Restaurant.
Children preferably in garden. Dogs welcome.

E
ESSEX

ARKESDEN

Axe and Compasses   Tel: 01255 250001

Arkesden, Essex, CB11 4EX
Greene King. Christou & Diana Themis, Lease.

If you are doing the touristy route you will probably have been to Clavering
to see one of Britain's smallest houses. Arkesden is just one mile north. Very
rural, this is an attractive popular local in a very pretty village. Basically a
spacious 17th century thatched pub which has been added to over the
years. Meals are served in either the bar or the restaurant. If you want just
bar food you can have sandwiches, home-made soup, mushrooms in garlic,
chicken leek and bacon crumble, steak and kidney pie or something from
the daily specials. A wider choice is available on the restaurant menu.
Greene King beers and a good wine list. Seats on the terrace among the
hanging baskets.

OPEN: 11–2.30. 6–11
Real Ale. Restaurant (not Sun eves).
Children in eating areas. No dogs.

BURNHAM-ON-CROUCH

Olde White Harte   Tel: 01621 782106

The Quay, Burnham-on-Crouch, Essex CM0 8AS.
Free House. John Lewis, licensee.

The Cowes of the East Coast and a mecca for thousands of yachtsman. The
largely Georgian High Street runs parallel to the river, The Quay, is too narrow
for vehicles so you walk past the yacht builders to get to the elegant, 17th
century Olde White Harte. You can't quite sail into the hotel but it does have
its own jetty, so if there is a high tide you can get really close, and believe
me, this is one of the places to be in Burnham and not only during Burnham

week. Enjoy a drink on the jetty or inside, among the beams in the comfortable bar. There is a good bar menu with a table d'hôte and à la carte menus in the restaurant. Tolly Cobbold IPA, Adnams Bitter and a good wine list.

OPEN: 11–3. 6–11. (11–11 Sat).
Real Ale. Restaurant.
Children if well-behaved. Dogs on leads.
11 Bedrooms en suite, eight others. Car park.

DAGENHAM

The Lord Denman   Tel: 0181 984 8590

270–272 Heathway, Dagenham, Essex
Wetherspoons. Dave Danskin, manager.

You have to admire Wetherspoons for taking on the most unlikely places and turning them into pubs. This was the local DSS building, now at least irate claimants have somewhere to drown their sorrows. Photos of 'local boys made good' are on the walls, among them Dudley Moore and Terry Venables. Named after the first Lord Denman, Lord Chief Justice of England, who lived in Dagenham from 1850 to 1852, there is a bust of Lord Denman in the bar. Reliable bar food and always six real ales, one of which is invariably cheaper than usual. On two levels, they have a special stairlift for wheelchairs. Seats in the garden.

OPEN: 11–11
Real Ale
No children. No dogs.

DEDHAM

Marlborough Head Hotel   Tel: 01206 323250

Mill Lane, Dedham, Essex CO7 6DH
Ind Coope (Allied). Brian & Jackie Wills and Linda Mowes, licensees.

One of the finest buildings in what is an attractive and busy village. The Marlborough Head was first licensed in 1704. This large, handsome, well beamed, friendly and comfortable pub has plenty of room for diners, and anyone taking morning coffee or afternoon tea. However it can get very busy, so arrive early if you want a table for lunch. Bar food includes soup, sandwiches, baked garlic mushrooms, quiches, savoury pancakes, cold smoked duckling, half a pheasant in wine and mushroom sauce, home-made puddings. Ind Coope, Burton and Flowers IPA under light blanket pressure. Seats in the patio garden and there is a large car park at the rear of the pub. Because of the Constable connection, this village gets very crowded during the summer, and parking can be difficult, (as I well know!). Alfred Munning's house, and a collection of his paintings can be seen at Castle House museum nearby.

OPEN: 10–11.
Real Ale.
Children in family room only. No dogs.
Bedrooms.

EARLS COLNE

Bird in Hand   Tel: 078722 2557

Coggeshall Road, Earls Colne, Colchester, Essex CO6 2JX T D
Ridley & Son. Colin & Lesley Eldred, lessees.

Mid-way between the villages of Earls Colne and Coggeshall, (an old wool village noted for its fine merchant's houses), and opposite the airfield used by the U.S. Air Force from 1942 to 1944 (now a Golf range – what else!), the Bird in Hand, situated as it was at the end of the runway, was regarded as a potential hazard. To lower its profile, the Americans decided to remove the pub's roof before it was inadvertently re-arranged by a low-flying aircraft. Now restored to its full height, you can see the 'before and after' photographs displayed in the saloon bar. Not a "foody" pub, it has, nevertheless, a full menu of favourite dishes – some of which are home-made, and these, understandably, are the most popular, and could be: a steak and kidney pie, beef lasagne or chicken curry. Home-made puds too. Ridleys range of ales; draught and bottled. Seats in the large garden.

OPEN: 12–2.30. 6–11 (7–10.30 Sunday)
Real Ale.
No children under 14. Dogs perhaps.
Wheelchair access.

FELSTED

The Chequers Tel: 01371 820226

Braintree Road, Felsted, Essex, CN6 3DL
Ridleys. Ruth Ripton, licensee.

In a quiet village, deep in the Essex countryside on the B1417 between the A120 and A 130. The saloon and private bars are quiet but a CD player is usually on in the public bar. Solidly built in the 19th century, the Chequers offers lunchtime and evening bar menus and barbecues on Sunday, weather permitting. Ridleys range of ales and John Smiths Bitter. Seats on the paved terrace overlooking Felsted School cricket field.

OPEN: 11–2.30. 6–11. (11–11 Sat,Sun & Summer)
Real Ale
Children allowed. Dogs welcome.

GREAT YELDHAM

White Hart Tel: 01787 237250

Poole Street, Great Yeldham, Halstead, Essex. CO9 4HJ.
Free House. Roger Jones, manager.

Built on the edge of the village in the 16th century, the half-timbered White Hart has recently been restored to its former beauty. A profusion of hanging baskets and tubs of flowers outside. Inside, low beamed ceilings, panelling and big log fires give it a wonderful ambience. Neither a pub nor a restaurant: two menus, but you can eat anywhere you like – informally in the pub, more formally in the no-smoking restaurant. From the snack menu you could have mushroom and sherry soup, chicken paté with toasted brioche and Cumberland sauce, a ploughmans with paté, cheese, plum chutney and bread, casserole of rabbit or grilled Lincolnshire sausages. The full menu offers hot mascarpone tart with poached garlic and grilled radicchio, spicy salmon and tuna patties with a peanut and cucumber dressing, baked fillet of cod with potato and onion tart and red pepper salsa, char-grilled sirloin steak with field mushrooms, roasted onions and roasted plum tomatoes. Delicious puds too and cheeses from Neals Yard. An extensive wine list; some wines by the glass. Adnams Best, Wadworths 6X, Charles West Bombadier and Fullers London Pride beers. Large gardens running down to the river Colne.

OPEN: 11–3. 6–11 (12–2. 7–10.30 Sun)
Real Ale. Restaurant. (not Sun Eve).
Children welcome. Dogs in garden only.

GOSFIELD

Green Man   Tel: 01787 472746

The Street, Gosfield, Essex
Greene King. John Arnold, lease.

Warm and friendly service and imaginative food are the hallmarks of this
pub. It has two small bars, and a no-smoking dining room. There is an
exceptional lunchtime cold table, with a wonderful choice of cold meats,
salmon or crab, game pies, salads, etc. The landlord is the whiz with the
carving knife. Home-made soups, fresh fish, lamb chops (done pink), roast
wild boar, pheasant in red wine, roast duck and home-made puddings.
Good, reasonably priced wine list. Greene King IPA and Abbot on hand
pump.

OPEN: 11–3. 6.30–11 (late supper licence)
Real Ale. Restaurant (no food and no restaurant Sun eves)
Well behaved children in eating area. Dogs if very restrained.

HORNDON ON THE HILL

Bell Inn   Tel: 01375 673154

High Road, Horndon on the Hill, Essex SS17 8LD
Free House. John Vereker, licensee.

An attractive 15th century coaching inn with a magnificent display of
hanging baskets and flowers in the summer. The Bell has been run by the
same family for over 50 years; when it was taken over in November 1938
they had no electricity and the pump in the courtyard was the only source
of water. Much has changed since then. Now the daughter of the house and
her husband run the pub, having added the nearby Hill House which they
manage as an attractive hotel. There's only one bar in The Bell and a
restaurant offering a wide choice of food and drink. Both the bar and the
restaurant can be busy, so arrive early to be sure of a table. Nothing frozen
here – even some of the vegetables are home-grown. Choice of interesting
soups, such as broccoli or mussels with saffron and vegetables. Rabbit and
bacon terrine, grilled salmon with mussels and chives and smoked chicken

and vegetable strudel, even corned beef hash with oyster mushrooms are just a few dishes from the changing blackboard menu. Home-made puddings as well. Good selection of wines, many by the glass or half bottle. The landlord has produced notes on what to drink with what, and you are also able to buy wine from him. Draught Bass, Hancocks IPA and Fullers ales on hand pump, plus a weekly changing guest beers. 144 different ales were tried last year. Seats outside in the courtyard. In competition with over 1,000 pubs, The Bell won the 1996 title "Free House of the Year" awarded by the paper `The Publican'. They must be doing something right!

OPEN: 11–2.30 (3 Sat). 6–11.
Real Ale. Restaurant.
Children in eating area. Dogs on leads.
14 en-suite bedrooms.

INGATESTONE

Cricketers   Tel: 01277 352400

Mill Green, Ingatestone, Essex CM4 0DS
Gray & Sons. Mrs E Marriage, tenant.

An interesting old building among the mix of Tudor, Georgian and Victorian houses in this attractive village. The pub overlooks Mill Green Common, where they once played cricket, and no doubt after the match, refreshed themselves in the bar. There is talk of using the green once more for its original purpose. Two bars, one of which is used as a restaurant. Bar snacks include: jacket potatoes, filled baguettes, ploughmans also fresh fish, steaks and daily specials. Greene King IPA and Abbot. A good choice of wines. Seats on the terrace overlooking the cricket green and in the garden at the back of the pub.

OPEN: 12–3. 6–11
Real Ale. No food Sun eves.
Children welcome. Dogs on leads.

LEIGH ON SEA

Crooked Billet   Tel: 01702 714854

51 High Street, Leigh-on-Sea, Essex SS9 2EP
Ind Coope (Allied). Andrew & Mairi Heron, managers.

Dating back to the 16th century, in what might be called a bracing position against the sea wall. Tudor beams and plasterwork were found when restoration work was carried out, and it is thought the pub was originally a farmhouse. From the lounge bar you can sit and look out to sea, warmed by a solid fuel stove. During the year there is a choice of over 6 different beers from the barrel. A beer festival is held twice a year in Spring and Autumn when more than 30 beers are served from casks in the cellar, which is open to the public. Bar food consists of home-made soups, filled rolls, ploughmans, a seafood platter is a speciality of the house, plus daily specials and some vegetarian dishes. There is a big terrace where pretty hanging baskets and window boxes are a feature during the summer, and from where you have a view of the working harbour.

OPEN: 11–11. Lunchtime meal snacks only.
Real Ale. No food Sun lunchtime.
No children. No dogs.

LOUGHTON

The Victoria Tavern   Tel: 0181 5081779

Smarts Lane, Loughton, Essex IG10 4BP
Charringtons. John Wilkes, tenant.

If you are walking the dog in Epping forest, this is the place to make for, muddy boots and all. Apart from the beer, you might come here for the food. "We're a very food oriented house" says the landlord, "we do everything, nothing frozen except the chips." Standard bar snacks: home-made soup, sandwiches, ploughmans and daily specials. From the blackboard: steaks, home-made pies, fish dishes, fish and chips – good satisfying fare. Thwaites Craftsman, Bass, Greene King IPA and varied guest ales. An aviary in the garden contains about eighty different birds: budgies, love-birds, cockatiels, finches and canaries.

OPEN: 11–2.30. 6–11. (12–3. 7–10.30 Sun.)
Real Ale
Children in garden only. Dogs on leads.

MILL GREEN

Viper   Tel: 01277 352010

Mill Green, Nr Ingatestone, Essex CM4 0PS
Free House. Fred Beard, licensee.

If you address a postcard quite simply to "The Viper Inn, England," you can ignore the town, county and postcode – it will reach its destination. The Viper is quite unique, probably named when there was an abundance of vipers (adders) on local common land: a 14th century listed building, with a pretty flowery garden in an enchanting wooded setting. It has four bars, two with carpets, two parquet (for those still in their walking boots). The food is simple bar food of the fill-a-gap variety, not sit down meals. There is a monthly changing choice of three ales from the smaller, less well known breweries. Seats outside in the attractive garden.

OPEN: 11–2.30 (3 Sat). 6–11.
Real Ale. Lunchtime snacks.
Dogs on leads.
Wheelchair access but difficult.

PELDON

The Peldon Rose   Tel: 01206 735248

Mersea Road, Colchester, Essex CO5 7QJ
Free House. Alan & Ariette Everett, licensees.

Aptly named – with its rose-pink walls – this mainly 14th century rambling country pub has two heavily beamed bars and a big no-smoking-dining conservatory which is only opened at weekends in the winter, but well used all week in the summer. Lots of tables in the bars, but the pub can get very busy. Seats in the garden in the summer. All the food is prepared and cooked "in-house": sandwiches, salads, lasagne, boeuf bourgignon, fresh fish when available, and other dishes. Sunday: roast beef and Yorkshire pudding. Daily cream teas in summer, and at weekends in winter. Boddingtons, Flowers Original and IPA, perhaps one guest on hand pump. Choice of wines.

OPEN: 11–2.30. 5.30–11.
Real Ale. Restaurant only Fri & Sat eves.
Children welcome away from bar. Dogs on leads.

PLESHEY

White Horse   Tel: 01245 237281

Pleshey, Chelmsford, Essex CM3 1HA
Free House. John & Helen Thorburn, licensees.

A mile long rampart, built in Norman times, encircles the village of Pleshey,

129

THE QUIET PINT

to protect it from the marauding natives. The pub itself dates back to the late 15th century; original timbers and floors can still be seen in the present bar. There is a new bar, so you have plenty of room to spread out. Seats on the terrace and in the garden during the summer. Extensive bar food: ploughmans, filled jacket potatoes, huffers (a local bread roll) with a variety of fillings, fish dishes, steak and something for the vegetarian. A full à la carte menu is provided in the restaurant. The pub also holds speciality months, during which they offer varying menus from different countries. You will need to telephone for details. A range of beers is available, selected from the best of British brewing. Nethergate Best and Tolly Original and regularly changing guest beers which could include Crouch Vale and Ridleys. There is an extensive list of wines from various parts of the world. Also a pub ghost, a lady in blue with her cat! The cat you see in daylight is real, and belongs to the pub.

OPEN: 11–3. 7–11.
Real Ale. Restaurant
Children welcome. No dogs.

RICKLING GREEN
Cricketers' Arms   Tel: 01799 543210

Rickling Green & Quendon, Saffron Walden, Essex CB11 3YG
Free House. Jo & Tim Proctor, licensees.

As you would expect from the name, The Cricketers' is in an enviable position overlooking one of the oldest cricket greens in North West Essex. At first sight a straightforward Victorian building, but it has hidden depths: it was originally a terrace of 16th century cottages, remains of which can be seen in the timbered saloon bar. A rambling old place with a reputation for interesting food – traditional French fish soup, a dish of smoked fish, their own chicken liver paté, chicken in apricot and cream sauce, medallions of lamb, liver and bacon, steaks cooked in various ways, a number of vegetarian dishes, mussels in various guises – a speciality of the house – balti curries, home-made puddings and much more. Whatever can be home-made on the menu – is. Apart from Flowers IPA the beers are nearly all from local breweries and change regularly, the only rule is that they have one strong bitter, a dark mild and one other bitter. Good wine cellar. Delightful terrace from where you can watch the cricket, or just relax and do nothing.

OPEN: 12–3. 6–11. (Summer Sundays. All day)
Real Ale.

130

N.B. There could be music in part of the pub, but one bar will always be music-free. Restaurant.
Children welcome. Dogs on leads.

SAFFRON WALDEN

Kings Arms   Tel: 01799 522768

Market Hill, Saffron Walden, Essex
Free House. Brian Banks, manager.

The street plan of Saffron Walden, with its wonderful 15th and 16th timber-framed houses, dates back to the 12th century when the original market was established under the castle walls. Originally Chipping (Market) Walden, it was renamed Saffron Walden after the discovery that the profitable saffron crocus grew well in the local soil. It's a lovely old town with a market place and tree-lined High Street. Not far from the market you'll find this comfortable, friendly pub serving traditional home-cooked lunches, ploughmans, sandwiches, sausages etc. Greene King IPA ale, Carlsberg and Kronenbourg on cask. Farm cider. Seats in the garden.

OPEN: 11–3. 5–11 (11–11 Sat).
Real Ale. No food Sunday.
Dogs on leads.

SHALFORD

The George   Tel: 01371 850207

The Street, Shalford, Essex, CM7 5HH
Free House. Ken & Elaine Lavery, licensee.

In a pretty village, the 15th century George is heavily timbered with low beams and a huge log filled inglenook fireplace. A friendly pub serving plenty of pub favourites – they have both a bar and full restaurant menu – something for everyone. Adnams Broadside, Greene King IPA, Wexford (an Irish Cream) and an occasional guest beer. Outside there are tables on the large terrace.

OPEN: 11–3. 7–11. (Sunday 12–3. 7–10.30)
Real Ale. Restaurant.
Children if eating only. No dogs.

STANSTED MOUNTFITCHET

Dog & Duck   Tel: 01279 812047

58 Lower Street, Stansted Mountfitchet, Essex, CM24 ALR
Greene King. Andrew Brennan, tenant.

An old pub 100 yards from the station and only 50 yards from Mountfitchet castle; built in Norman times and destroyed by King John. This is a busy place, noisy with traffic, but the quiet side streets have some interesting buildings. The Dog and Duck, over 400 years old, weatherboarded and beamed, is a fine traditional Essex pub. Two bars: public and saloon, serving a satisfying bar menu: all sorts of filled rolls, chicken Kiev, sausage egg and chips – that sort of thing. Greene King ales and some guest beers. Tables in the garden.

OPEN: 10–2.30. 5.30–11.
Real Ale.
Children preferably in garden. Dogs very welcome, bowls of water for them.

STOCK

Hoop   Tel: 01277 841137

21 High Street, Ingatestone, Essex
Free House. Albert Kitchin, licensee.

Food all day in this 450 year old pub and they offer, on average, 500 different ales over the year: some on hand pump, some straight from the cask. They provide a good selection of dishes, with the emphasis on fish: grilled monkfish or skate, swordfish, trout florentine with dill sauce, paella. The all day menu is simpler: soups, omelettes, hotpot. The range of ales, including some from the tiny independent breweries, is so extensive it is best to go and see what's on offer. There is a beer festival on May 1st each year at which you have a choice of 150 ales. Farm cider, wines by the glass, mulled wine in winter. Seats outside in the pretty garden.

OPEN: 11–11.
Real Ale. Meals & snacks all day.
Children in eating area. Dogs on leads.

TILLINGHAM

Cap & Feathers
Tel: 01621 779212

8 South Street, Tillingham, Nr Southminster, Essex CM0 7TH
Crouch Vale. John Moore, tenant.

A traditional, old-fashioned 15th century pub. Clapboard and tiles – so familiar in the eastern counties of England. Cosy, low-beamed timber rooms have a timeless quality which encourages you to linger and appreciate all that's on offer. There is a no-smoking family room, and an area with an old bar billiards table that takes one old shilling to operate. Bar food changes daily. The pub smokes its own food so there could be smoked beef or trout also beef and venison pies, soups, lasagne and home-made puddings. Crouch Vale Woodham IPA, Best Bitter, SAS, Willie Warmer in winter and a guest beer. Farm cider and English wines.

OPEN: 11.30–3. 6–11.
Real Ale.
Children in No-Smoking family room. Dogs on leads.
Bedrooms.

WIDDINGTON

Fleur de Lys
Tel: 01799 540659

High Street, Widdington, Saffron Walden, Essex CB11 3SG
Free House. Robert Bunten, licensee.

Percy the Peacock, who gave this pub his vote of approval, is sadly missed. A resident of the local wildfowl park, he decided that village life was more congenial. A born escapee, he was returned several times but prefered the village to wander in for the odd snack, and the pub tree as his des.res. Now he seems to have escaped for ever, as no-one has seen him for some time. Only one bar in his old haunt and a no-smoking family room. The emphasis here is on the food, but there is always a good choice of beer on offer. Generous sandwiches, home-made soups, garlic mushrooms. Curries are a favourite. Choice of fish, venison and local game, vegetarian dishes and home-made puds. On Sunday there is always a roast and occasionally fresh fish. Adnams Broadside, Batemans, Ridleys, Burton Ale and Nethergate IPA. There are seats on a lawn at the side of the pub.

THE QUIET PINT

OPEN: 12–3. 6–11.
Real Ale. Restaurant, not Sun evening.
Children in Restaurant & No-smoking family room. Dogs on leads.
Folk music Fri evening.

WOODFORD GREEN

Travellers Friend Tel: 0181 5042435

496/498 High Road, Woodford Green, Essex IG8 0PN
Free House. M J Morris, licensee.

Just by looking at the address you can surmise that two houses have been made one, presumably when first licensed in 1832. If you happen to go upstairs you can see the join. An interesting feature of the partially panelled, main bar are its interesting "snob screens" – opaque glass screens, a foot square, which rotate to form a solid barrier for customers who want to conduct private business with each other without being overheard or their lips being read by anyone else. Traditional English lunchtime menu. A choice of sandwiches, lasagne, chicken curry, a roast and various salads. Ridleys IPA, Courage Directors and Best. Westons draught cider and two guest beers.

OPEN: 11–11 Mon–Sat. (12–3. 7–10.30 Sun).
Real Ale. No food evenings or Sunday.
Children welcome. Dogs on leads.
Al Fresco Jazz band twice yearly.

G

GLOUCESTERSHIRE

ALDERTON

Gardeners Arms   Tel: 01242 620257

Alderton, Tewkesbury, Glos.
Free House. J Terry, licensee.

Six miles east of Tewkesbury, in a village well off the beaten track, you'll find this 16th century, black and white thatched pub to whose door someone has clearly beaten a path, as it is consistently fully booked for lunch on Sundays. This isn't surprising as it is renowned for its imaginative food and well kept ales. Recently enlarged and refurbished, the Gardeners Arms is as relaxed and welcoming as ever. Bar food is served at lunchtime only: soup, ploughmans, paté – always a wide choice of dishes – all of generous proportions. Juicy home-cooked ham seems to be popular; also blackcurrant sorbet with brandy snaps. In the evening there is an à la carte restaurant, when the menu shifts up a gear: fresh Scottish fillet of salmon poached in a wine, cream and dill sauce, fillet of halibut, roast guinea fowl stuffed with spinach and grapes served with a Cumberland sauce, whole King Prawns pan-fried with garlic, chilli and ginger butter, steaks and racks of lamb. Set roast on Sunday, usually two sittings – book well in advance. Theakstons XB, Theakstons Best, Marstons Pedigree also Guinness, Gillespies, and several ciders. Seats on the two attractive terraces and in the garden.

OPEN: Mon–Thu: 11–2. (11–2.30 Fri–Sat) 6.30–11. Sun: 12–3; 7–10.30.
Real Ale. Only a roast lunch Sun. Restaurant. (Singer/guitarist plays every Thursday evening)
Children welcome. Dogs in bar lunchtime only.
Wheelchair access.

THE QUIET PINT

AMBERLEY

Black Horse   Tel: 01453 872556

Littleworth, Amberley, Stroud, GL5 5AL
Free House. Patrick O'Flynn, licensee.

Facing West with wonderful views of the surrounding countryside, including Minchinhampton Common which is owned and managed by The National Trust, the Black Horse is a friendly local pub – local in the true sense of the word as it is communally owned. One bar, one no-smoking family room and a new conservatory. Familiar pub food: soup, ploughmans, sandwiches, steak and kidney pie, chicken dishes and salads. Archers Best, Fergusons Dartmoor, Tetleys, Wadworths 6X, Youngs and other guest beers. Seating on the terrace and in the pretty garden.

OPEN: 12–3. 6–11. (12–11 Summer)
Real Ale.
Children welcome. Dogs on leads.

APPERLEY

Coalhouse Inn   Tel: 01452 780211

Apperley, Glos GL19 4DN
Free House. Mr & Mrs McDonald, licensees.

The Coalhouse is situated amid green fields at Coalhouse Wharf, on an isolated stretch of the River Severn between Tewkesbury and Gloucester. In summer you can sit out on the grassy bank by the river. In winter, when the Coalhouse is cut off by floods, you hail a passing boat – in some winters the river overflows into the bar! Informal, welcoming, with a buzz of conversation, it offers a traditional pub menu of well cooked and well presented food. The local Floodwater Bitter is a favourite; other ales include Eldridge Popes Royal Oak Strong Ale, Wadworth 6X, Guinness and various draught lagers. Draught cider.

OPEN: 12–2.30. 7–11 (6–11 summer).
Real Ale.
Children welcome. Dogs on leads.

ASHLEWORTH QUAY

Boat Inn   Tel: 01452 700272

Ashleworth Quay, Glos GL19 4HZ
Free House. Irene Jelf & Jaquie Nicholls, licensees.

Run by the Jelf family for hundreds of years, this small 15th century pub on
the banks of the river Severn offers the sort of welcome you would expect
from a pub with centuries of experience serving the traveller. It has two,
timeless, simply furnished rooms and a small back tap room with a couple
of settles and the casks of ales. Locally baked rolls for lunch, filled with
proper ham or mature cheddar and served with home-made pickle. Beers
include Smiles Best Bitter, Arkell BBB, Oakhill Yeoman 1767, and guest ales.
Westons Farm cider. Seats in the flowery sunny courtyard.

OPEN: 11–2.30. 6–11 (11–2.30. 7–11 winter).
Real Ale. Lunchtime snacks.
Children welcome. No Dogs.

BISLEY

Bear Inn   Tel: 01452 770265

George Street, Bisley, Glos GL6 7BD
Pubmaster. N S Evans, tenant.

An extra accolade here, as the licensees have ripped out the piped music
– so all is as it should be in this lovely 16th century inn. Architecturally it is
very attractive, with a colonnaded front supporting the upper storey, under
which is a small flagstone sitting area; it also has seats in the garden. Using
fresh local produce, the menus change daily: lots of filled French sticks with
salad, fried potatoes with garlic and herb butter, Mediterranean fish pie,
rabbit in cider, rosemary and mushrooms, vegetable pasties, home-made
burgers and other dishes. Daily specials. Local cheeses and home-made
puds are listed on the blackboard. Bass, Flowers Original, Tetleys, Castle
Eden and Old Speckled Hen on hand pump.

OPEN: 11–3. 6–11.
Real Ale. No food Sun.
Children in own room. Dogs on leads.

BLAISDON

Red Hart   Tel: 01452 830477

Blaisdon, Longhope, Glos.
Free House. David Burton, licensee.

The Red Hart is in an area famous for its plums. The village is a delight in spring, surrounded by plum orchards in blossom, and lane verges covered in daffodils. Inside, the beams of the pub are inscribed with past guest ales: 589 so far, growing by about 20 a week. Once a barrel is finished, a new one from a different brewery takes its place. You will get a warm welcome from an enthusiastic landlord with a good line in bantering abuse to and from the locals. Join in if you wish! There is a wide range of home-cooked food from crusty smoked ham rolls, steak, mushroom and ale pie to Cajun Turkey and a choice of vegetarian dishes. Home-made puds to follow. The same menu available in both the bar and the restaurant. Seats in the large garden.

OPEN: 12.30–3. 7–11
Real Ale. Who knows what's on offer, you have to go and see.
Children welcome, Dogs on leads.
Sometime live trad jazz on the terrace.

BRIMPSFIELD

Golden Heart   Tel: 01242 870261

Nettleton Bottom, Birdlip, Glos GL4 8LA
Free House. Catherine Stevens, licensee.

There are two main bars in this well-beamed 16th century country pub divided into several distinct areas, two of which are no-smoking. There is also a children's room. They have a blackboard menu and dishes vary from well-filled sandwiches, stuffed pancakes, fresh fish, steak & ale pie to more uncommon offerings such as Kangaroo, wild boar with chestnuts, ostrich steaks (now you know where your investment got to!) and the usual variety of salads. Outside there are seats on a sunny terrace. Timothy Taylors Landlord, Bass, Hook Norton, Marstons Pedigree on hand pump, or from the barrel. Beer festivals are held in May and August . Guest barrels behind the bar are changing all the time. Scrumpy and wine by the glass.

OPEN: 12–2.30. 6–11.
Real Ale.
Children welcome. Dogs on leads.

BROAD CAMPDEN

Bakers Arms   Tel: 01386 840515

Broad Campden, Nr Chipping Campden, Glos GL55 6UR
Free House. Carolyn Perry, licensee.

Popular with walkers following the Heart of England Way. Big log fires in the beamed bar during winter, seats outside on the terrace in summer. Reasonably priced bar food: soups, paté, ploughmans, the very popular pork chop in cider, Moussaka, beef in beer casserole, Chicken supreme in white wine sauce, fishermans pie and smoked haddock bake are among the fish dishes. Several vegetarian dishes and daily specials from the blackboard. Fruit crumbles, steamed puddings and other favourites for afters. Ales change all the time, but five usually on hand pump, mainly from small independent breweries such as Stanway, Donnington Wickwar, Hook Norton and lots more. Folk music nights the 3rd Tuesday of every month.

OPEN: 11.30–2.30. 6–11 (12–3. 7–10.30 Sun)
Real Ale.
Children welcome. No dogs in pub.
Folk night 3rd Tues in month.

BROCKWEIR

Brockweir Country Inn   Tel: 01291 689548

Nr Chepstow, Gwent NP6 7NG
Free House. George & Elizabeth Jones, licensees.

This pub, close to the Welsh border and by some strange postal logic placed in Wales, is really in Gloucestershire. It's a favourite with energetic people tramping the path by Offa's Dyke. The Dyke runs from Prestatyn at its north end, to Chepstow in the south. This defensive earthwork is thought to have been constructed by the Mercian King Offa in the 8th century. The 16th century Brockweir offers a welcome respite from the onward march. Traditional bar snacks and more substantial dishes always available. Three of the favourites are: pork in cider, beef in Guinness and a tuna fish bake, all made "in house". Freeminer Bitter, brewed not far away in the Forest Dean (Freeminer supply the House of Commons), Hook Norton Best and a changing guest on hand pump, also real cider. The ales are beautifully kept; Mr Jones, a retired chemist, is very proud of his beers.

OPEN: 12–2.30 (3 Sat). 6–11.
Real Ale.
Children in family room. Dogs on leads.
Bedrooms.

CHEDWORTH

Seven Tuns   Tel: 01285 720242

Chedworth, Cheltenham, Glos GL54 4AE
Free House. Brian Eacott, licensee.

Nearer to Cirencester and Northleach than Cheltenham, this is an attractive
17th century Cotswold pub – very popular during the summer walking
season. In winter there will be a big log fire in the lounge bar. All the noisy
fruit machines, video games, pool table etc are in a separate room beyond
the public bar. In the evening there is a full à la carte menu in the lounge bar;
a popular bar menu the rest of the time. Sunday roasts. George's Traditional
Bristol Bitter and Old Ambrose Bitter are brewed especially for the Seven
Tuns by a small Bristol Brewery; John Smiths and Courage Best are on
draught. Plenty of tables outside.

OPEN: 12–2.30. 6.30–11. (Sats: 11.30–3. 6.30–11.) Closed Mon
lunchtimes.
Real Ale.
Children & Dogs in bottom bar only.

CLEARWELL

Wyndham Arms   Tel: 01594 833666

Clearwell, Nr Coleford, Glos GL16 8JT
Free House. John & Rosemary Stanford, licensees.

In the centre of the village of Clearwell, in a valley on the edge of the Forest
of Dean, the 600 year old Wyndham Arms continues to do what it has been
doing for centuries: looking after the traveller in the best way possible. In the
comfortable beamed bar is an excellent choice of food: chicken liver paté,
a choice of open sandwiches, egg and prawn mayonnaise, whitebait,
smoked local wild salmon, a hot or cold seafood platter, steaks and a lot
more. The 18 dish hors d'oeuvre trolley is very popular. Chef's specials too.
Most of the vegetables, fruit and herbs home-grown. All food is cooked to
order, so expect a little delay. Seats outside on the terrace during the

summer. If you are lucky enough to be staying here and exploring the countryside, the Wyndham Arms can provide you with a well packed hamper. Bass and Hook Norton on hand pump. Excellent choice of malt whiskies and a good wine list. Some wines by the glass.

OPEN: 11–11.
Real Ale. Restaurant.
Children welcome. Dogs on leads.
Good wheelchair access.

COCKLEFORD

Green Dragon   Tel: 01242 870271

Cockleford, Nr Cowley, Cheltenham GL53 9NW
Smiles. Jamie James, manager.

A traditional stone-built, 17th century Cotswold pub. Both the public and lounge bar have huge inglenook fireplaces, flagstone floors in one bar, low ceilings everywhere and a landlord who when last measured was 6ft 2in, and who at the end of the day feels he has developed a permanent stoop and is really 5ft 8in! No real dining room – you eat where you can find somewhere to rest your plate – but there is a small secluded dining area for privacy. Quite an extensive menu, everything is cooked 'in house'. The standard menu has about 40 dishes; the specials board another 18. A lot of game on the winter menu, shot by the landlord, so you know where it has come from, and it is properly hung. Trout from the trout farm about 50 yards from the pub. The pub garden backs onto the farm, so clutching your drink, you can watch the trout being fed. Smiles beers – Exhibition, Best and Brewery. Always five guest beers which could be: Theakstons Old Peculiar, Greene King Abbot, Batemans, Hook Norton Old Hooky, Marstons Pedigree or Fullers London Pride. They choose from a pool of about 40 differant beers. Concise wine list and a range of malt whiskies.

OPEN: 11–3. 6–11. (12–3. 7–10.30. Sun)
Real Ale
Children welcome. Dogs on leads.
Car park. Wheelchair access.

COLN ST-ALDWYNS

New Inn   Tel: 01285 750651

Coln St-Aldwyns, Nr Cirencester, Glos GL7 5AN
Free House. Brian Evans, licensee.

Between Fairford and Bibery, flower baskets and ivy-covered walls make this 16th century Cotswold village pub very appealing. It has a classy restaurant and a chef to match who's aiming high. The fixed price restaurant menu is thought out daily and could include: seared escalope of salmon with a Caesar salad, lobster and crayfish bisque, pan fried red mullet or roast breast of duck flavoured with port, warm plum and almond tart to finish, selection of cheeses too. There is also an impressive bar menu at lunchtime and in the evening; whisky and kipper paté, tomato and goats' cheese crostini with basil, salmon fish cakes with a chive sauce, poached salmon, braised shoulder of lamb, moussaka of vegetables, even a ploughmans. Delicious sounding puds. Hook Norton and Wadworths 6X ales and other guest beers on hand pump. Seats outside in the garden. Summer barbecues.

OPEN: 11.30–2.30. 5.30–11 (11–11 Summer Sats).
Real Ale. Restaurant.
Children in eating area. Dogs on leads.
Wheelchair access. Bedrooms.

CORSE LAWN

Corse Lawn Hotel   Tel: 01452 780479

Corse Lawn, Glos GL19 4LZ (nr Tewkesbury but actually in Worcs.!)
Free House. Denis Hine, licensee.

As the name implies, this is not a pub but the bar of an utterly relaxed and welcoming hotel. Corse Lawn House, now an elegant country house hotel, was originally a Tudor inn which burnt down early in the 18th century and was rebuilt in 1745 in the Queen Ann style as a coaching inn. An interesting feature is the old "coach wash" at the front of the hotel which has been retained as an unusual ornamental pond. The proprietor is French, the staff English, and the atmosphere Franglais. Food from the bar/bistro could include: sandwiches, omelettes, Mediterranean fish soup, gallantine of duckling with orange chutney, cassoulet with chicken breasts, garlic sausage and haricot beans, shoulder of lamb provençal, jugged venison with port and mixed herbs and good puddings. Flowers Ale and Goachers Bitter.

Hein cognac and over 300 wines. Corse Lawn is off the beaten track and takes its name from the wide mile-long green either side of the road.

OPEN: 12–2. 6–11.
Real Ale.
Children welcome. Dogs on leads.
Bedrooms.

DURSLEY

Old Spot Inn Tel: 01453 542870

Hill Road, Dursley, Glos
Free House. Ric Sainty, licensee.

When Ric and Ellie Sainty took over The Old Spot – built in 1776 and a school throughout the last century – they were urged by some patrons "to give them a bit of music". The furthest they ever got was an occasional evening of live folk. "Now," says Ellie, "we're hallowed ground!" Such a very friendly welcoming pub makes The Old Spot a compulsory stop on any journey through Dursley. Don't expect gourmet food, though. All you will get are sandwiches of rare beef and home-cooked ham. Well kept local Uley brewery ales, including Old Ric – named after the landlord – are made with Uley's own spring water. Other beers include Draught Bass, Worthington Best, Old Spot Prize Ale, and Pigor Mortis, which they brew for Christmas. Guest ales too. The pub has its own boules pitch, and a beer garden.

OPEN: 11–11. (12–3. 7–10.30.Sun)
Real Ale.
Children at landlord's discretion. Dogs on leads.
Wheelchair access poor but possible.

EBRINGTON

Ebrington Arms Tel: 01386 593223

Ebrington, Nr Chipping Campden, Glos GL55 6NH
Free House. Gareth Richards & Andrew Geddes, licensees.

Obviously no music, but no machines either. Only the TV goes on for the Five Nations Rugby Match. There is also an enthusiasm for dominoes. The local since 1764, it has one beamed, flagstoned bar with an inglenook fireplace and an adjoining dining room. The menu is written on the beams of the bar

143

and it can take you some time to read it all. Traditional bar food: sandwiches, sirloin steak baguette, local sausages, lasagne, chicken Kiev, eggs and chips, omelettes, steak & kidney pies and steaks. The fresh cod is their speciality. Hook Norton Best, Donnington SBA and guest beers on hand pump. Farm cider. Seats outside on the sheltered terrace.

OPEN: 11–2.30. 5.30–11 (11–11 summer Sats).
Real Ale. Restaurant.
Children in eating area. No dogs.

GUITING POWER

Ye Olde Inne   Tel: 01451 850392

Winchcombe Road, Guiting Power, Nr Cheltenham, Glos GL54 5UX
Free House. Bill & Julia Tu, licensees.

At the far end of the village, Ye Olde Inne has been freshened up with a facelift by its licensees. It's a 17th century stone building with three small beamed rooms. The main bar has a big log fire, the public bar has the darts board and there's a dining room – although you can eat anywhere you can find a table. Bar food includes: soups, steak & kidney pies, chicken in a sherry vinegar and tarragon sauce, spicy nut roast and some Burmese and Thai dishes – such as Burmese chicken curry with noodles – introduced by the landlord. Seats in the garden with views over the surrounding countryside. Hook Norton and Bass, plus guest beers on hand pump. Several malt whiskies.

OPEN: 11.30–3. 5.30–11 (11.30–2.30. 6–11 winter).
Real Ale. Restaurant.
Children in public bar area and restaurant. Dogs in public bar only.
Good wheelchair access.

HILLESLEY

The Fleece   Tel: 01453 843189

Chapel Lane, Hillesley, Nr. Wotton-under-Edge, Glos.CL12 7RD
Whitbread Lease. Mrs Celia Rollo, licensee.

An unspoilt – Grade II listed – village local, in a small Cotswold village surrounded by glorious countryside. The Fleece still retains the definite demarcation between the public and saloon bar, just as it was years ago.

Low ceilings and open log fires in both busy bars. A bar menu and daily specials board gives you a lot of choice: ploughmans, steak pies, gammon, steaks and scampi on the bar menu; specials can be a salmon dish, fillet steak in a sauce or steak Diane. Whitbread ales and guests from Smiles or the Uley Brewery. Seats in the garden. You are near the Cotswold Way, so there are good walks nearby.

OPEN: 11.30–3. 6.30–11. (12–3. 7–10.30 Sun)
Real Ale
Children welcome. Dogs in garden only.
Three bedrooms.

KINGSCOTE

Hunters Hall   Tel: 01453 860393

Kingscote, Tetbury, Glos GL8 8XZ
Free House. David Barnett-Roberts, licensee.

First licensed in the 14th century, this eye-catching, creeper-covered inn is a popular local. It has a back room with pool, darts and a jukebox; also a no-smoking family gallery above the bars. The garden is planned for children. Bar food changes daily; there will be a cold buffet in the dining room at lunchtime and other dishes which range from prawns cooked in garlic butter and lemon, smoked chicken and bacon salad, whitebait, fresh mussels mariniere, sweet and sour pork, venison and orange casserole, pork apple and cider casserole to home-made puds. A restaurant menu features in the evening. Bass, Hook Norton, Marstons Pedigree and Uley Old Spot on hand pump. Wines by the glass, and a selection of malt whiskies. A summer barbecue in the children oriented garden.

OPEN: 11–3.30. 6–11.
Real Ale. Restaurant (No Sandwiches Sun).
Live music some Sunday evenings.
Children welcome. Dogs on leads.
Bedrooms.
Wheelchair access to pub and bedrooms.

LECHLADE

Trout Inn Tel: 01367 252313

Lechlade on Thames, Glos GL7 3HA
Courage. Bob & Penny Warren, lease.

A lovely place to stop if you are walking the Thames Footpath. Lechlade is an attractive village with a number of handsome Georgian buildings, and it is where the Leach and Coln rivers join the young Thames. The Trout, which dates back to the 13th century, has been considerably re-built since then, but inside there are pleasant, low-beamed bars, one of which is over 350 years old, and the other a mere stripling of 100, and usually, there is an outside bar functioning during the summer. In the restaurant the menu is dependable – as dependable as the popular bar food: home-made soups, paté, salmon, steaks and locally produced sausages, daily specials and home-made puds. The pub does get very busy. There is a no-smoking area in the restaurant. Wadworths 6X, John Smiths Yorkshire and Courage Best ales. They have their own boules pitch. On a warm day you can either sit in the big garden, or on the river bank, to watch the water flow by.

OPEN: 10–3. 6–11 (all day Sats summer).
Real Ale. Restaurant.
Children in eating area of bar. Dogs on lead (not in dining or children's room).
N.B. If the radio is intrusive, please let us know. Live Jazz Tues & Sun eves.

LITTLETON-ON-SEVERN

White Hart Tel: 01454 412275

Littleton-on-Severn, BS12 1NR
Smiles. Shelley & Philip Berryman, licensees.

The garden is at the front of this fine old pub – a pretty cottagey garden with seats. Very near the Severn Bridge, studying the map, you see that the county boundary does a quick change in mid river, I'm not sure we are even in the right county! Plenty of room in this well cared for old pub; four bars and a family room. A wide choice of bar food available, ranging from home-made soup, filled crusty rolls, ploughmans, steak and kidney pie, fish pie, vegetarian dishes and daily specials. Smiles range of ales, two guests, one of which is Wadworths 6X, the other changes regularly. There are also seats on the terrace at the back of the pub.

OPEN: 11.30–2.30. 6–11. (11.30–11 Sat. 12–3. 7–10.30 Sun.)
Real Ale
Children in the Garden Room. Dogs on leads.
Four en suite bedrooms in a converted barn.

MISERDEN

Carpenters Arms   Tel: 01285 821783

Miserden, Gloucestershire.
Free House. Jean M. Jones, licensee.

In a picturesque Cotswold village, roughly equi-distant from Cirencester, Cheltenham and Stroud. One of only two buildings in the village not owned by the Wills family (the tobacco Wills') – the other is the church! A friendly, welcoming place, very popular as a serious food place, but still retaining an excellent public bar feel. Not even a gaming machine to disturb the sleeping dogs. Good bar menu: filled jacket potatoes, a ham or cheese ploughmans, hot crispy bacon rolls, or a choice of nine other fillings. All the ham is home-cooked as are most of the dishes on the full menu: Garlic mushrooms topped with melted Stilton, smoked trout fillet with salad, vegetable pie with a flaky pastry top, seafood platter, cajun chicken, or if you are really hungry – the Carpenters Arms mixed grill will sort out the men from the boys. Flowers IPA, Boddingtons, Abbot Ale and an extensive wine list.

OPEN: 11–3. 6–11
Real Ale
Children welcome. Dogs on leads.

NAILSWORTH

Weighbridge Inn   Tel: 01453 832520

The Longfords, Nailsworth, Minchinghamton, GL6 9AL
Free House. Janina Kulesza, licensee.

The building dates back to 1220 but they have had the builders in since then, so that there are now three, traditionally furnished rooms housing an interesting collection of country artefacts. No restaurant food, just good pub grub. Two-in-one pie is a speciality of the house: half steak and mushroom and half cauliflower cheese with a short pastry crust; also steak & mushroom pie, Turkish sweetcorn and pepper pie, vegetable and lentil crumble, pizzas and puddings. The ales change frequently but there could be Marstons Pedigree, Wadworths 6X, and John Smiths. Other guest beers too. A good number of wines by the glass or bottle. Seats outside in the sheltered garden.

OPEN: 11–2.30. 7–11 (6.30–11 Sat).
Real Ale.
Children in rooms away from bar. Dogs on leads.

NEWLAND

Ostrich   Tel: 01594 833260

Newland, Nr Coleford, Glos GL16 8NP
Free House. Richard & Veronica Dewe, licensees.

Charming, 16th century pub in a little village between the Wye Valley and the Forest of Dean. One low-beamed bar with big winter log fires. Popular with walkers, but very muddy boots off at the door. About thirty light dishes are available from the lunchtime bar menu. There is also a more extensive menu –all home-cooked – running to over 70 items, ranging from wild boar, venison, pheasant, moules marinière to soups and home-baked bread. In the evening there are over 25 dishes to choose from. Usually eight different ales on hand pump. There is also a German keg lager and farm ciders.

OPEN: 12–2.30 (3 Sat). 6.30–11.
Real Ale.
No Children. Dogs on leads.
Bedrooms.

OAKRIDGE LYNCH

Butchers Arms   Tel: 01285 760371

Oakridge Lynch, Nr Stroud, Glos GL6 7NZ
Free House. Peter & Brian Coupe, licensees.

East of Stroud on the Eastcombe Bisley road, along high-sided lush Gloucestershire lanes, it is well worth hunting out the Butchers Arms for its lunchtime sandwiches, ploughmans, plus cauliflower cheese, beef and ale pie and omelettes. Evening meals are served in the restaurant only. Archers Best, Bass, Hook Norton Old Hooky and Theakstons Best are among the ales kept. Plenty of room to park in the detached car park and there are seats in the garden from where you can enjoy views over the village to the valley below.

OPEN: 12–3. 6–11.
Real Ale. Restaurant Wed–Sat eves, Sun lunch.
Children in anteroom only. Dogs on leads.

REDBROOK

Boat Inn   Tel: 01600 712615

Lone Lane, Penalt, Monmouth, Gwent, S Wales
Free House. Steffan & Dawn Rowlands, licensees.

Amazingly situated on the bank of the River Wye; clinging on would be more
to the point. Strictly speaking the Boat is in Wales – via a footbridge across
the Wye from its Gloucestershire car park. Very popular with our energetic
friends, so walking boots and hairy socks are the norm. You will find a genial
bar – looking very smart, all the seat covers and curtains have been replaced
– serving good, familiar bar food including the house dish of Panhaggerty
(cheese, potato, onion and garlic) which they have been serving for years,
boozy beef pie, vegetable turkari curry, pork in cider hot pot, Italian style
lamb casserole , filled jacket potatoes and good puds to finish. All the food
is home cooked. There is a garden, (and from what I remember, parts of that
are perpendicular), from where you can watch the river. Up to ten ales from
casks behind the counter: Bass, Boddingtons, Butcombe, Theakstons Old
Peculiar among them, but they change all the time.

OPEN: 11–3. 6–11 (11–11 Sat)
Real Ale.
Children welcome, so are dogs.
Folk music Tues eve. Jazz Thurs eve.

SAPPERTON

Bell Inn   Tel: 01285 760298

Sapperton, Cirencester, Glos GL7 6LE
Free House. Gordon & Violet Wells, licensees.

On the side of a ridge facing the beech woods along the Frome River valley,
Sapperton attracts both walkers and canal enthusiasts. The two-and-a-half
mile Sapperton Tunnel was cut through the hill in 1789 to link the Thames
and the Severn rivers. The eastern entrance is now restored and is well
worth a visit. After the walk or the sightseeing, head for the bars of the Bell
Inn. Good value bar food: soups, sandwiches, local Gloucester sausages,

and grilled gammon steaks. Tables at the front of the pub. Flowers Original, Bass, Whitbreads West Country Pale Ale Wadworths 6X and others, all on hand pump.

OPEN: 11–2.30. 6.30–11.
Real Ale.
Children in eating area. Dogs on leads.

SAPPERTON

Daneway Inn   Tel: 01285 760297

Sapperton, Cirencester, Glos GL7 6LN
Free House. Liz & Richard Goodfellow, licensees.

The Daneway Inn is at the end of the derelict Sapperton tunnel. The Cotswold Canals Trust is working towards opening both the Thames and Severn Canal, which links the Thames near Lechlade to Stroud, and the adjoining Stroudwater Canal, from Stroud to Gloucester. Having already restored the eastern entrance, the Trust has recently finished restoring the castellated western entrance to the tunnel. Originally built to accommodate the canal workers, the Daneway has a wonderfully grand Dutch fireplace in the lounge bar which came out of the long-since demolished Amberley House. Lunchtime bar food varies from filled rolls, baked potatoes and ploughmans to lasagne and a beef in ale pie. There are additions to the menu in the evening. Bass, Wadworths 6X, Archers Best and Daneway Bitter, which is brewed locally, plus a guest beer. Farm cider. Tables in the pretty garden overlook the Canal and the river valley.

OPEN: 11–2.30 (3 Sat). 6.30–11.
Real Ale.
Children in no-smoking family room. No dogs.

SHEEPSCOMBE

Butchers Arms   Tel: 01452 812113

Sheepscombe, Nr Painswick, Glos GL6 7RH
Free House. Johnny & Hilary Johnston, licensees.

Dating back to 1670, the Butchers Arms is very much the village local. Facing due south with wonderful views, it is so sheltered you can sit outside in comfort in the early spring. Very traditional, with a timeless atmosphere, huge log fires, walls covered with old pictures and prints, no fruit machines or juke box, just lots of chat. Good, varied bar menu – smoked mackerel or smoked trout, Ardennes paté lasagne, omelettes, seafood platter, mixed grills, filled jacket potatoes, filled rolls and daily specials from the blackboard. Evening specials, such as poached salmon with prawn sauce, mussels cooked in garlic butter, half roast duck with Grand Marnier and orange sauce, home-made "pepperpot" beef, steaks, mixed grills and home-made puds. Hook Norton Best, Fullers London Pride and Abbot Ale plus guest beers. Farm ciders and a good wine list. Local singing groups visit on special occasions.

OPEN: 11–11 (11–2.30. 6–11 winter).
Real Ale. Restaurant.
Children in eating areas. No dogs.
Live music on special occasions.
Wheelchair access to pub and restaurant.

SLAD

The Woolpack   Tel: 01452 813429

Slad, Nr. Stroud, Glos.
Free House. David Tarrat, licensee.

From Stroud, NE on the B4070, travel along the glorious Slad valley – Laurie Lee's 'Cider with Rosie' country – until you reach Slad. The village and The Woolpack perch on the hillside, looking across the valley to the woods opposite. A delightful 'unimproved' village pub. Just an agreeable room, with small additional rooms either end, and through the window behind the bar a view across the valley. One room is a no-smoking family room. The terrace is even more unpretentious and the view even more spendid. A wide range of reasonably priced dishes, a particularly good chicken tikka masala, served with bowls of raisins, coconut and mango chutney. The sauté potatoes are worthy of a mention says our researcher. Worth a trip for the Old Spot beer, brewed not far away at Uley; also Boddingtons, Bass, Guinness and three ciders.

OPEN: 12–2.30. 6–11. (7–10.30 Sun)
Real Ale.
Children welcome. Dogs on leads.
Occasional live music evenings.

STOW-ON-THE-WOLD

Queens Head　　　　　　　　　　　　　　　Tel: 01451 830563

Market Square, Stow-on-the-Wold, Glos GL54 1AB
Donnington. Timothy Eager, tenant.

Among the fine stone buildings in Market Square you will easily find the Old Queens Head, pretty as a picture with its climbing roses and hanging baskets. Inside are two bars: the lounge bar at the front, and a family room at the back where the landlord has put the games and fruit machine and – with a macabre sense of humour – his coffin (made of yew, by the way – very grand), which is listed as pub furniture on the tax return. The bar menu offers soups, ploughmans, sandwiches, savoury flans, cottage pie, cheese and potato pie, seasonal specials and good home-made puds. There are seats outside in the courtyard, and at the front of the pub. Donningtons ales, and mulled wine in winter.

OPEN: 11–2.30. 6 (6.30 Sat)–11.
Real Ale.
Children welcome. Dogs on leads.
N.B.There is music in the family room. Occasional Jazz Sun.

WESTBURY-ON-SEVERN

Red Lion　　　　　　　　　　　　　　　　Tel: 01452 760221

Westbury-on-Severn, Glos. GL14 1PA
Free House, W.J.Parry, licensee.

Just a 100 yards from Westbury Court's 17th century water garden, now owned by the National Trust, the Red Lion – right on the road (A48) – is a fine pub with a traditional atmosphere and lots of jolly, friendly local banter. The decor has a baseball theme with a collection of caps brought by customers and friends from all over the world. The large menu of freshly-cooked food is popular, so it's better to book: peppered chicken breast in garlic cream, fresh salmon with cream and dill mayonnaise, pork medallions in port and cranberry and fresh cod and chips among others. Our researcher says lots of scrummy puds. Five different ales served each week, these could be : Yates Bitter, Wickwar Ale, Brains SA, Everards Tiger, Buchanans Original, Mansfields Old Baily and Wye Valley Brew. Good selection of malt whiskies, South African and New World wines. Seats in the garden.

OPEN: 11–2.30. 7–11

Real Ale.
Children welcome. No Dogs.
Car park.

WOODCHESTER

Ram Inn   Tel: 01453 873329

Station Road, South Woodchester, Nr Stroud, Glos.
Free House. Michael & Eileen McAsey, licensees.

Gloucestershire does have the most wonderful scenery and from the Ram
Inn the views are spectacular. Traditionally furnished, the beamed bar has
no less than three log fires during winter. An interesting, changing menu
includes the usual sandwiches and ploughmans, maybe spinach roulade
with a cream cheese and smoked salmon filling, plaice with a prawn and
mushroom stuffing, Italian beef casserole, spicy pork loin with a brandy and
apricot sauce, fillet of steak with a cream and pepper sauce, venison in red
wine; always fresh vegetables. The ales change frequently but there are
usually eight or nine on hand pump. Serious beer drinkers flock here.

OPEN: 11–3. 5.30–11 (11–11 Sat).
Real Ale. Restaurant.
Children welcome. Dogs on leads.

H
HAMPSHIRE

BENTWORTH

Sun Inn   Tel: 01420 562338

Bentworth, Nr Alton, Hants GU34 5JT (at Sun Hill off A339 from Alton)
Free House. Richard & Jan Beaumont, licensees.

Originally two cottages, this fine old 17th century pub is tucked away down a country lane at the edge of the village. Two connecting, beamed, comfortable bars, with big log fires make it especially appealing during the winter. A newly built extension allows more people to enjoy the praiseworthy catering. Daily specials on the blackboard which could be watercress or asparagus soup, a choice of pasta dishes, smoked haddock pancakes, Mediterranean lamb casserole, Somerset pork, sweet and sour chicken, as well as sandwiches, ploughmans, filled baked potatoes, ham and eggs, salads and home-made puddings. Ruddles Best, Wadworths 6X, Marstons Pedigree, Courage Best, Cheriton Pots, Ringwood Best, Hampshires' Sun Special, Worldhams' Old Dray and Gales country wines. Tables outside amongst the flowering tubs.

OPEN: 12–3. 6–11. Closed Sunday nights Nov–Easter.
Real Ale. No food Sun evening Nov–Feb.
Children in garden room. Dogs on leads.
Occasional Morris Dancers.
Wheelchair access.

BOLDRE

Red Lion   Tel: 01590 673177

Ropehill, Boldre, Nr Lymington, Hants
Eldridge Pope. John & Penny Bicknell, lease.

On the edge of the New Forest, not far from Lymington, this 17th century, flower-festooned pub has all those artefacts you associate with past country life – including mantraps and chamber pots! – displayed around its four well-beamed rooms. Usual range of reliable bar food, plus meals in a basket, lots of salads, some vegetarian dishes and quite a choice of elaborate ice creams to follow. Menu changes weekly and could include jugged hare, pheasant in red wine, rabbit chasseur, fresh salmon fishcakes and braised oxtail, plus home-made puddings to follow. All Eldridge Pope ales. Wines by the glass. Seats in the attractive garden.

OPEN: 11–3. 6–11.
Real Ale. Restaurant.
No children under 14 inside pub. No dogs.
Wheelchair access.

BROUGHTON

Tally Ho!   Tel: 01794 301280

High Street, Broughton, S020 8AA
Free House. Frank Bartlett, licensee.

In a village of timbered houses on the Wallop brook, the Tally Ho! is a Georgian building belonging to the family that also own The Flower Pots at Cheriton. It is opposite the 13th century Norman church. Totally refurbished three years ago, it is now a comfortable pub serving good reliable bar food: home-cooked curries, chillies, hot-pots, properly cooked ham, filled jacket potatoes, sandwiches, ploughmans and daily specials. The ales come from the Cheriton Brewery which includes the award winning Pots' Ale, also Diggers Gold and Best Bitter. There is a lovely, colourful garden at the back of the pub.

OPEN: 12–2.30. 6–11. (12–3. 7–10.30. Sun)
Real Ale. No food Tuesdays.
Children welcome in garden. Dogs on leads.
Wheelchair access at the back.

BURITON

Five Bells   Tel: 01730 263584

48 High Street, Buriton (off A3. S of Petersfield)
Free House. John Ligertwood, licensee.
N.B: One bar has music, one is without.

Close to the South Downs Way, the Five Bells offers a welcome haven to walkers and locals alike. Low-beamed bars, log fires, good ales and an inventive menu. Substantial lunchtime snacks: filled baguettes, jacket potatoes, ploughmans and salads, otherwise the menu changes regularly – whatever takes the fancy of the chef, but there could be sardines in garlic butter, devilled whitebait, steaks, liver and bacon casserole, dressed local crab, game in season, casseroles, always some vegetarian dishes, a good choice of fish and home-made puddings. A three course menu is available in the dining room and there are also Sunday lunches. Ballards Best, Adnams Best, Ind Coope Burton, Ringwood Old Thumper and True Glory, Tetleys, Eldridge Popes Thomas Hardy and Friary Meux. Seats on the terrace and in the sheltered garden.

OPEN: 11–2.30 (11–3 Fri & Sat). 5.30–11.
Real Ale. Restaurant not Sun eve.
Children in restaurant & snug. Dogs in public bar.
Jazz last Mon, Folk or Blues each Wed in month.

CHERITON

Flower Pots   Tel: 01962 771318

Cheriton, Alresford, Hants SO24 0QQ
Own Brew. Joanna Bartlett, Patricia Bartlett, licensees.

Bought in the early 19th century by the retired head gardener of Avington Park (Nell Gwynne lived for a time at Park Mansion – worth a visit), the pub, with its past horticultural leanings, is aptly named. Popular locally, it even has its own brewery – The Cheriton Brewhouse – providing several reasonably priced ales to go with the good value bar food. You will find well-filled jacket potatoes, sandwiches, baps and hot-pots. Their own beer includes Cheriton Best, Diggers Gold and Pots' Ale. Seats outside at the front and the rear.

OPEN: 12–2.30. 6–11.
Real Ale. No food sun.
Children in family room. Dogs on leads.
Bedrooms. Wheelchair access.

DROXFORD

White Horse Inn   Tel: 01489 877490

South Hill, Droxford, Southampton, Hants SO32 3PB
Free House. Paul Young & Darren Moore, licensees.

Not far from Soberton – a peaceful Meon-valley village with a flint church tower, reputedly built in the 16th century by a butler and dairymaid – is the contemporaneous White Horse, a family run old coaching Inn, with a quiet, beamed lounge bar, no-smoking restaurant, but a public bar with games, juke box and MUSIC. They serve a good selection of bar food which could include: home-made soup, sandwiches, plain or toasted, gammon steak, salads and vegetarian dishes. The home-made pies are very popular: steak pie cooked in Guinness, fish pie and various game pies. Occasionally they will have wild boar sausages and smoked duck. Home-made fruit pies and crumbles to finish. Morlands Old Speckled Hen, Wadworths 6X, Charles Wells Bombadier, Greene King Abbot Ale, also Tanglefoot, Exmoor Gold, Hog Best and Hobgoblin – all from the small independent breweries. Seats in the sheltered, flowery courtyard.

OPEN: 11–3. 6–11 (Public bar open all day Sat & Sun but there is MUSIC)
Real Ale. No-smoking Restaurant.
Children in family room and restaurant. Dogs under control.

EMSWORTH

Kings Arms   Tel: 01243 374941

19, Havant Road, Emsworth, Hants. PO10 7JD
Gales. Adrian & Penny White, tenants.

This is a 'sometimes' pub. If there is a deathly 'ush, the landlord will sometimes put on a little light classical music to take the chill off the early morning silence....... it soon fades out. On the Havant road (A259) westward out of Emsworth, 50 yards from the mill pond and the ducks, look for the flowers; the black and white Kings Arms is right behind them. Just one bar with a small no-smoking area. Adrian runs the 'front of house', Penny is in the kitchen – which is why, and they said it, they are still married! Ploughmans, salads, steaks etc. on the bar menu. Home-made fresh crab gratin, Moroccan chicken, cheese and vegetable pie and pineapple upside down pudding from the blackboard, daily specials could include: stilton and bacon mushrooms, cauliflower moussaka or Victorian beef-cake and a Hampshire six cup pudding. A selection of wines by the glass and the bottle. Well kept Gales beers and guest ales. Gales country wines. Outside there is a prize-winning garden.

OPEN: 11–2.30. 5.15–11. (12–3. 7–10.30. Sun)
Real Ale
No children in bar. Well behaved dogs on leads.

IBSLEY

Old Beams Inn   Tel: 01425 473387

Ibsley, Nr Ringwood, Hants
Free House. R Major & C Newall, licensees.

An attractive, half-timbered, 600 year old thatched pub, looking as pretty as a picture when the cherry trees are out in the spring. Inside is one large open space and a conservatory extension. There is always a good choice of well-cooked meals with lots of daily specials, the favourite dish is fish – any sort. The impressive cold buffet – cold meats, seafood and lots of salads – is also very popular, or you can have quiche, pork in cream and mustard sauce, grilled fish, lasagne, chillies, not forgetting ploughmans and sandwiches. Quite a range of ales: Gibbs Mew, Bishops Tipple, Ringwoods Best, Old Thumper, Gales HSB and Bass. Imported bottled beers and wines by the glass. Seats in the garden among the trees.

OPEN: 10.30–2.30. 6–11 (10.30 winter).
Real Ale. Restaurant (not Sun eve).
Children in eating areas and family room. Small dogs only.
Wheelchair access.

LANGSTONE

Royal Oak   Tel: 01705 483125

19 High Street, Langstone, Havant, Hants PO9 1RY
Whitbread. Stuart Warren, manager.

A 16th century pub on the edge of a natural harbour – at extra high tides the local swans could join you for a drink as the water nearly reaches the front door. Comfortable in winter with its open fires, it is appealing in all seasons. Traditional range of bar food: home-made soups, well filled French bread, a vegetarian dish, local fish and a roast of the day. Flowers Original, Gales HSB, Boddingtons, Whitbread Pompey Royal and Fuggles on hand pump. Seats at the front of the pub or in the garden behind, where there is a children's corner with goats and rabbits.

OPEN: 11–11.
Real Ale.
Children in eating area. Dogs on leads in part of pub.

OVINGTON

Bush Inn   Tel: 01962 732764

Ovington, Nr Alresford, Hants SO24 0RE
Free House. Geoff & Sue Draper, licensees.

To appreciate this pretty cottagey pub fully, try coming during the week, or out of season, when it is a little quieter. In an idyllic position on the fast-flowing River Itchen, it is popular not only for its excellent trout stream, but for its riverside paths where you can either work up an appetite or walk off the meal you have just enjoyed. Inside the pub there are three comfortable bars, each with roaring log fires in winter. The usual traditional bar meals are readily available. There are daily specials on the blackboard which lists a short and more adventurous choice of dishes: creamy broccoli and salmon soup, smoked haddock fillet on spinach with a cheese and herb glaze, loin of pork Alsacienne, skate wings and a cassoulet. A two course lunch is served in the restaurant on Sundays. (Must book). Gales HSB, Flowers Original, Wadworths 6X and usually a guest beer. Various country wines. Seats overlooking the river and, naturally enough, lovely walks.

OPEN: 11–2.30. 6–11.
Real Ale. Evening restaurant (not Sun).
Children in eating area lunchtimes & restaurant evenings. Dogs on leads.

PRIORS DEAN

White Horse Inn   Tel: 0142 0588387
Known as The Pub with No Name.

Priors Dean, Nr Petersfield, Hants GU32 1DA (Clutching a good map, you go up a track past E Tilstead/Privett crossroads, between Petersfield & Winchester).
Gales. Roger Datchler, licensee.

When locals tell you about a pub they have known all their lives, you assume it's fairly easy to find. This one is not. If there were a "hunt the pub" game, this one would be starred as "very difficult". High on the Downs, with views on either side, this 17th century farmhouse has no pub sign. Simple and traditional, with lovely open fires in winter, think of a country pub 20 or so years ago, and you will know what to expect. In those days you were lucky if you got a nut from the cardboard stand on the counter or a packet of crisps (with blue salt twist) from a tin marked Smiths. Now everything is cooked to order; menus vary with the seasons – as do the specialities. You can always get sandwiches, soup (in winter made on the Aga), and ploughmans. Ballards Best, Courage Best and Directors, No Name Best, No Name Strong, Fuggles, Bass, Theakstons Old Peculiar, Gales Festival Mild, Butser and IPA are among the ales on offer, plus guest ales. Considerable number of country wines, including wine from a local vineyard. Seats in the garden, from where you may see the hot air balloons taking off or a Tiger Moth landing. There are occasional visits from those wonderful old steam road rollers and the pub is a meeting point for vintage cars and motorbikes. If you want to pitch your tent, you can do that too.

OPEN: 11–2.30 (11–3 Sat). 6–11.
Real Ale. No meals or snacks Sun lunchtimes.
Children not allowed in. Well behaved dogs on leads.
Wheelchair access.

ROTHERWICK

Coach & Horses   Tel: 01256 762542

The Street, Rotherwick, Nr Basingstoke, Hants RG27 9BG
Badger. Sean McAusland, manager.

Here you can be sure of a bowl of soup and a sandwich any time during the day, and when you are travelling across country you really appreciate pubs like this. It's 16th century, covered in creeper and surrounded by flowers; and inside there are attractive, small, beamed rooms, one of which is no-smoking. About five different varieties of sausage are on the menu, steak & kidney and other pies, stews, steaks and Sunday roast. Children's dishes. Well-kept beers: Gribble Black Adder, Badger Best, Hard Tackle, and Tanglefoot and Wadworths 6X. Seats outside amongst the flowers.

OPEN: 11–11.
Real Ale. Restaurant.
Children in eating area. Dogs on leads.

ROWLANDS CASTLE

The Castle Inn   Tel: 01705 412494

1 Finchdean Road, Rowlands Castle, Hants. PO9 6DA
Gales. Stephen Thomas and Annabel Viney, tenants.

Recently renovated. The original wood and flagstone floors have been restored. Both public and lounge bars are panelled and have open fires. All the food is freshly made using locally bought ingredients. From the bar snack menu you could choose home roasted ham or stilton ploughmans, sandwiches with several different fillings, liver and bacon casserole, chicken piri piri and rice or beef vindaloo, rice and poppadoms. From the restaurant menu: stilton and cauliflower soup, crispy bacon and mushrooms in garlic cream, grilled sardines, minted lamb chops with rosemary, darne of salmon in a dill sauce, a vegetarian dish or two, and tempting puds. Gales HSH and Butser on handpump, also Gales 777 Mild, Best and Smooth; one guest ale, also on handpump. Gales country wines – all 21 of them! Lots of space in the garden. Only 200 yards from Stansted Park, so there are good walks nearby.

OPEN: 11.30–3.30. 6–11. (12–10.30. Sun)
Real Ale. Restaurant.
Children welcome. Dogs too.
Disabled facilities.
Bedrooms. Car park.

SOUTHWICK

Red Lion   Tel: 01705 377223

High Street, Southwick, Nr. Fareham, Hants. PO17 6EF
Gales. Mr & Mrs Paul & Linda Dunn, licensees.

On the A333 Portsmouth to Wickham (which has some fine Georgian houses), the Red Lion is a comfortable old village pub serves snacks at the bar and a full meals from an à la carte menu. Over half the seating area is no-smoking. Most of the food is home-made, such as smoked haddock and broccoli mornay or giant Yorkshire pudding filled with sausage, tomato, mushrooms, bacon and scrambled egg; chips too – that should fill a few gaps. Gales Butser, Best, HSB, Force 8, seasonal Winter Brew and Christmas Ale. Gales country wines.

OPEN: 11–2.30. 6.30–11 (12–3. 7–10.30 Sun)
Real Ale
Children welcome. No dogs.

THE QUIET PINT

STEEP

Harrow Inn   Tel: 01730 262685

Steep, Petersfield, Hants GU32 2DA
Free House. Edward C McCutcheon, licensee.

Another pub that is difficult to find, but here all you have to do is locate
Sheet Church and turn left, follow the sign to Steep – over the motorway
bridge and hey presto! (This isn't a typographical error, Sheet and Steep are
two different places). The Harrow Inn, probably 15th century, is beamed,
hung with hops and dried flowers, with old oak benches in the public bar
which has a big inglenook fireplace. Beer is served through a hatch from the
barrels behind. Unchanging, wonderfully traditional – to be treasured. Home-
cooked hams, scotch eggs, soups and salads. Flowers, Boddingtons and
Whitbread beers. Country wines. Tables in the wild garden.

OPEN: 11–2.30 (11–3 Sat). 6–11.
Real Ale.
No children. Dogs on leads.

TICHBORNE

Tichborne Arms   Tel: 01962 733760

Tichborne, Nr Alresford, Hants SO24 0NA
Free House. Christine & Peter Byron, licensees.

A village which takes its name from the Tichborne family who lived here from
1135. The Tichborne Dole ceremony, was started in 1150 by Richard de
Tichborne. It is celebrated on March 25th each year, when flour is distributed
to the villagers. Thatched, as are many buildings in the Itchen Valley, the
Tichborne Arms is very much the centre of village life. Very popular, it can
get busy – the home-cooked bar food being a particular attraction. Using
fresh local produce, there is usually a soup, sandwiches, toasties,
ploughmans, well filled baked potatoes and salads plus daily specials such
as: liver, bacon and onion casserole, steak, ale and stilton pie, chicken
breasts with apricots in brandy. Wadworths 6X, Boddingtons, Flowers IPA
and Fuggles IPA from the cask. Tables in the garden.

OPEN: 11.30–2.30. 6–11.
Real Ale.
No children under 14. Dogs on leads.
Wheelchair access.

UPHAM

Brushmakers Arms   Tel: 01489 860231

Upham, Nr Bishops Waltham, Hants (village signposted from Winchester).
Free House. Sue & Andy Cobb, licensees.

Brushes for every occasion. Not quite, but there is quite a collection hanging around the pub. It has a comfortable, good-sized bar divided by a wood-burning stove in a central fireplace. Better than average choice of bar food and a Sunday roast. The favourites from the menu are: braised beef in mustard sauce, pan fried duck breast with black cherries, monkfish thermidor and tagliatelle with bacon and Stilton. Bass and Ringwood Best on hand pump plus two guest beers. A choice of malt whiskies and country wines. Seats outside on the terrace and the lawn.

OPEN: 11.30–2.30. 6–11.
Real Ale. Children welcome away from bar. Dogs on leads.

VERNHAM DEAN

George Inn   Tel: 01264 737279

Vernham Dean, Andover, Hants SP11 0JY
Marstons. Candy Lacy-Smith, Derek Pollard, tenants.

A rambling, friendly, popular, attractive old village pub in a pretty garden with its own vegetable patch – so you will know most of the vegetables accompanying the home-cooked food will be produced "in-house" so to speak. Soups, toasted sandwiches, selection of ploughmans, interesting savoury pies and game in season. Marstons Pedigree and Best on hand pump. Seats and tables in the lovely garden.

OPEN: 11–2.30 (11–3 Sat). 6–11.
Real Ale. No meals/snacks Sun eve.
Children in family room. Dogs on leads.

WELL

Chequers Inn   Tel: 01256 862605

Well, Odiham, Hants RG29 1TL
Free House. Rupert Fowler, Terry McGrath licensees.

Deep in the lovely Hampshire countryside, at its best on a glorious early summer's day, you will find the 17th century Chequers beamed and panelled, with shelves of books to read if you are waiting for someone, or just want a book with your beer. Home-cooked food. The menu which is chalked on the blackboard in the bar changes daily, and is quite enterprising. There could be pasta, coronation chicken, seafood vol au vents, smoked salmon and scrambled eggs and other dishes. Flowers Original, Boddingtons and Strongs Country ales. Good range of wine. Tables in the garden at the back and on the vine covered terrace at the front of the pub.

OPEN: 11–3. 5.30–11.
Real Ale. Restaurant, Thurs, Fri. and Sat. eves only.
Children welcome. Dogs on leads.

WEST MEON

Thomas Lord   Tel: 01730 829244

Peter Lane, West Meon, Nr Petersfield, Hants. GU32 1LN
Whitbread. Peter Lane, lease.

Don't be fooled by those black boxes you see on the walls: the equipment might be there, but this pub is run by someone who doesn't think background music suits a country pub, nor does he think it necessary. We couldn't agree more. The name, Thomas Lord, is of great significance to any cricketing enthusiast. Thomas Lord, founder of Lord's cricket ground died in 1832, and is buried in West Meon church yard. A popular village pub with a public and lounge bar – no restaurant – just tables in the lounge bar. Ploughmans, sandwiches and a blackboard menu: haddock and prawns in onion sauce covered in mashed potato, pan fried lemon sole, turkey roast in Roquefort cheese and sour cream, a familiar steak and kidney pie or lamb cooked with mint and spices. Whitbread ales, Fullers London Pride and Ringwood Best Bitter as the permanent guest. Peter Lane says the locals would lynch him if he took off the Ringwood! Large secluded garden. Wonderful walks along the old Meon Valley railway line.

OPEN: 11–3. 6–11. (12–3.7–10.30 Sun)
Real Ale
Children welcome. Dogs on leads.

WINCHESTER

Wykeham Arms   Tel: 01962 853834

75 Kingsgate Street, Winchester, SO23 9PE
Eldridge Pope, Mr & Mrs Graeme Jameson, lease.

South of the Cathedral Close you'll find one of the best pubs in town. Six rooms radiate from a central bar (where the serious drinking goes on), so there is plenty of room for you to sample the extremely popular bar food. The lunchtime menu changes daily so either book a table, or get there early to avoid disappointment as all Winchester seems to beat a path to the door. Specials on the blackboard which could include French onion soup, seafood chowder, Wyke cottage pie, red pepper, onion and pesto quiche, grilled tuna steaks, duck confit with rocket salad or a hot or cold open sandwich. There is also an interesting restaurant menu along with an impressive wine list. If you have to wait, make your way to the room at the back where you will find a set of Ronald Searle's 'Winespeak' prints: they are quite hilarious and put any wine-pseud in his place. Several no-smoking areas. Eldridge Pope Dorchester, Hardy and Royal Oak ales. Seats on the terrace and small lawn.

OPEN: 11–11. No meals/snacks Sun. Real Ale. Evening restaurant (not Sun).
No children. Dogs on leads.
Bedrooms.

H
HEREFORD, SHROPSHIRE & WORCESTERSHIRE

ASTON ON CLUN

Kangaroo Inn   Tel: 01588 660263

Clun Road, Aston on Clun, Shropshire SY7 ATW
Free House. Bob & Pam Wright, licensees.

It has been called The Kangaroo – no one knows why – since 1820 – and like Johnny Walker whisky, "it's still going strong". It is located in an area that has deep-rooted connections with the novelist Mary Webb and the poet A.E. Housemans, who called this part of the country "the quietest under the sun". From the top of nearby Hopesay Hill you get marvellous views of the Long Mynd to the north and the Welsh hills to the west. If you don't make it to the top of Hopesay, you can still appreciate the splendid views of the Clun Valley from the pub garden. The Kangaroo has a juke box, but it's rarely played except in the late evening, presumably to help clear the pub. There are, however, plenty of quiet areas, including the dining room. It is famous for its home-made pies – steak & kidney, game, venison in season, vegetarian, kangaroo pies, not forgetting the house speciality – Alligator Casserole – steaks too (local, beef), fish, chicken Kiev and some vegetarian dishes. Bass, Worthingtons, Highgate Mild and one guest beer. Varied wine list.

OPEN: 12–3. 7–11 (12–3. 7–10.30 Sun).
Real Ale.
Children in family room. Dogs on leads.

BEWDLEY

Little Pack Horse   Tel: 01299 403762

31 High Street, Bewdley, Worcs DY12 2DH
Free House. Peter & Sue D'Amery, licensees.

Busy, cheerful and slightly eccentric, this 16th century town pub has tremendous appeal, full of fascinating objects, including an incendiary bomb

166

(dud, I hope). Reasonably priced traditional bar food of the home-made variety: soups, filled baked potatoes, chilli, lasagne, salads, steaks and their own "Desperate Dan pies", these come in three sizes, with the "mini Dan" for small appetites. Beers do change, there are usually about 30 and among them you could find: Ind Coope Burton, Marstons, Holt Plant and Deakins Entire, also Lumphammer Ale which is brewed for the "Little Chain" of pubs to which the Little Pack Horse belongs. Note: there is no nearby parking.

OPEN: 11–3. 6–11 (all day summer Sat & Sun)
Real Ale.
Children in back bar or stable room. No dogs.

BIRTSMORTON

Farmers Arms   Tel: 01684 833308

Birts Street, Nr Malvern, Worcs WR13 6AP
Free House. Jill & Julie Moore, licensees.

Situated in a country lane, this black and white timbered pub with its low-beamed, convivial, rambling interior, offers a good range of bar food. This includes sandwiches, ploughmans, salads, steak & kidney pie, trout and almonds, steaks and good puddings. Hook Norton Old Hooky and some guest beers on hand pump. Seats in the garden during summer. Good walking country.

OPEN: 11–2. (3 Sat). 6–10.
Real Ale.
Children welcome. Dogs on leads.
Self-catering cottage available.

BISHOP'S CASTLE

Three Tuns   Tel: 01588 638797

Salop Street, Bishop's Castle, Shropshire SY9 5BW
Own Brew. Dominic Wood, licensee.

Pubs that have been brewing their own beers for several centuries are now few and far between. The Three Tuns is a fine example of one that has been brewing for the last 300 years. The brewery, now a listed building, was rebuilt in Victorian times, but was first mentioned in 1642. The inn and a black and white barn next to it probably date from that time. Inside, the pub retains many original features, including heavy oak beams and a good Jacobean staircase. The bar menu includes a number of fish and vegetarian dishes, a selection of Indian curries, steaks and pub specials. From the brewery comes XXX Bitter, Mild, a stout called Jim Wood's and the winter ale is Old Scrooge. Halls and Westons ciders. Interesting small wine list. Seats on the terrace and in the sheltered summery garden. The pub has its own garden centre, open from Easter to October. Lovely walking country.

OPEN: 11.30–3. 6.30–11 (perhaps longer in summer).
Real Ale. Restaurant.
Children welcome if well behaved. Dogs in bar & snug.

BRETFORTON

Fleece   Tel: 01386 831173

The Cross, Bretforton, Nr Evesham, Worcs.
Free House. N J Griffiths, licensee.

On the edge of the Cotswold hills, the village of Bretforton dates back to a Saxon deed of 714 AD and The Fleece is one of the gems of the village. Originally a medieval farmhouse, it became an inn during the 19th century. During its lifetime it has been added to and extended and these alterations can be seen by the changes in the timber framing at the front of the pub. Once completely thatched, the roof is now a mixture of thatch and stone. Beer was brewed in the back kitchen, continuing well into this century. The same family had lived here for over 500 years and when Miss Taplin died in 1977, she left The Fleece and all its wonderful contents to the National Trust who run it as an unspoilt country pub. Inside remains much as it was throughout the 19th century; the family collection of furniture, pewter, china and other ornaments and artefacts are still in their place. An unique interior which must be seen to be appreciated (don't miss the witch's marks still on the flagstones in front of the fire). It seems a bit mundane to talk about food and beer, but special as this place is, it is still the village local and as such provides good ales and an equally good choice of generous, varying bar food. Uley Old Spot and Pig's Ear, M and B Brew X1 and Everards Beacon Bitter. Country wines and farm ciders.

OPEN: 11–2.30. 6–11
Real Ale. (no food Mon eve, or Sun eve Jan & Feb)
Children welcome. No dogs.
Occasional live entertainment, visiting Morris men.

BRIDGES

Horseshoe Inn   Tel: 01588 650260

Bridges, Nr Ratlinghope, Shrewsbury, Shropshire SY5 0ST
Free House. John & Brenda Muller, licensees.

The 16th century Horseshoe is under the westerly side of the Long Mynd, a ridge of hills rising to 1700 ft, from where you get commanding views of the beautiful Shropshire countryside. From the seats in front of the Inn you can overlook the little river Onny. A short bar menu is served at lunchtime only: sandwiches, ploughmans and a few hot dishes – enough to give the walkers among you the energy to continue. Adnams Bitter and Extra, Shepherd Neame Spitfire and two guest beers. In 1995 The Horseshoe was voted CAMRA pub of the year for the Shrewsbury & W. Chropshire area. Westons farm cider. On a fine summer day the sky will be filled with the gliders from the Long Mynd Gliding Glub taking advantage of the standing wave the ridge is famous for.

OPEN: 11–3. 6–11
Real Ale.
Children in own room. Dogs on leads.
Wheelchair access to main bar and WC's.

BRIMFIELD

Roebuck   Tel: 01584 711230

Poppies Restaurant, Brimfield, Nr Ludlow, Shropshire SY8 4NE
Free House. Carole Evans, licensee.

If you want to do some serious eating, this is really a restaurant with a pub attached; but it is still a pub – with a restaurant; very much the village local, so if you want a pint and above average bar food, this is the place to come. The choice is considerable: hot crab pot with toast, warm salad of smoked chicken with sun-dried tomatoes, crispy bacon and tomato croutons, fish cakes with parsley sauce, smoked haddock and tarragon tart with leek sauce, old fashioned steak & kidney pie and a fantastic choice of puddings. Fifteen different English farmhouse cheeses. There is an even more extensive menu in the restaurant, where they also do set three-course lunches. Woods and Hobsons ales, Morlands Old Speckled Hen and a weekly guest. Half bottles of wine from a good wine list.

OPEN: 12–2.30. 7–11 (closed Sun & Mon)

THE QUIET PINT

Real Ale. Restaurant.
Children welcome. Dogs in the snug bar.
Bedrooms.

BROADWAY

Collin House Hotel   Tel: 01386 858354

Collin Lane, Broadway, Worcs, WR12 7PB (1.5 miles outside village)
Proprietor, John Mills.

The honey-coloured Cotswold stone of the buildings in Broadway, makes it
one of the most perfect Cotswold villages. Pretty houses, neat gardens, lots
of flowers, and of course, the antique shops, make it one of 'the places to
see' on the tourist circuit. Collin House is a small country house hotel with
an attractive bar. This isn't the sort of place to go to if you just want a drink,
they are only licensed to serve drinks if you are eating. Lunch is served in
the bar and restaurant every day except Sunday, when they only do a roast
meal. Full dinner in the restaurant every night, and, except at weekends, they
serve a 'Cotswold supper' which is a light two course meal. Donningtons
traditional ales and Carlsberg lager on draught. Good wine list too. There is
a garden to sit in, and as they are at the foot of the Cotswold hills, there are
plenty of walks.

Hotel opening hours
Real Ale
Children not in dining room in eve. Dogs in garden.
Bedrooms.

BROMSGROVE

Golden Cross Hotel   Tel: 01527 870005

20 High Street, Bromsgrove, Worcs. B61 8HH
Wetherspoon. Tony Rudenko, manager.

When Wetherspoon's opened the Golden Cross, the surrounding publicans
gave it about 6 weeks - no music you see. They couldn't imagine how
anyone could run a quiet pub. Well, he who laughs last laughs longest. Now
you know. It's how you run a pub that makes it successful, music is not a
requirement. Standards are high, the beer is reasonable, facilities are good,
the food is reliable. An old, run-down commercial hotel has been knocked
about and transformed into a busy, popular pub. The menus are standard

throughout the Wetherspoon chain and change three times a year. The beer, always about six regulars: Courage Directors, Theakstons Best & XB, Youngers Scotch Bitter, Banks Mild and Morlands Old Speckled Hen and guest ales. The new long bar has 21 hand pumps! They drink a lot of beer here.

OPEN: 11–11. (12–10.30. Sun)
Real Ale
No children. No dogs.
All wheelchair facilities.

CARDINGTON

Royal Oak   Tel: 01694 771266

Cardington, Nr Church Stretton, Shropshire SY6 7JZ
Free House. John Seymour, licensee.

You will find the creeper-covered 15th century Royal Oak behind the church in the small village of Cardington. In lovely countryside, not far from the Stretton hills; climb to the top and you have the most wonderful views over a picturesque valley. Inside the pub there is a rambling, well beamed bar with a big inglenook fireplace with good log fires during the winter. Varied, reliable bar food at lunchtime includes the traditional ploughmans, soups and sandwiches, plus a selection of hot dishes. Bass, Hobsons and Wadworths 6X ales. Tables on the terrace at the front of the pub with views over the undulating countryside.

OPEN: 12–2.30. 7–11. (closed Mons except bank hols)
Real Ale. No evening food.
Children at lunchtime only. Dogs on leads.

CORFTON

Sun Inn   Tel: 01584 861239

Corfton, Nr Craven Arms, Shropshire SY7 9DF
Free House. Teresa & Norman Pearce, licensee.

They say it's the oldest licensed premises in Corvedale – between Ludlow and Much Wenlock. An expert looking at the original timbers – which you can still see inside – would date it as 17th century. The lounge bar has a dining area where you have a choice of an à la carte menu or bar snacks, and a children's menu. The daily offerings are written on the blackboard in the lounge.There is a regularly changing selection of dishes: lamb and leek casserole, liver and bacon, lamb Shrewsbury, gammon, and various steaks; a fish menu, vegetarian menu, steak menu, childrens menu and somewhere, there is bound to be a pudding menu. Flowers IPA, Boddingtons Mild and Bitter and Wye Valley are the permanent ales but approximately 120 guest ales are brought in over the year. Seats in the garden. They keep chickens for their eggs, the ducks for their eggs too I hope, (no duck on the menu!), the rest of the produce used is nearly all local.

OPEN: 11–2.30. 6–11 (12–3. 7–10.30 Sun)
Real Ale.
Children welcome. Dogs on leads.
Wheelchair ramps to all parts of pub.

DEFFORD

The Cider House (Monkey)　　　　　　　　Tel: 01386 750234

Woodmancote, Defford, Hereford, Worcs NR8 9BW (No pub sign. The last cottage after Oak Public House.)
Free House. Graham Collins, licensee.

An experience not to be missed. Simple and unspoilt, there are only a few of these unique places left in the country – what you might call a dying breed, to be preserved at all costs. This black and white cottage without any inn sign is a traditional cider house. Cider is served from a barrel into a jug, through a hatch, into a mug. Beer available in cans (very 20th century), nuts and crisps. You can also bring your own picnic to enjoy with the cider. (No hamper charge!)

OPEN: 11–2.30. 6–10.30 (11 Fri & Sat). Closed Mon eves & all day Tues.
Cider. No food.
No dogs.

ELMLEY CASTLE

Queen Elizabeth Inn　　　　　　　　　　Tel: 01386 710209

Main Street, Elmley Castle, Nr Pershore, Worcs. WR10 3HS
Marstons. Tony Howells, tenant.

No food here, not even a bar snack, so it's just a nut, crisp and the beer. One of the loveliest villages in the country, Elmley Castle, at the foot of Bredon Hill, is full of timbered cottages; a stream runs alongside the main street. The castle has long disappeared, but from Bell Castle, an 18th century folly built on the slope of Bredon Hill, you can, on a clear day, see eight counties. After all that excitment, down to the early 16th century Queen Elizabeth Inn for a refreshing drink, and yes, she did call in. Marstons Best Bitter and Pedigree. There is a garden. The surroundings are beautiful, and there are good walks nearby.

OPEN: 12–3. 7–11
Real Ale. No food
Children – just about. Loves dogs.

FOWNHOPE

Green Man   Tel: 01432 860243

Fownhope, Nr Hereford HR1 4PE
Free House. Arthur & Margaret Williams, licensees.

Close to the meandering River Wye in the lovely Herefordshire countryside, this black and white timbered 15th century inn has a fascinating history. It had Civil War connections; it was then an 18th century petty sessions court, after that a coaching inn and now it's an hotel where everyone is welcome. Comfortable, with big log fires, it has a no-smoking dining room and a residents' lounge. Good value bar food, soup, sandwiches, plain or toasted, a "Tom Spring" steak sandwich with mushrooms and onions should set you up for the day, a choice of salads, vegetarian dishes, a seafood platter, a roast on Sundays, also children's meals. Well kept ales: Hook Norton Best, Courage Directors, Marstons Pedigree and Sam Smiths OB on hand pump. Farm ciders. Overlooking the river, the attractive garden has lots of room for drinks and afternoon tea. An unique sign, which was commissioned decades ago, hangs over the entrance to the coachhouse yard and reads in part: "You travel far, You travel near, it's here you find the best of Beer, You pass the East, You pass the West, if you pass this, you pass the Best."

OPEN: 11–3. 6–11.
Real Ale. Two Restaurants.
Children welcome. Dogs on leads.
Wheelchair access.

HANLEY CASTLE

Three Kings   Tel: 01684 592686

Hanley Castle, Worcester WR8 0BL, N of Upton upon Severn off B4211
Free House. Mrs Sheila Roberts, licensee.

Run by the same family for eighty-five years, it is a wonderfully unspoilt pub
without even a cigarette machine. Several small rooms, each with their own
atmosphere, in this attractively timbered 15th century building. A good
choice of bar snacks, ranging from soups and sandwiches to ploughmans
and omelettes. Gammon and egg, and a toasted bacon and mushroom
sandwich are the most popular items. Specials, which can take half an hour
to prepare include: beef Wellington, salmon and halibut Wellington, grilled
trout and steaks. A selection of puddings. Beer is served through a hatch
and includes Thwaites and Butcombe Bitter plus three guest beers. Over 50
malt whiskies and some farm ciders. Seats at the front of the pub
overlooking the village green.

OPEN: 11–3. 7–11.
Real Ale. No food Sun eves.
Children in family room. No dogs.
Bedrooms.
Live music Sun & alternate Sat eve. Folk alternate Thurs

HEREFORD

The Sun Inn   Tel: 01432 266403

71 St. Owen Street, Hereford (near the Bath Street junction)
Free House. Mayo Evans, licensee.

Hereford, a Cathedral city, was founded in 700 AD on the banks of the River
Wye. The Sun is a city pub doing what a pub always did: provide a friendly,
quiet congenial haven, in which to sit and contemplate life, enjoying a
decent drink. This is a variation on a crisp and nut pub, only this time
substitute pork scratchings for the crisps. Good choice of beers: Marstons,
Boddingtons, Flowers IPA, Guinness, Murphys, Draught Heineken, Hereford
Bitter and Whitbread's Welsh Bitter. Tables in the beer garden.

OPEN: 11–3. 6–11 (12–4ish. 7–10.30. Sun)
Real Ale
Children welcome. No dogs.

KEMPSEY

Walter de Cantelupe Inn
Tel: 01905 820572

Main Road, Kempsey, Worcs WR5 3NA
Free House. Martin Lloyd Morris, manager/owner.

Not far outside Worcester, this was originally just a cider house, but since being taken over in 1991 by the present owner, the inn has been gaining an enviable reputation for its food. When possible, locally produced vegetables, meat and cheese are used to create a reasonably priced, well chosen menu. If they take longer that 10 minutes to make your sandwich you will get it free – now there's a thought. Hot baguettes filled with either roast beef or home cooked smoked ham moistened with a rich meat stock are very popular, seafood pot, pasta, curry, and other dishes. During the six week asparagus season they have a special menu featuring locally grown asparagus. Quality wines by the glass. Regular free tasting sessions. Marstons Bitter, Sedgley Surprise from Sarah Hughes Brewery at Dudley and Wadworths 6X. The customers voted with their beer glasses for Sedgley Surprise. Dents Ramsbottom as the guest ale, but this can changes to something else from another of the smaller breweries. Seats in the flowery hidden garden.

OPEN: 12–2.30. 5.30–11 (12–3; 7–10.30 Sun)
Real Ale. (Closed lunch Mon except Bank holidays)
Children lunchtime & until 8pm. No dogs.

KNIGHTWICK

Talbot Hotel
Tel: 01886 821235

Knightwick, Nr Worcester WR6 5PH. (At Knightsford Bridge off A44 Worcester-Bromyard.)
Free House. Ann & Wizz Clift, licensees.

Set in a lovely part of Worcestershire on the banks of the River Teme. The Talbot, parts of which date back to the 14th century, continues to provide hospitality as it has been doing for the past 500 years. Beamed, comfortable bars, panelled dining room, imaginative, well cooked food, well-kept ales and good wines. A daily changing menu for both the bar and restaurant: fresh scallops beignets, king prawns and garlic noodles, rabbit pudding, Middle Eastern lamb casserole, liver & bacon, three fish pie, salmon steak poached in white wine, vegetarian dishes and much more. Good home-made puds to follow. Hobsons Bitter, Worthingtons and Bass on handpump. Wines by the glass. Seats outside and opposite the pub. Lots of walks nearby.

OPEN: 11–11.
Real Ale. Restaurant.
Children in eating area until 7.30. Dogs on leads.
Bedrooms.
Morris Dances winter Wed.
Wheelchair access is possible.

LEDBURY

Feather's Hotel Tel: 01531 635266

High Street, Ledbury, Herefordshire HR8 1DS
Free House. D.M.Elliston, licensee.

Situated in the main street of this unspoilt market town, The Feathers, three storeys high, is a dazzling example of timber-framed building at its best. Architecturally a jewel. Inside there is a big, well-beamed, very attractive bar and an elegant restaurant. Good lunchtime snacks: home-made soups, spinach and ricotta tartlet with mixed leaf salad, Feather's seafood and spinach lasagne, casserole of local rabbit with rosemary and coarse mustard, vegetarian dishes, grills, and imaginative puddings. Three course Sunday lunch. Marstons Bitter, Worthington BB and Bass on hand pump plus two guest beers. Large wine list and choice of malt whiskies and farm ciders.

OPEN: 11–11.
Real Ale. Restaurant
Children in eating area. Dogs on leads.
Bedrooms.
Live music Wed.
Wheelchair access.

LEOMINSTER

Grape Vaults Tel: 01568 611404

Broad Street, Leominster, Herefordshire HR6 8BS
Free House. Mrs Pauline Greenwood, licensee.

One of the nicest small 17th century pubs: lately very well restored, it has all the advantages of an English country inn, but in town. No fruit machines, computer games or juke box. Just the hum of conversation and the chink of glasses. Wide ranging bar menu of home-cooked food: soups, deep-fried brie in ale batter, steak & kidney pie, cottage pie, ham and leak pie with potato topping, ham on the bone and fresh cod in their own beer batter – using Marstons Best! Ales could be Banks Mild, Marstons Bitter, and Pedigree – these do change – 28 different guests made an appearance last year.

OPEN: 11–3. 5–11. (12–3; 7–10.30 Sun)
Real Ale.
No children. Dogs on leads.
Wheelchair access just possible.

LUDLOW

The Unicorn   Tel: 01584 873555

Corve Street, Ludlow, Shrops. SY8 1DV
Free House. Alan, Elizabeth & John Ditchburn, licensees.

About ten minutes walk from the centre of Ludlow, a town full of architectural treasures. The half-timbered Unicorn dates from 1635, its oak panelled, beamed bar reflecting its great age. Two dining areas, one with a view over the flood meadows on the other side of the river. Better than average pub grub with daily additions listed on the blackboard: – ham served with a parsley sauce, black pudding with a cider and mustard sauce – always some vegetarian dishes. In the restaurant: chicken wrapped in bacon in a cream and mushroom sauce, half a chicken roasted in ginger wine and apple sauce, fillet of cod with crab and prawn bisque – lots more of well thought out, well cooked dishes. Beers are always Bass and Worthington. Seats on the terrace of this attractive pub with views over the River Corve (quite small, fringed with willows) which merges with the River Teme in Ludlow.

OPEN: 12–2.30. 6–11. (12 until empty. 7–10.30 Sun)
Real Ale. Restaurant.
Children welcome. Dogs on leads.
Wheelchair access to the back of the pub.

LUGWARDINE

Crown & Anchor   Tel: 01432 851303

Cotts Lane, Hereford. Off A438 E of Hereford.
Free House. Nick & Julie Squires, licensees.

In what is virtually a dormitory village for Hereford, the old timbered Crown and Anchor was closed for some time but has now been brought back into the fold. It has comfortable, friendly bars plus one room especially for families. They offer a good variety of traditional bar food and well kept ales. Eel pie is one of the specialities of the house, the eels caught in the nearby River Lug. Worthington BB, Hook Norton Best, Bass and a weekly changing guest beer all on hand pump. A range of wines.

OPEN: 11.30–11.
Real Ale.
Children welcome. Dogs on leads.

OMBERSLEY

Crown & Sandys Arms   Tel: 01905 620252

Ombersley, Droitwich, Worcs WR9 0EW. Turn left at roundabout in village.
Free House. R E Ransome, licensee.

Considerably older than it looks, the original timber-framed inn was remodelled in the early 19th century and is enclosed in the Dutch gabled shell you see today. Situated at the south end of the attractive village of Ombersley, it has comfortable, beamed and timbered bars with huge inglenook fireplaces. There is an interesting, imaginative choice of home-cooked food, bar meals and daily specials using local game, wild boar, venison cooked in various ways, fresh fish, vegetarian meals and an à la carte menu in the restaurant. Daily specials on the blackboard. They also have a fine wine list. House wines by the glass, and some country fruit wines. Traditional draught ales – Hook Nortons Best, Woods, Hobsons and varying guest ales on hand pump. Tables in the garden during the summer.

OPEN: 11–2.30. 5.30–11.
Real Ale. Restaurant. Standard bar food and snacks always available.
Children if well behaved. Not babies. No dogs. Guide dogs excepted.

OMBERSLEY

Kings Arms   Tel: 01905 620315

Ombersley, Droitwich, Worcs WR9 0EW
Free House. Chris & Judy Blundell, licensees.

The old timbered pub has been rearranged inside to give more space for diners, but it still has rambling, beamed rooms with good log fires in the inglenook fireplaces. Plenty of choice from the changing menu, including tried and tested pub fare with specials such as soup, garlic crevettes, gratin of mussels farcis, kidneys in curry cream sauce, aubergine parmigiana, medallions of chicken with a cranberry glaze, steak and kidney pie, vegetarian dishes and a selection of home-made puddings. Draught Brew X1, Bass, Worthingtons, Wadworths 6X and a range of malt and Irish whiskies. Tables in the courtyard amongst the summer flowers.

OPEN: 11–2.45. 5.30–11 (12–10.30 Sat).
Real Ale. Food all day Sunday.
Children, not under six, in eating area till 8.30. No dogs.
Wheelchair access.

PEMBRIDGE

New Inn   Tel: 01544 388427

Market Square, Pembridge, Hereford HR6 9DZ
Free House. Jane Melvin, licensee.

In the small, medieval village surrounded by meadows and orchards, the New Inn was 'new' in the 14th century, very much the same date as St Mary's Church. A charming, traditional pub with two beamed bars and not a right angle between them. Well chosen home-cooked food: soups, mussels in garlic, salmon terrine, lamb and mint hot-pot, leek and pepper lasagne, duck in elderberry wine and interesting puddings. Ruddles Best and County plus one guest beer a month. New world wines and a considerable range of malt whiskies. Tables outside with views of the church, whose separate bell tower was used as a refuge during the Welsh Border wars.

OPEN: 11–3. 6–11 (6.30–11 winter).
Real Ale. Restaurant (no Sun evening)
Children in eating area until 9pm. No dogs.
Bedrooms.

PULVER BATCH

White Horse   Tel: 01743 718247

Pulver Batch, Nr Shrewsbury, Shropshire SY5 8DS
Whitbread. James Macgregor, lease.

Everywhere you go in Shropshire seems to unveil another vantage point from where you can see another aspect of this glorious county; the White Horse is no exception. It is at the end of the village from where there are magnificent views. Dating from the 13th century, it has rambling, beamed, traditionally furnished rooms, well decorated with blue and white plates, mugs, copper kettles, pictures and other interesting objects. Sturdy bar food: soups, ploughmans, lasagne, casseroles, trout and steaks. A longer, more sophisticated menu is a feature during the evening. Wadworths 6X, Flowers Original and Boddingtons are the regular ales. Lots of malt whiskies, and wine by the glass. No garden but there is a big car park.

OPEN: 11.30–3. 7–11.
Real Ale.
Children welcome. Dogs on leads.

SHREWSBURY

Three Fishes   Tel: 01743 344793

Fish Street, Shrewsbury, Shrops. SY1 1UR
Whitbread. John Sims, leaseholder/licensee.

Fifteenth century, (next door was built in 1460), open all day; one bar, beamed and timbered, this is just the place to refresh yourself before another foray onto the streets of one of the finest Tudor towns in England. More of a thirst quencher really, only bar snacks available but there are a number of rotating guest ales to accompany the Whitbread range of beers.

OPEN: 11.30–11
Real Ale
Children welcome. Dogs on leads.
Wheelchair access.

SHREWSBURY

The Armoury   Tel: 01743 340525

Welsh Bridge, Shrewsbury, SY1 1HH
Free House. Barbie Dixon-Bate, licensee.

On the bank of the River Severn, this pub is having a pontoon built so customers can sit in mid-stream, drink, eat and watch the water flow by. The Armoury has only been open since April 1996. Originally a bakery built just after the last war. There was a shortage of bricks at the time so they used all available ones from an old armoury that had been demolished – no more bricks meant rather large windows. Interesting choice of bar food: ploughmans with several different cheeses, including Shropshire Blue; lots of fillings for the sandwiches; tapenade with warm Italian bread, avocado with prawns and pink grapefruit in a citrus dressing, salmon and smoked haddock fishcakes with a lemon mayonnaise, scrambled egg and smoked salmon on a toasted muffin, char-grilled Mediterranean vegetables with couscous and tomato sauce, lots more including Armoury Pie – beef, bacon, red wine and mushrooms. Puds too. Real coffee. Timothy Taylors Landlord, Boddingtons, Wadworths 6X, Woods Shropshire Lad and two guest beers. Views across the river.

OPEN: 11.30–3. 5–11 (11.30–11 Sat. 12–10.30 Sun)
Real Ale
Children welcome. No Dogs.

TELFORD

Coalbrookdale Inn   Tel: 01952 433953

12, Wellington Road, Coalbrookdale, Nr Ironbridge, Shrops. TF8 7DX
In Business Ltd., Mike Fielding, tenant.

Late Georgian, first licensed in 1813, this listed building is near the Museum of Iron, part of the Ironbridge Gorge World Heritage site, an important centre in Britain's industrial revolution. Built in 1779, the bridge over the Severn was the first iron bridge in the country. Just one bar in the pub, but with two fires, one of them a little Coalbrookdale cast iron grate. There is an extensive bottle collection and some pub memorabilia. Lunchtime bar food: baguettes with lots of different fillings, daily specials. In the evening there will be a different menu – all home-cooked: spicy chicken stir fry and Dale ale pie are a couple of dishes from the menu. Courage Directors, plus 30 different beers a week. 900 beers in four and a half years. Once he has sold his quota of "barrellage", specified by the pub's owners, the landlord is free to buy beers from any brewery he chooses. The pub is built into a bank, so there is no garden, but there is a side terrace with seating for about twenty people.

OPEN: 12–3. 6–11
Real Ale
Children welcome. Dogs on leads.

WENLOCK EDGE

Wenlock Edge Inn   Tel: 01746 785403

Hilltop, Wenlock Edge, Shropshire TF13 6DJ
Free House. Stephen Waring, licensee.

Wenlock Edge is a 400 million year old coral reef. The inn, by comparison, is a mere stripling, dating back to the 17th century. In fact, it was only licensed as a pub in 1925. Run by the Waring family, it has a reputation for creating a very friendly, welcoming atmosphere, and for serving English cooking at its best. Good stews, garlic mushrooms in cream and sherry, honey baked ham with either salad or hot vegetables, venison casserole, and steaks in the evening and very more-ish puds. Websters Yorkshire Bitter and two locally brewed ales: Hobsons Best and Town Crier and one guest, currently Ruddles Best. Selection of malt whiskies and wines by the glass. There are Monday storytelling evenings when a local group swops stories from "the Edge". Ask about Ippikin, a thief who lived in a cave near Lilleshall Quarry.

OPEN: 11.30–2.30; 6–11 (6.30–11 winter). Closed Mon lunch.
Real Ale. Restaurant. (No meals Mon except Bank Hols)
Children in restaurant (not under 10 after 8pm). Dogs on leads in bar.
Bedrooms.

WEOBLEY

Ye Olde Salutation   Tel: 01544 318443

Market Pitch, Weobley, Hereford HR4 8SJ
Free House. Chris & Francis Anthony, licensees

Still the village local, where you can meet for a drink and a chat, though this old pub has gained a reputation for its imaginative food. Chorizo sausage on a bed of pan fried potatoes with roasted peppers and chives, home cured gravadlax, pot roasted quail in port wine, fillet of Brill on a bed of samphire with red pepper sauce, and those are just a few of the seasonal specials. Hot filled rolls (home-baked bread), vegetarian dishes and interesting puds to finish. There is an à la carte menu in the no-smoking restaurant and a very popular 3 course lunch on Sundays. Wadworths 6X, Bass, Hook Nortons Best and Westons cider. Over 120 differant wines and 20 malt whiskies. Seats on the terrace at the back of the pub.

OPEN: 11–3. 7–11.
Real Ale. Restaurant (not Sun evening)

Children in eating areas. No dogs.
Wheelchair access to eating area only.

WHITNEY-ON-WYE

The Rydespence Inn   Tel: 01497 831262

Whitney-on-Wye, Hereford, HR3 6EU. 1.5 miles W. of village on A 438.
Free House. Peter & Pamela Glover, licensees.

The stream in the garden of this wonderful, timbered old inn, which
overlooks the Wye valley and Black mountains, marks the boundary
between Wales and England. Originally a manor house, it was, until the
coming of the railways, an assembly point for drovers en route to the English
market towns; even as far as London. The 140 acres surrounding the inn
was divided up into penny, ha-penny and farthing fields, so if you didn't have
many animals for overnight grazing, a farthing field would do. What you now
have is a comfortable, charming, inn. Two bars in the 16th century part of
the building; heavily beamed, one with a big log fire; serving bar meals
lunchtime and evenings. There is also a very attractive restaurant. From the
bar menu you could choose: ploughmans platters with crusty bread, filled
jacket potatoes, Rydepsence chicken liver paté studded with smoked
pigeon breast and served with Cumberland sauce, brochette of king prawns
and monkfish, mushroom provençale with fresh tagliatelle and garlic bread,
seafood pie, seafood platter, beef lasagne, Heals farm Devon sausages in
onion gravy, steaks, grills, several vegetarian dishes – all this and more,
everything is freshly prepared. Good selection of home-made ice-creams
and sorbets. Robinsons Best Bitter, Draught Bass and Brains SA. Interesting
wine list. Local cider. Seats on the sunny terrace and in the large garden.

OPEN: 11–2.30. 7–11.
Real Ale. Restaurant.
Children welcome. No dogs.
En suite bedrooms.

WOOLHOPE

Butchers Arms   Tel: 01432 860281

Woolhope, Herefordshire, HR1 4RF
Free House. Patrick Power, licensee.

Down a lane, just outside the village, you'll find this black and white half-timbered 14th century country pub. Two low beamed bars, log fires in winter, the windows opening onto the flowery terrace in the summer. Lots of pub favourites on the menu: sandwiches, ploughmans, salads, lasagne, chillis, steaks, also Woolhope pie, made with wild rabbit, bacon and cooked in cider. There is a vegetarian dish or two, and some home-made puds. The menu is constantly changing – go and be surprised. A separate restaurant open only on Saturday evenings. Hook Norton Best, Old Hooky and guest beers. A stream borders the garden. There are very good walks nearby.

OPEN: 11.30–3. 6.30–11.
Real Ale. Restaurant.
Children welcome. Guide dogs only.
Wheelchair access. Car park.

WOORE

The Falcon Tel: 01630 647230

London Road, Woore, Nr Crewe CW3 9SF. (Really in N. Shropshire)
Marstons. Norman Cannon, tenant.

Now this is something new. A pub with a bookie's office in the car park. Not surprising really. This was an old coaching inn – licensed to keep 12 horses during the day, six at night – so they are keeping in touch with their equine past. A really sporty place. Until recently The Falcon had its own cricket field and during the 19th century prize fights used to take place in the field at the back – the organisers often bringing fighters over from America. One such fight started in Newcastle-under-Lyme, was stopped by magistrates, to be re-started at The Falcon, ten miles away, watched by 7000 spectators. Now the only arguement will be over who has what from the menu. Specialising in fish, the landlord is never certain what is available from the Manchester fish market, but there will be about 25 different dishes, anything from haddock in batter to lobster thermidor. Famous for its food – fish in particular – it was voted Pub chef of the year in 1993, and was a finalist in 1995, so you know they can cook. Marstons Bitter, Pedigree and every two weeks, there is a Head Brewers choice. Nearly 50 different whiskies, and wine to go with the fish. Seats in the garden.

OPEN: 11.30–3. 6.30–11 (12–3.30. 7–10.30 Sun)
Real Ale. Restaurant.
Children – but not young children and not evening. No dogs.

H
HERTFORDSHIRE

ALDBURY

Valiant Trooper   Tel: 0144 2851203

Trooper Road, Aldbury, Nr Tring, Herts HP23 5RW
Free House. Dorothy O'Gorman, licensee.

Here's another pub that's ideally situated for the country walker and anyone
looking for a good pint and bar food in the lovely, wooded Chiltern hills, not
far from the Ridgeway Path. Short, familiar bar menu plus blackboard
specials: cottage pie, mixed grill, liver and bacon casserole or fish pie; all
home-cooked using fresh ingredients – no chips. Bass, Fullers London Pride
and John Smiths Bitter plus two weekly changing guest beers. Farm ciders.
Charming, cottagey garden to sit in. (Recognised as one of the best value
pubs in Hertfordshire.)

OPEN: 11–11 (12–2.30. 7–10.30 Sun).
Real Ale. Restaurant (not Sun eve); No meals/snacks Sun or Mon eve.
Children in one room lunchtime. Dogs on leads.

ARDELEY

Jolly Waggoner   Tel: 01438 861350

Ardeley, Nr Stevenage, Herts SD2 7AH
Greene King. Barron Perkins, lease.

Off the B 1037 before you get to Cromer windmill, this is a charming 15th
century pub in a quiet village. Quarry tiles, beams, open fireplaces and a 40
seat restaurant – all newly done-up. Popular bar food: soups, sandwiches,
ploughmans, local sausages, salads and daily specials. Greene King Abbott
and IPA; occasional guest ales. Seats in the attractive garden. Good walks
nearby.

OPEN: 12–2.30. 6–11 (7–10.30 Sun)

Real Ale. Restaurant.
Children over 7. No dogs.
Wheelchair access.

BARLEY

Fox & Hounds   Tel: 01763 848459

High Street, Barley, Nr Royston, Herts SG8 8HU
Own Brew. Rita Nicholson, licensee.

This is a rambling, beamed 15th century village local that brews its own beer.
The selection is not limited to what is brewed in-house, however: there are
usually between eight and ten other ales on offer, with many more during the
real ale festivals licensee Rita Nicholson organises from time to time. There
is an extensive choice of bar food. A huge blackboard menu virtually covers
one wall and nearly all the food is home-made. Lots of pies, casseroles,
curries, steaks and seafood. Lighter bar snacks available at lunchtime, as
well as a selection of vegetarian and vegan dishes, a children's menu, and
a carvery on Sundays. Half the dining area is non-smoking. The Fox and
Hounds' own ales are: Nathaniel's Special (standard) and Flame Thrower (
strong). Ciders, wines by the glass and a selection of malt whiskies. There
is a barbecue in the garden; also a skittle alley.

OPEN: 12–2.30. 6–11 (12–11 summer Sats).
Real Ale. Evening restaurant .
Children in family room & restaurant. Dogs on leads.
Wheelchair access to dining room and WC's.

CHENIES

Red Lion   Tel: 01923 282722

Chenies Village, Rickmansworth, Hertfordshire WD3 6ED.
Free House. Heather & Mike Norris, licensees.

A four-square, white painted old pub, hung about, if that is the right word to
use, with a wonderful display of hanging baskets. Inside, there is a large
main bar and a small dining area in what was the original 17th century
cottage. A varied selection of very popular, home-cooked bar food could
include: soup, game paté, pasta in a basil sauce, french sticks with a hot or
cold filling, jacket potatoes, several different pies including the special
"Chenies lamb pie", salmon, spinach and cream cheese parcels or even

duck Wellington. All dishes are served with fresh vegetables, but NO CHIPS. Also filled French sticks, baps and jacket potatoes. Daily specials from the blackboard. Wadworths 6X, Benskins Best, Notley Ale and Lion Pride, brewed for the pub by The Rebellion Beer Co. They have a short wine list, and house wines by the glass. If you want a little "culture," Chenies Manor House – a Tudor Manor built by the Earl of Bedford in 1526 and still with its original Tudor garden – is not far away.

OPEN: 11–2.30, 5.30–11
Real Ale.
No children. Dogs on leads.

FLAUNDEN

Bricklayers Arms   Tel: 01442 833322

Hogpits Bottom, Flaunden, Herts HP3 0PH
Free House. David Winteridge, licensee.

This small, popular, low-built, creeper-covered pub has an appealing beamed interior. It is so popular that it is filled to the gunnels at weekends. During summer week-ends they cope by overflowing into the attractive garden. In winter, though, it's first come, first served, to a place by the fire. Well chosen, imaginative food is one of the attractions, along with the well kept ales and friendly atmosphere. Good generous bar food is served at lunchtime and ranges from the familiar soups and filled baked potatoes, ploughmans and sandwiches, to cottage pie, vegetable bake, curried chicken, fish pie, steak in ale pie, steaks and daily specials. An à la carte menu is served in the dining room during the evening. Chiltern Celebration Ale, Brakspears Special, Vale View Edgars Golden Ale and two guest beers. Seats in the lovely cottagey garden. Good walks nearby.

OPEN: 11–2.30 (11–3 Sat). 6–11.
Real Ale. Restaurant.
Children in restaurant. Dogs on leads.

FLAUNDEN

Green Dragon   Tel: 01442 832269

Flaunden, Nr Hemel Hempstead, Herts HP3 0PP
Free House. Richard Knight, tenant.

Another hunt the pub game. The landlord says "you have to know how to get here." Well, I've looked at the map and it seems to be about three miles from Hemel Hempstead and south of Chipperfield – pubs have a habit of being on remote country roads. When you do arrive they have a comfortable saloon, public bar, snug and a collection of green dragons behind the bar. "Light bites" for a quick snack: garlic mushrooms, Everglade eggs – with mayonnaise gherkins and olives; various sandwiches, filled jacket potatoes and lots more. A restaurant menu too, offering poached salmon, scampi, beef in red wine or roast duck. Marstons Pedigree, Greene King IPA, Abbotts and one guest beer. Seats in the small, well kept garden.

OPEN: 11–3. 5.30–11. (11–11. Sat. 12–3. 7–10.30.Sun)
Real Ale. Restaurant.
Children in garden or restaurant. Dogs on leads in one bar only.

HIGH WYCH

Rising Sun   Tel: 01279 724099

High Wych, Nr Sawbridgeworth, Herts CM21 0HZ
Free House. Stephen Prior, licensee.

A small village pub on a what used to be a quiet village street, now busy and noisy with traffic. The Rising Sun has been in the Prior family since 1929: it's one of those pubs that belongs to different periods 'all bits and pieces.' A classic layout: small public bar, saloon bar and tap room (without carpet). No food – crisp and nut country this – just beers. Courage Best, Directors and a guest beer from one of the smaller breweries. Relax in the quiet garden at the back of the pub.

OPEN: 12–2.30. 5–11. (12–3 Fri & Sat)
Real Ale.
Children welcome in tap room. Dogs on leads.

KINSBOURNE GREEN

The Fox   Tel: 01582 713817

469, Luton Road, Kinsbourne Green, Harpenden, Herts AL5 3QE
Allied Domecq. Phil Stringer, manager.

On the outskirts of the village, you are really spoilt for choice in The Fox on a cold winter night. The lounge bar has two fires: lose your space in front of the first, there is always the second. Still no room ? – you'll find yet another in the old panelled snug. Traditional pub grub from the menu: sandwiches, ploughmans, scampi, and between ten and fifteen different dishes on the daily changing specials board. Nine real ales at any one time. Ind Coope Benskins BB and Burton, Tetley Bitter, Eldridge Pope Thomas Hardy's Ale and Royal Oak. The rest are constantly changing guests.

OPEN: 11–2.30. 5.30–11.
Real Ale.
Children welcome. Dogs on leads.

NORTH MYMMS

Woodman   Tel: 01707 650502

Warrengate Road, North Mymms, Herts AL9 7TT
Free House. John Stewart, manager.

Very popular with the students from the local veterinary college, this nice old pub, built in 1732, serves interesting food and good ale. Traditional bar food, but the emphasis is on offering restaurant food at pub prices. John Stewart, the manager, is from Inverness and frequently goes to Scotland to bring back supplies, so you will find salmon, pheasant and grouse in season and other game dishes featured on the menu. Courage Directors, Best, Bitter, Wadworths 6X and Marstons Pedigree. Large garden at the front, and a beer garden at the back overlooking the surrounding countryside.

OPEN: 11–3. 5.30–11.
Real Ale. No food Sun.
No children. No dogs.

NUTHAMPSTEAD

The Woodman   Tel: 01763 848328

Nuthampstead, Nr Royston, Herts SG8 8NB
Free House. Ian and Sandra Johnson, licensees.

Thatched and weatherboarded outside, beams and inglenook fireplace inside. Dating back to the 16th century, it has more than a nodding aquaintance with the 20th century. A memorial outside The Woodman commemorates members of the United States Air Force who lost their lives in the last war. The 398 Bomb Group flew Flying Fortress' out of Nuthampstead airfield, and the Association regularly returns for a reunion.

The Bar snack menu consists mainly of basket meals, lasagne and vegetarian dishes. An à la carte menu features in the restaurant – mainly grills; steaks, salmon and chicken – very traditional fare. Ales vary, but could be from the Dark Horse Brewing Co. A pleasant garden to sit in. In winter they do shooting lunches – for all those very hungry people and their dogs.

OPEN: 11–3. 5–11 (11–3. 7–10.30)
Real Ale. Restaurant.
Children welcome. Dogs too.

SAWBRIDGEWORTH

King William IV   Tel: 01279 722322

Vantorts Road, Sawbridgeworth, Herts
Courage. Derek Tunmore, tenant.

A fine old pub on a quiet lane, with an affable host and clientele. Some years ago it was voted "Friendly Pub of the Year". Beer is well kept, all the food is locally supplied, freshly cooked and good value. The special "Willie's Sausages" are made by the local butcher, 100 yards or so from the pub. No juke box, just a TV in the snug off the main saloon and normally switched on only for major sporting events. Courage beers, Beamish stout and a guest. No garden, but there are seats outside the front of the pub, so you can watch the world go by.

OPEN: 11–11.
Real Ale. No food Sunday.
Children welcome. Dogs on leads.
Occasional live music.

ST ALBANS

Rose & Crown   Tel: 01727 51903

10 St Michael Street, St Albans, Herts AL3 4S6
Greenalls. Neil Dekker, tenant.

The town was named after the Christian martyr, St Alban, beheaded on the hill on which the cathedral now stands. The 300 year old Rose and Crown, in the shadow of the 9th century Abbey, was built alongside the original Watling Street, and opposite the remains of the Roman town of Verulanium. Inside, the old pub is well beamed, with a big inglenook fireplace – and no right angles! The landlord specialises in American style sandwiches with names like Frank Sinatra, Lucille Ball, Johnny Appleseed and others. Many-layered, try these and you know you have had a sandwich. "Serf's" sandwiches available too, (roast beef, paté, ham or cheese) plus hot pub dishes: moussaka, lasagne or chilli con carne. Greenalls original, Adnams, Tetleys, Wadworths 6X and a guest beer, farm ciders and choice of malt whiskies. Plenty of tables outside in the garden among the flowers. The car park is built over the gates of the old Roman town.

OPEN: 11–3. 5.30–11 (6–11 Sat).
Real Ale. No food Sunday.
Children in eating area. Dogs on leads.
Live music Thurs & Mon eves.
Wheelchair access to pub.

THUNDRIDGE (Nr Wadesmill)

Sow & Pigs   Tel: 01920 463281

Thundridge, Nr Ware, Herts SG12 0ST
Greenalls. Meriel Riches, tenant.

A comfortable, friendly village local. It has a small, panelled central bar, with rooms off, one of which is the dining room. With a name like this you are not surprised when bacon or ham feature in the menus, but that is not the only dish offered here. Usual variety of bar food, with daily specials: steaks, chicken dishes, sausage and onions and their own "very special" fish and chips. Adnams, Greenalls Original, Shipstones and Wadworths 6X plus guest beer. Picnic tables on the sheltered area by the car park.

OPEN: 11–3. 6.30–11 (6–11 Sat)
Real Ale. Restaurant.
Children in eating area. No dogs.

WATTON AT STONE

George & Dragon   Tel: 01920 830285

High Street, Watton at Stone, Herts SG14 3TA
Greene King. Kevin Dinnin, lease.

Pink-washed and on the main road – you can't really miss it, nor should you if you want a relaxed, civilised pub, complete with daily newspaper, proper napkins, interesting pieces of furniture, plus a reputation for good imaginative food. Carbonnade of Beef, Salmon in whisky and lemon juice, lamb's liver in cream and brandy and black pepper sauce, chicken breast in light pastry with bacon and onion in white wine sauce plus light snacks such as: cornets of smoked salmon filled with avocado mousse, filleted smoked eel and bacon served on a bed of dressed mixed leaves, millionaire's bun which is fillet steak and a bread roll, or billionaire's bun which has twice as much steak! And if you really must, sandwiches, ploughmans and home-made puddings too. Very popular with everyone from near and far. Greene King ales, short wine list and choice of malt whiskies. Some tables in the restaurant are non-smoking. Seats in the attractive garden.

OPEN: 11–2.30. 6–11 (11–11 Sat)
Real Ale. Restaurant (not Sun eve)
Children in family room & restaurant. No dogs.
Occasional live entertainment.

K
KENT

BIDDENDEN

Three Chimneys   Tel: 01580 291472

Biddenden, Nr Ashford, Kent TN27 8HA (1 mile W of village on A262)
Free House. C F Sayers & G A Sheepwash, licensees.

Set in the Kentish Weald, famous for its hops and cherries, a mile and a half
west of the attractive village of Biddenden, you'll find this black and white
15th century country pub. Sitting slightly below the level of the main road,
it is easy to miss, so you have to watch out for the inn sign depicting a man
and a three-armed signpost. Friendly, busy, with rambling low-beamed bars
and log fires in winter. Good imaginative food on offer: home-made soups
– devilled crab or chilled mint and stilton, egg and anchovy mousse, duck
and orange paté, ham and parmesan pancakes, rabbit in cream and
mustard sauce, steak and oyster pie, mushroom stroganoff are just a few
examples. The blackboard menus are seasonal – spring, summer autumn
and winter. Four puddings, served with local Jersey cream, change daily.
There is a family garden room and tables in the pretty garden filled with
shrubs, roses and nut trees. Range of eight or more ales tapped from behind
the bar could include: Marstons Pedigree, Morlands Old Speckled Hen,
Brakspears, Fremlins, Adnams Best, Harveys Best, Wadworths 6X and
Harveys Old Ale in winter. A strong local cider, local wines and a varied wine
list. Wines by the glass and half bottles.

OPEN: 11–2.30. 6–11
Real Ale. Restaurant.
Children in restaurant. Dogs on leads.
Occasional live entertainment.
Wheelchair access to pub only.

BOSSINGHAM Nr. Canterbury

The Hop Pocket   Tel: 01227 709866

Bossingham, Nr. Canterbury, Kent CT4 6DY. (Between Bridge and Stelling Minnis)
Free House. Mike Austin, licensee.

One pub in the village. You really can't miss it. It's right on the road looking a bit like a Victorian station master's house. At first glance you may think there is a queue to get in, but that's the bus stop. Inside there are hops; these hang about on the un-real beams accompanying the bank notes that are stuck to the ceiling. One big bar, wooden floors, small fireplace and a huge number of blackboards. Some list the fruit wines, or the take-away cask ales; others, the menu. You are quite spoilt for choice but service can be slow. Shepherd Neame Spitfire and Master Brew, Timothy Taylors Landlord, Harveys Sussex and Hopback Summer Lightening. Small garden with some picnic tables, and a large play area beyond the car park.

OPEN: 12–3. 7–11. (12–3. 7–10.30 Sun)
Real Ale
Children welcome. Dogs on leads.

CHIDDINGSTONE

Castle   Tel: 01892 870247

Chiddingstone, Nr. Edenbridge, Kent TN8 7AH.
Free House. Nigel Lucas, licensee.

Tucked in the lea of Chiddingstone Castle – whose mock 19th century medieval façade conceals a 17th century interior – the Castle Inn dates back to 1420. Originally Waterslip House, the building was first licensed and renamed in 1730. Still the centre of village life, it is part of an unspoilt Tudor village which was bought by the National Trust in 1939 for £25,000, and is considered to have one of the finest village streets in Kent. The Castle's heavily beamed saloon and public bar can get very crowded in summer, so arrive early to be sure of room to eat. An extensive bar menu is available: home-made soup, home-made paté, a plate of smoked salmon, local pork sausages, a daily pasta (read the blackboard), lots of different salads, filled jacket potatoes, sandwiches, ploughmans and of course daily specials. Some very interesting Spanish ice creams to follow plus other puddings. More elaborate, two or three course meals available in the saloon bar or restaurant. The ales are Larkins Traditional, Harveys Best and one other guest ale. There is an extensive wine list featuring wines from all over the world. Outside is a very pretty vine hung courtyard, with tables.

OPEN: 11–3. 6–11 (all day Sat & Sun).
Real Ale. Restaurant.
Children welcome. Dogs on leads.

CHILLENDEN

Griffins Head   Tel: 01304 840325

Chillenden, Nr Canterbury, Kent CT3 1PS (off Eastry/Nonington road)
Shepherd Neame. Mark J Copestack, tenant.

A typical country pub where you may meet the local farmer, half the cricket team, vintage car enthusiasts or just people dropping in. Dating back to 1286, the Griffins Head is heavily beamed and rambling, with two big inglenook fireplaces. The rooms are decorated with old photographs, a collection of oil pressure lamps and heaters, a formidable number of unusual beer bottles and artefacts relating to the brewing trade. Only one bar serving three different areas, and a dining room. Shepherd Neame ales: Spitfire, Master Brew, Best Bitter and Bishops Finger. Lots of picnic tables in the large garden; a barbecue in the middle of the car park, lit at weekends during the summer. On the 1st Sunday of every month the local vintage car enthusiasts meet and admire each others' vehicles – the landlord is a car enthusiast, not only of vintage, but of racing cars too. The Griffin has its own cricket pitch, cricket eleven, and keen followers.

OPEN: 11–11.
Real Ale. No food Sun eves.
No children. Dogs on leads.
Annual Jazz Festival.

CHISLEHURST

Ramblers Rest   Tel: 0181 467 1734

Mill Place, Chislehurst, Kent BR7 5ND
Courage. Peter Grierson, tenant.

Situated on a large wooded common, close to Chislehurst cricket ground and golf club, access to the pub is along a driveway off the Chislehurst/Bromley road (A 222). The Ramblers Rest is just what you would expect of a 17th century Kent building – painted clap-board under a Kent peg tiled roof. Bedecked with flowers during the summer, its inside is a wealth of beams and a warm welcome. Familiar, well tried bar food served at lunchtime only: steak and kidney pie, spaghetti bolognese, chilli, fishermans pie, toasties, sandwiches, salads and ploughmans. Courage ales plus guest beers. Seats in the secluded garden.

OPEN: 11–3. 5.30–11.
Real Ale.Bar menu. No food evenings or Sunday.
Children in eating area. Dogs on leads.

COBHAM

Darnley Arms   Tel: 01474 814218

The Street, Cobham, Kent DA12 3BZ
Free House. Trevor & Beryl Howard, licensees.

Cobham village, written about in Charles Dickens' Pickwick papers, stands at the gates of Cobham Hall, the former residence of the Earls of Darnley, now a school. The present Darnley Arms is a mere stripling, dating back only to the 18th century, but there has been an inn on this site for over 600 years. Rumour has it that there is a tunnel connecting the pub to the nearby church – quite a way to go for the communion wine! Good range of bar food: sandwiches, ploughmans, home-made pies, egg mayonnaise, tiger prawns, various fish dishes and grills. Steamed pudding or ice cream for afters. Courage ales on handpump and a selection of wines and liqueurs.

OPEN: 11–3. 6–11. N.B. Closed Sunday evenings.
Real Ale.
Children if well behaved. No dogs.

DARTFORD

Wat Tyler   Tel: 01322 272546

80 High Street, Dartford DA1 1DE
Free House. Ian Duncan, owner/licensee.

One of the busiest pubs in Dartford. "The policy of no juke box or background music is very much appreciated by the Wat Tyler's clientele", says the landlord, who is, as we write, just about to take over The Black Horse in Stansted, Kent. The Wat Tyler is bang in the middle of Dartford. A long, narrow 14th century pub, reputed to be THE Wat Tyler's cottage – he of the Peasants' Revolt. Traditional pub grub served in the bar plus a daily special. This could be roast beef and Yorkshire pudding, beef strogonoff or chicken curry. Sandwiches too. In the evening the function room is available for pre-arranged dinners and parties. Theakstons Old Peculier, Youngs Special, Courage Best and two guest beers.

OPEN: 10–11 (12–10.30 Sun)
Real Ale
Children welcome, (under control). Dogs on leads.

ELHAM

The Kings Arms   Tel: 01303 840242

The Square, Elham, Nr Canterbury, Kent CT4 6TJ
Whitbread. Edward Walsh, licensee.

The Church and some attractive Georgian and earlier houses form the Square in this very attractive village, set in a valley of chalk hills on the road from Canterbury to Folkestone (the scenic route). The main door of the Kings Arms opens into the fairly small bar, behind which is a spacious dining room. A favourite with locals having a pre-prandial drink, it is also a very popular place to have lunch. Jolly, friendly, blissfully quiet except for contented chat and the thump of darts. A fairly extensive menu: sandwiches, filled potatoes, salads, beef stroganoff, whole trout, chicken Kiev, chicken tagliatelle with garlic bread, vegetarian dishes and many more. Whitbreads, Fremlins Bitter, Flowers Original and Murphys. Choice of wines. Seats in the garden and a couple of tables at the front of the pub overlooking the square. Parking is hit and miss. One of the locals turns up in a pony and trap and ties up in the old stable yard! Probably the best way to arrive.

OPEN: 11–3. 6–11.(12–3, 7–10.30 Sun.)
Real Ale, Restaurant.
No children in public bar. Dogs on leads

FAIRSEAT

Vigo Inn   Tel: 01732 822547

Fairseat, Nr Wrotham, Sevenoaks, Kent TN15 7JL
Free House. Mrs P J Ashwell, licensee

On top of the North Downs, the North Downs Way passes the pub en route to Trosley Country Park. Originally an old drovers' inn, the paddock next to it will probably still accomodate your cattle or horses. When you have settled your livestock, and got your drink in hand, you can join in a game of 'Dadlums' – an old table skittles game that is so unusual, it is listed in the Guinness Book of Pub Games. Food is limited to sandwiches, a crisp and a nut. Quite a selection of well kept ales: Youngs Bitter, Ramsmooth, Special and Oatmeal Stout, Harveys Mild and Best Bitter. Also Flagship Ensign Beer from the Chatham Dockyard Brewery. Liefmans Kriek Belgian Cherry Beer and Framboise Beer, lots of local fruit juices plus wine by the glass and farm cider. If you've parked your horse or cattle, you can keep an eye on them from the garden at the back of the pub.

OPEN: 12–3 Tues–Sun. 6–11 Mon–Sat. 7–10.30 Sun.
Real Ale. Not even a sandwich Sunday.
Children. Dogs on leads.

FAVERSHAM

Albion Tavern   Tel: 01795 591411

Front Brents, Faversham Creek, Faversham ME13 7DH
Shepherd Neame. Patrick Coevoet, tenant.

Literally up the creek. Faversham creek this time. Opposite the pub, on the other side of the river, is the Shepherd Neame brewery. You can't miss the brewery so you will easily find the pub – just remember there is a river in between, and it is muddy, very. Sit in the pub bar and enjoy uninterrupted views across the creek and sample something from the varied and imaginative menu. Choose a typically English dish such as steak and ale pie, a salad, even a ploughmans, or a meal with a touch of je ne c'est quoi-spinach crèpes with Roquefort and mushrooms, a carré d'agneau, fresh fish from the boats at Whitstable and a tarte tatin to finish. Shepherd Neame range of ales and some guests. Good wines to go with the food. Picnic tables at the front of the pub overlooking the river.

OPEN: 11–3. 6.30–11 (12–3. 6–10.30 Sun)
Real Ale.
Children, not at the bar. Dogs in garden.

FORDCOMBE

Chafford Arms Tel: 01892 740267

Fordcombe, Tunbridge Wells, Kent TN3 0SA
Whitbread. Barry Leppard, licensee.

A recently extended, attractive and comfortable village local, where the same licensee has presided for the past 30 years. An extensive bar menu includes speciality fish dishes based on fresh supplies from Hastings. Apart from the home-made country soup, you could have smoked salmon paté, Greenland prawns, local Weald-smoked trout, fresh Dover sole, dressed crab and prawns, grilled local trout, prawn Provençale, meat dishes too, a selection of vegetarian dishes, a ploughmans, filled Yorkshire pudding, toasted sandwiches, ordinary sandwiches or a salad. That should set you up for the day. Larkins Traditional, King & Barnes Sussex and Flowers Original and changing guests. Outside there is a large, award winning garden, with lots of secluded areas in which to enjoy your drink.

OPEN: 11–3. 6–11. (12–4. 7–10.30 Sun)
Real Ale
Children welcome, dogs as well, as long as they are both well-behaved.

GROOMBRIDGE

Crown Tel: 01892 864742

10 The Walks, Groombridge, Kent
Free House. Bill & Vivienne Rhodes, licensees.

Together with a charming terrace of tile hung 18th century cottages, this Tudor pub is in an enviable position, situated on the edge of the sloping village green, with views over the green towards the village below. Inside the Crown there are lots of beams, ancient timbers, and an inglenook fireplace. A good varied menu – home-made soup, lots of salads, steak & mushroom pie, home-cooked ham, properly cooked vegetables, sandwiches and Sunday roasts. Harveys IPA, Courage Directors and Ruddles County, local farm cider, house wines by the glass. Groombridge Place is very near and well worth a visit.

OPEN: 11–2.30 (3 Sat). 6–11 (11–11 Summer Sats).
Real Ale. Restaurant (evenings). No food Sun eves.
Children in restaurant. Dogs on leads.
Occasional Morris dancers.
Bedrooms.

HADLOW

Artichoke Inn   Tel: 01732 810763

Park Road, Hamptons, Hadlow, Kent TN11 9SR (off Hadlow/Plaxtol road)
Free House. Terence & Barbara Simmonds, licensees.

This remote little pub is in an area noted for its hop gardens and orchards. Part of the Hampton Estate until 1950, it's been a pub since the late 16th century, so they've had lots of practice. As there are only two small beamed rooms, it can be quite a squeeze if it's busy. During the summer you can spread out on the covered front terrace, enjoy your drink and admire the surrounding countryside. Good reliable home-made bar food – pork in a garlic and cider marinade, casseroles, vegetable pies, steak & kidney pies, king prawns, steaks and a number of pasta dishes. A ploughmans is only available weekday lunchtimes. Greene King Abbot, Youngs Special and Fullers London Pride on hand pump.

OPEN: 11.30–2.30; 6.30–11 (closed Sun eves in winter)
Real Ale. Restaurant (not Sun eve)
Children in eating area. No dogs.
Car park.

IVY HATCH

The Plough   Tel: 01732 810268

Coach Road, Ivy Hatch, Nr Sevenoaks TN15 ONL
Free House. Daniel Humbert, manager.

A well sign-posted, roadside inn in a small hamlet. Very popular at lunchtime. Firstly, there is no music and secondly, the food is above average: (evenings too, but then – please note – you have music). The saloon and public bars are now knocked into one, still with a big log fire and several distinct seating areas. An attractively furnished conservatory extension completes the picture. Monsieur Humbert, the manager, is also the chef. You can have a light snack, or a full meal. Food is something English, something French – all highly praised; the menu is constantly changing, so go and be surprised. Adnams ales and two guests beers which change every month. Larkins is a favourite. Well chosen wine list, some by the glass. Tables at the side of the pub, beyond the car park.

OPEN: 12–3. 6–11. (12–3. 7–10.30 Sun)
Real Ale
Children over 8 in conservatory lunchtime only. No dogs.
Wheelchair access.

KINGSDOWN

Zetland Arms Tel: 01304 364888

Wellington Parade, Kingsdown, Deal, Kent CT14 8AF (pub on the beach
at the end of South & North roads)
Scottish & Newcastle. T. J. Cobbet, tenant.

Nothing much to look at, (one longs to get at it with a paint brush), but in a
wonderful position to take full advantage of those glorious summer days.
You collect your pint and sandwich, sit on the sea-wall and gaze out to sea.
When a North easterly gale is blowing you can watch the waves crashing
against the sea defences from the safety of the bar – or if you're very
unlucky, watch them sweep past you, straight through the bar. That has to
be one humdinger of a storm – and they do have them. Only one bar, always
very popular, with helpful, friendly staff. Food is fairly traditional with dishes
such as quiche, fish and chips, a pint of prawns and crab or prawn
sandwiches. Shepherd Neame Master Brew, Ruddles County, Websters
Yorkshire Bitter, Courage Best and Guinness on handpump. Carlsberg and
Holstein lagers also on draught. Water for the dog.

OPEN: 11–3, 6–11 (12–3, 7–10.30 Sun), 11–11 Summer.
Real Ale.
Children welcome. Dogs on leads.

LUDDESDOWN

Cock Inn Tel: 01474 814208

Henley Street, Luddesdown, Kent DA13 0XB (nr Meopham)
Free House. Andrew Turner, licensee.

On a country lane in a tiny hamlet near Luddesdown, a remote village at the
junction of four valleys between Gravesend and Meopham. The Cock Inn,
has been a public house since the early 1700's; before that it was probably
a farmhouse. Evidence of its age can still be seen as some of the old
supporting timbers are still in place. Make for the comfortable lounge bar
with its big log fire; here is peace and quiet – there's music in the public bar.

THE QUIET PINT

Hearty pub snacks from a short, well chosen menu: toasted sandwiches, filled jacket potatoes, pint of prawns, dressed crab, a selection of pies – steak pie and venison pie – and a rack of pork ribs. A range of cask conditioned ales is kept. Adnams is the main beer, another eight or more are changed regularly. Two farm ciders and some lagers. Seats in the large garden and picnic tables at the front of the pub.

OPEN: 12–2.30.5–11. (12–11 Sat. 12–10.30 Sun)
Real Ale.
Children's room, no children in the bar. Dogs on leads.
Wheelchair access

MARSHSIDE

Gate Inn   Tel: 01227 860498

Boyden Gate, Nr Marshside, Canterbury, Kent CT3 4EB (off A28 Canterbury/Margate road nr Upstreet.)
Shepherd Neame. Christopher Smith, tenant.

Down a lane off the Canterbury to Margate road, this friendly, busy, unspoilt country pub has just two connecting rooms warmed by a central fireplace. Offering a well cooked, simple menu, the pub has a thriving trade. Fresh local produce is used whenever possible – sandwiches, hot torpedoes (filled French bread), filled jacket potatoes, gateburgers, lots of home-made pickles, spicy sausage hotpot, home-made flans and puddings. At lunchtime the dining area is no-smoking. Shepherd Neame ales are tapped from the cask. In summer you can sit outside by the stream and feed the assortment of ducks and geese that have made their home there. (No duck à l'orange here!)

OPEN: 11–2.30 (3 Sat). 6–11. (12–3 6–10.30 Sun)
Real Ale.
Children in eating area and family room. Dogs on leads.

MATFIELD

The Wheelwright Arms   Tel: 01892 531973

The Green, Matfield, Kent TN12 7JX
Shepherd Neame. Alec and Joan Jessup, licensees.

On the edge of the green in a pretty village about 6 miles from Tunbridge Wells. Early 17th century, the pub has just one bar and serves an extensive bar menu. All the usual things plus a "lot of wet fish" and a wildlife section in various guises: alligator, boar, kangaroo and those ostriches again – all very popular. They do have a vegetarian dish or two, but this pub menu leans towards the carniverous. A lot of cricket is played on the green, the Wheelright Arms has its own cricket eleven and hosts matches throughout the season. All the teams appreciate the well kept Shepherd Neame beers: Master Brew, Spitfire, Bishops Finger, the new brew Autumn Gold and seasonal Winter Porter. There is a small area beside the pub with a few tables, and a small terrace in front with a more seats.

OPEN: 11.30–3.30. 6–11. (11–11 Sun – all those cricket matches)
Real Ale
Well behaved children & dogs welcome.

PLUCKLEY

Dering Arms   Tel: 01233 840371

Pluckley, Ashford, Kent TN27 0RR (nr station)
Free House. James Buss, licensee.

All H E Bates' fans know Pluckley – home of Pop Larkins. They made very good bricks in Pluckley too. It also has the reputation of being the most haunted village in England. Originally a hunting lodge for the Dering family, the Dering Arms has the distinctive arched "Dering" windows which can be found on all the Estate houses. The same windows, thought to bring good luck, are seen even further afield in houses nearer Canterbury. Imposing in its architecture, the main beamed bar has high ceilings, stone floors and a huge fireplace. There is also a small intimate restaurant serving some interesting dishes. The pub provides good, varied menus, using the finest local ingredients. Bar snacks include an all day breakfast; the specials from the blackboard range from mussels in cider and cream sauce, potted shrimps, pasta with Stilton and basil sauce, whole crab salad, rack of lamb with herb crust, pheasant casserole with red wine sauce, many more fish dishes: potted crab, fillet of halibut and local trout, home-baked pies, steaks, selected cuts of pork and lamb to good puds. Every meal is prepared to order. Gourmet evenings are held several times a year. Ales include specially brewed Dering ale and Goachers Maidstone ale. Good range of wines and local farm cider. Garden parties and musical evenings are held in the large garden. Telephone for details.

OPEN: 11–3. 6–11.
Real Ale. Restaurant (closed Sun evening)
Children in restaurant and eating area. Dogs on leads.
Bedrooms.
Wheelchair access to pub.

SMARDEN

The Bell

Tel: 01233 770283

Bell Lane, Smarden, Nr. Ashford TN27 8PW
Free House. Ian Turner, licensee.

As we go to press, this pub is up for sale. Negotiations are going on with Youngs brewery and as most of Youngs pubs are free of music everything should be alright. Still, who knows. Let's hope for the best. Addresses are so misleading, but you can't really miss this pub. It's on a country road about three minutes from Headcorn, and not far from Smarden. Tile-hung, by itself, and with a very big sign. First hung in the late 18th century, before that, it was an inn without a name. Spacious and rambling, with low beams, exposed, creaking timbers, flagstone floors and inglenook fireplaces – all the requirements for a traditional country inn. Food too. Good filling fare from sandwiches and ploughmans to the daily specials: pork in a Dijon mustard sauce, chicken creole, steak, kidney and mushroom pie; also salads, gammon and steaks. Shepherd Neame Master Brew, Morlands Old Speckled Hen, Harveys IPA, Marstons Pedigree, Flowers Original, Fremlins and Goachers Light Ale. About 40 wines, some by the glass. Seats in the secluded garden among the fruit trees.

OPEN: 11.30–2.30. 6–11 (12–3. 7–10.30 Sun)
Real Ale
Children welcome in two bars only. Dogs on leads.
Car park. Bedrooms.

SMARDEN

The Chequers

Tel: 01233 770217

The Street, Smarden, Nr Ashford
Free House. Frank Stevens, licensee.

You really can't miss the Chequers. There are three roads into this attractive village: two of them nearly end up in the pub. Just the sort of pub you wish you lived near. A 14th century, comfortable, welcoming place with lots of beams, two bars, two dining areas and two open fires. More a foody pub, but plenty of local support for the beer. Quite a lot of fish on the menu: pepper-crusted monkfish in a red pepper sauce, wing of skate with black butter, baked trout in fresh herbs, grilled lemon sole or grilled tuna meunière. You could start with a cream of carrot soup, a choice of patés, mussels or prawns, followed by crispy roast duckling, Scotch sirloin steak or lamb cutlets with rosemary. Bar snacks too: a hot-pot, something with pasta, fisherman's pie and a vegetarian dish or two. Ruddles County, Old Speckled Hen, Draught Bass, Youngs Special and Draught Worthington beers. A good wine list to go with the good food. The car park is at the back of the pub, beyond that, grass, seats, and a pond with ducks.

OPEN: 10–3. 6–11. (12–3. 7–10.30 Sun.)
Real Ale. Restaurant.
Children, if well behaved. Dogs on leads.
Wheelchair access.

SNARGATE

Red Lion   Tel:01797 344648

Snargate, Kent. on B2080 Brenzett-Appledore road.
Free House. Doris Jemison, licensee.

In an area filled with Red Lions, this one is in open country between Snargate and Appledore. The pub has somewhat flexible opening times, so don't expect the door to be unlocked on the dot. When the door is open you walk straight into the bar, large enough to accomodate at least six people sitting down, and only a few more than that standing. This bar is also the passageway to the other two, equally small, totally unspoilt rooms. Timeless is the word you would use; beers from the barrel, crisps from the box, maybe a nut! – and coal fires in winter. The gas light fittings are still there, although electricity has crept in as there is a spotlight over the dartboard. You come here for the experience, the good ale, not the comfort. Ales are Batemans XB Bitter, Rother Valley Level Best, (brewed at Northiam) and Goachers Light Ale.

OPEN: Roughly from 11–3. 7–11. (12–4, 7–10.30. Sun).
Real Ale
No children No dogs inside.

SOLE STREET

Compasses Inn   Tel: 01227 700300

Sole Street, Crundale, Canterbury, Kent CT4 7ES (country lane between Godmersham and Petham)
Free House. John & Sheila Bennett.

Off the beaten track along a quiet lane between Godmersham and Petham. Two rooms front and back in this 15th century pub. Polished flagstone floors and a restored bread oven in one, polished boards, beams and log fire in the other. Varied bar food – soups, filled rolls, ploughmans, steak & kidney pie, salmon cod & mushroom pie and puff pastry parcels with various fillings. The blackboard specials change several times a week. There is a large garden with an aviary, goats, sheep and a climbing frame – presumably for the children, not the goats. Fullers London Pride and ESB, Boddingtons, Shepherd Neame Master Brew and Fremlins Bitter, a local cider and fruit wines. Lots of interesting walks nearby.

OPEN: 11–3. 6.30–11.
Real Ale.
Children in garden room. No dogs.

STANSTED

Black Horse Tel: 01732 822355

Tumblefield Road, Stansted, Nr West Malling
Free House. Ian Duncan, licensee.

High on the chalk downs above Wrotham. The yew tree, in the grounds of the 13th century St Mary's church, is reputed to be 1,000 years old. The Black Horse is the centre of village life; not only can you buy a pint but you can post a letter as the pub is also the post office. Now owned by Ian Duncan, who also owns the Wat Tyler in Dartford, things will inevitably change, but there will never be any piped music. Beers will be Theakstons Old Peculiar, Youngs Special, Courage Best, two guests and three Draught Lagers. Food will be filling pub favourites. As this is a good walking area, you need to be well stoked-up for the onward march.

OPEN: 10–11. (12–10.30 Sun)
Real Ale
Children under control. Dogs on leads.

STAPLEHURST

Lord Raglan Tel: 01622 843747

Chart Hill Road, Nr Staplehurst TN12 0RN
Free House. Andrew Hutchison, owner/licensee.

A thoroughly unspoilt country pub, near Chart Hill where you get fine views over the surrounding orchards. The oldest bit of the pub is 17th century; it's full of old beams, creaking floorboards with open log fires. The bar menu offers various sandwiches and ploughmans, and the blackboard menu may list pork in an orange sauce, beef in ale pie, lamb curry, chilli or smocked salmon. This menu changes all the time – it depends on what is available. Harveys Best Bitter, Goachers Light or Dark plus a guest beer. As befits the area, there is an orchard garden.

OPEN: 12–3. 6–11 (12–3. NOT SUN EVES)
Real Ale. Dining Room.
Children welcome. Dogs on leads.
Car park. Wheelchair access.

SUTTON VALENCE

Swan Inn   Tel: 01622 84321

Broad Street, Sutton Valence, Maidstone, Kent
Whitbread. Ronald Hamer & Brenda Mason, licensees.

The village of Sutton Valence is built on the slope of a steep hill six miles south of Maidstone. Famous for its public school which was founded in 1576, the village has a number of notable buildings, one of which is the Swan Inn. Built in 1467, well before the public school was thought of, the Swan is a comfortable, well beamed, friendly, old pub with two bars, public and saloon, and a separate restaurant. No foreign food in the restaurant, just good wholesome familiar English fare: steaks, gammon, chops, Dover sole and King prawns. Bar snacks range from scampi to egg and chips and sausage and chips. Not a big menu, but what they do, they try to do well. Ales are Fremlins, Flowers Original and Wadsworths 6X, Guinness and several lagers. On a sunny day it is wonderful to sit outside this pub, look at the countryside and watch the world meander past.

OPEN: 11–3. 6–11.
Real Ale
Children welcome. Dogs on leads.

TOYS HILL Nr WESTERHAM

Fox & Hounds   Tel: 01732 750328

Toys Hill, Nr Westerham. Kent
Greene King. Hazel Pelling, licensee.

Several years ago this fine old establishment with not a juke box to be seen, let alone piped music, won a fight with Allied Lyons to retain the look and feel of a pub. The Brewery had plans for modernising it with restaurants, fun areas and music. But the locals rebelled; and after several months of wrangling Allied Lyons gave in. "We don't like anything that destroys the harmony of the place – and that includes mobile 'phones, which are disruptive and noisy", says Hazel Pelling. "Anyone thinking of making a call is hurled straight into the gents' lavatory or the car park." Food is limited to lunchtime snacks –ploughmans, caulifower cheese etc. Sundays and Bank Holidays filled rolls only. Greene King IPA, Abbot Ale, Guinness on handpump. Cider and Harp lager. Let the correspondent who told us about this pub have the last word. She said, "The Fox is rather like a front room; furnished with somewhat battered sofas and chairs. In winter there are two log fires, which add to the cosy atmosphere. And there's NO POP MUSIC, which is heaven!" Shows what you can do if you try.

OPEN: 11.30–2.30. 6–11 Mon–Fri. 11.30–3. 6–11 Sat. 11.30–3. 7–11.30 Sun.
Real Ale
Children with parents in special area, lunchtimes only. Dogs on leads.

IN THE LICENSED TRADE BACKGROUND MUSIC POLICY CAN CHANGE OVERNIGHT

The entries in this Edition of the Quiet Pint were correct at the time of going to press. However, changes can occur very quickly in the licensed trade and a pub that has been free of background music can adopt a different policy overnight. The editors cannot therefore be held responsible for such changes and we rely on our readers to keep us informed.

L
LANCASHIRE

BALDERSTONE

Myerscough Hotel
Tel: 01254 812222

Whalley Road, Balderstone, Blackburn, Lancs BB2 7LE (on A59)
Robinsons. John Peddar, tenant.

Very much a favourite meeting place for lunch during the week, this friendly country pub is popular with businessmen and families from the nearby British Aerospace plant. You really can't miss it as a Canberra bomber and Lightening fighter are parked on the other side of the road. Plenty of room in the beamed, comfortable bars where they serve good, traditional bar food. Robinsons ales and Hartleys XB plus a good selection of malt whiskies.

OPEN: 11.30–3. 5.30–11.
Real Ale.
Children in front room till 8.30. No dogs except guide dogs.
Wednesday Quiz night.
Bedrooms.

BARNSTON

Fox & Hounds
Tel: 0151 6481323

Barnston Village, Wirral, Merseyside, L61 1BW
Free House. Helen Leech, licensee.

On the site of an 18th century pub, the one you see today was built in 1911, but pictures of the original pub can be seen in the bar. Pitch pine woodwork, the bar and snug are tiled; carpet in the lounge bar. Home-cooked pub grub: soup, sandwiches, ploughmans, well filled baked potatoes, salads and changing specials from the blackboard. Courage Directors, Marstons Pedigree, Ruddles County and Best, Websters Yorkshire and one guest. They have a flowery courtyard and pretty garden. Attractive surroundings and good walks.

THE QUIET PINT

OPEN: 11–3. 5.30–11. (11–11 Fri. Sat & Sun)
Real Ale
Children welcome. Dogs on leads.
Wheelchair access.

BLACKSTONE EDGE

White House   Tel: 01706 378456

Blackstone Edge, Little Borough, Rochdale, OL15 0LG
Free House. Neville Marney, licensee.

A great favourite with walkers on the Pennine Way, which crosses the road
outside this windswept old pub high on the moors. There is a warm welcome
in the main bar with its glowing coal fire. From another room you have a view
over the moors: you can see either where you came from or where you are
going. Alternatively, if it all looks too tiring: book a taxi home. Daily specials
as well as the usual bar food: home-made soups, sandwiches, quiche, steak
& kidney pies, garlic mushrooms, salads and steaks. Children's portions.
Marstons Pedigree, Moorhouse Pendle Witches' Brew, Theakstons Best and
Black Sheep Bitter. Farm ciders and several malt whiskies. Remove the
muddy boots and leave them in the porch. Only clean shoes or socks inside
the bars.

OPEN: 11.30–3. 7–11.
Real Ale. Restaurant.
Children welcome. No dogs.
Wheelchair access.

BRINDLE

Cavendish Arms   Tel: 0125 4852912

Sandy Lane, Brindle, Nr Chorley, Lancs
Burtonwood. Peter Bowling, tenant.

Cheerful village pub with lots of comfortable seating inside, on the terrace
and small lawn. In the bar there are interesting stained-glass partitions
depicting a skirmish near the river estuary between the Vikings and Anglo-
Saxons. There are also a number of Devonshire family heraldic emblems on
display – hardly surprising as they bought the village in the 16th century.
Good familiar bar food: home-made pies, lasagne, crispy cod, roast beef
and Yorkshire pudding and daily changing specials. Burtonwood ales and
a range of malt whiskies.

OPEN: 12–3. 5.30–11.
Real Ale. Restaurant (no meals or snacks Sun eve)
Children in eating areas. No dogs

CHORLTON-CUM-HARDY

Beech Inn   Tel: 0161 881 1180

72 Beech Road, Chorlton-cum-Hardy, Greater Manchester.
Whitbread. Edna Thomas, manager.

A very popular pub, not far from the village green and on the western edge
of Greater Manchester. You won't get fed, apart from the essential crisp and
nut, so you'll be here to enjoy the beer: Boddingtons, Whitbread Trophy
Bitter, Timothy Taylors Landlord and Best, also Morlands Old Speckled Hen.
Beer garden at the back of the pub.

OPEN: 11–11 (11–10.30 Sun)
Real Ale
Children until 5pm. Dogs, small ones only.

CROSBY, LIVERPOOL

Crow's Nest   Tel: 0151 9313081

63 Victoria Road, Crosby, Liverpool, Merseyside
Boddingtons. Norman Thomas, licensee.

You know just where you are when you read the sign outside this pub. "No
music, no pool, no fruit machines, no footballers and no food." It is just
serious drinking here. Good traditional beer and conversation. Frequented
largely by professionals – teachers, barristers and the like. A few years ago
the brewery proposed installing a juke box but a petition forestalled that for
a couple of years. Then one did suddenly appear, but customers were
"persuaded" not to use it and it soon vanished. A popular local with bar,
snug and lounge. Cains Mild, Boddingtons and various lagers, stouts and
cider. The garden should be laid out by now, ready to be enjoyed.

OPEN: 11.30–11
Real Ale.
Children allowed if well behaved. No dogs.

DIDSBURY

Royal Oak   Tel: 0161 434 4788

729 Wilmslow Road, Didsbury, Greater Manchester M20 0RH
Marstons. Vince Crolla, tenant.

What wonderful choices: cheese and ale, sherry and port. For years the landlord has been tracking down cheeses from all sorts of places – a truly knowledgeable cheese enthusiast who has created a sort of Paxton and Whitfield in Manchester. A choice of two cheeses – and this is no mean sliver, more a hunk – with a chunk of bread and salad. You should get yourself over there rapidly. If you're not into cheese you can usually get soup and paté. Marstons Pedigree Bitter, Burton Ale, Bateman Mild and a guest beer plus sherries and port from the barrel. Delicious with cheese.

OPEN: 11–11.
Real Ale. Lunchtime snacks, not weekends or Bank Holidays.
No children. No dogs.

DIDSBURY

Station Hotel   Tel: 0161 445 9761

682 Wilmslow Road, Didsbury, Greater Manchester M20 0DN
Marstons. Saxon Bain, manageress.

A small pub among the shops. Look for the floral display and that will be the Station Hotel. The size of a terrace house with three rooms: one a bar, one a lounge and the other a games room. Only sandwiches available. Marstons Pedigree, Best, Head Brewers Choice, Batemans Mild and a guest beer. "No garden, but do hanging baskets count?"

OPEN: 11–11.
Real Ale
Children – possibly. Dogs on leads

GREASBY

Irby Mill   Tel: 0151 6040194

Mill Lane, Greasby, The Wirral, Merseyside L49 3NT
Greenalls. Tony Johnston, licensee.

Although a millers' cottage until 1980, no milling had been done since the

212

mill blew down in 1898. You can see old photographs of the mill in all its' glory in the bar. The Irby Mill is a very small sandstone pub covered in hanging baskets. They compare it to drinking in a railway carriage – long and narrow. Flagstones in the bar, carpet in the lounge. Lunchtime food only: sandwiches, ploughmans, Cumberland sausages and lasagne – reliable pub fare. Greenalls ales, also a guest beer policy enabling them to take beers from all over the country. The standards are Cains, Tetley, Theakstons and Boddingtons. Irby Mill backs onto National Trust land, so is surrounded by good walking country.

OPEN: 11.30–11. (11.30–10.30 Sun)
Real Ale. Lunchtime food only, seven days a week.
No children. No dogs.

GOOSNARGH

Bushells Arms   Tel: 01772 865235

Church Lane, Goosnarsh, Preston, Lancs PR3 2BH
Whitbreads. David & Glynis Best, tenants.

An extremely popular pub, not far from the M6 (exit 32). The home-cooked food here – based on fresh local produce – leans imaginatively towards the Mediterranean and especially Greece, although Lancashire hotpot, Cumberland sausage casserole and the like are not forgotten. Daily specials are listed on the blackboard and two of the eating areas are non-smoking. Tetleys and Boddingtons ales. A good wine list features a monthly special choice. There are seats outside in the garden.

OPEN: 12–3. 6–11. Closed some Mondays.
Real Ale.
Well behaved children in eating area until 9 pm. No dogs.
Wheelchair access to pub.

HESWALL

Black Horse   Tel: 0151 342 2254

Village Road, Lower Heswall, Merseyside P60 0DP
Bass Taverns. Kevin McCardle, manager.

Over a hundred years old, the Black Horse, once a hotel, is well known as somewhere to come and have a chat. It has the equiment to play the dreaded wallpaper music, but Kevin McCardle, who took over the pub last year, won't use it. "Mine's a talking pub at our clients request," he says. Whatever music they do play is live – an Irish night, for example a pianist dropping in and playing for a pint. Inside there is a big lounge and a conservatory. Standard English fare: sandwiches, jacket potatoes, crusty rolls with hot fillings, sizzling steaks, and mixed grills – all served with chips. Daily specials, vegetarian dishes – good filling pub food. Worthington BB, Stones BB amd M&B Brew X1 and varying guest ales. No garden and a very small car park.

OPEN: 11.30–11.
Real Ale. No food Sundays
No children. No dogs.

LIVERPOOL

The Philharmonic   Tel: 0151 7091163

36 Hope Street, Liverpool L1 9BX
Allied Domecq. Phil Ross, manager.

Built as a Gentlemans Club in the late 19th century, regarded as a magnificent "Gin Palace" palace by the staff, this Grade I listed building is a monument to the excellence of Victorian craftsmen. Tiled, gilded, carved, stained and etched. Whatever could be decorated, was. Exuberant is a word that comes to mind. Standard, reliable pub menus: one for the bar and one for the restaurant. Tetleys, Ind Coope Burton, Jennings and Walkers. Some malt whiskies and a cask cider.

OPEN: 11.30–11. (12–3.7–10.30 Sun)
Real Ale. No food Sunday. Restaurant
Children in restaurant. No dogs.

LIVERPOOL

Roscoe Head   Tel: 0151 7094490

24 Roscoe Street, Liverpool L1 2SX
Tetley Walker. Margaret Jayce, licensee.

This friendly mid-Victorian city pub doesn't seem to have altered much since it was built. "Tiny little pub", says the landlady: "a little snug, two little parlours and a little bar." The larger of the two parlours is known as the tie room – they started collecting the occasional tie and it caught on. Customers bring in ties that mean something or have a history: now they have about 190, including one for Japanese prisoners of war. Each one is numbered and identified on a chart – it is quite a sight. People come on pilgrimages to view them. Food served at lunchtime only – reliable pub grub: curries, steak pie, chicken pie, sausages, that sort of thing. Ind Coope Burton, Jennings Bitter and Tetley Walker mild, no guest beers. No outdoor drinking area. A conversation pub.

OPEN: 11.30–11. (12–11. Sat)
Real Ale
No children. No dogs.

LYTHAM

The Taps   Tel: 01253 736226

Henry Street, Lytham, Lancs FY8 5LE
Whitbreads. Ian Rigg, manager.

This one's really for the true beer enthusiast. It is not far from the beach, so there's a sea-shore theme running through the pub (fish, boats and things) – but the real interest here is in the beer. In one year a thousand different varieties of ale were offered – not all at once! No doubt all the others being brewed will be tasted by the Taps' patrons in due course. At that rate you take pot luck (if that's the expression with beer), as who knows what's on offer and when! Traditional bar food with home-made daily specials.

OPEN: 11–11.
Real Ale. Lunchtime meals & snacks, not Sunday.
Children in eating area at mealtimes. Dogs on lead.

MANCHESTER

Circus Tavern   Tel: 01612 365818

86 Portland Street, Manchester M14 GX
Tetley Walker. Kathleen Corless, licensee.

If you want to find the smallest pub in Manchester – here it is. So small there is only room for one beer – Tetley Walker Bitter. No room to cook – certainly no where to put a plate! So a bag of crisps and a nut, neither of which take up much space, is all you will get. Well known for being small, a timeless little gem.

OPEN: 11–11
Real Ale
Children welcome. Dogs – well yes, if well behaved.

MANCHESTER

Moon under the Water   Tel: 0161 834 5882

68–74 Deansgate, Manchester M3 2FN
Wetherspoon. Dave and Jane Smith, managers.

They say this is the biggest pub in the country, and it probably is. Situated in the heart of the city, the Moon under the Water was built on the site of the old ABC cinema. There are three separate bars on two levels and a passenger lift. Not many of our pubs have one of those. Decorations include pictures, photographs and slightly un-nervingly, especially commissioned sculptures of Manchesters' famous five. They sit in cinema seats on the first floor: Ena Sharples from Coronation Street, Sir Robert Peel, Emily Pankhurst, Hattie Jacques and horror actor, Christopher Lee. Eclectic I think you would call that choice. Console yourself with the five or six real ales and the guest ale this chain always provides. Bar snacks, or a full menu if you're hungry. Good solid reliable fare plus a daily special or two.

OPEN: 11–11
Real Ale
No children. No Dogs.

MELLOR

Devonshire Arms   Tel: 01614 272563

Longhurst Lane, Mellor, Nr Marple, Greater Manchester SK6 5PP
Robinsons. Brian Harrison, tenant.

This Mellor is between the A626 and the A6015, very near the Cheshire border. There is another Mellor in Lancashire, but this is the one you want. The Devonshire Arms is a cheerful, friendly pub with a reputation for good imaginative home-made food. It has a constantly changing menu but there is a leaning towards curries and spicy dishes. Varied soups, steamed fresh mussels, chicken and peppers in spicy sauce, smoked sausage, vegetarian dishes, steaks and home-made puds. Robinsons ales, lots of malt whiskies and a good selection of wine.

OPEN: 11–3. 5.30–11.
Real Ale. Meals & snacks lunchtime & Mon evening.
Well behaved children in eating area. No dogs.
Trad Jazz Thurs eve.

POULTON-LE-FYLDE

The Thatched Public House   Tel: 012253 891063

Ball Street, Poulton-le-Fylde, Lancs FY6 7BG
Greenalls. Brian Ballantine, manager.

If you are looking for a thatched building – it was thatched, until 1906 – you look in vain. Now with a tiled roof, this popular, very traditional pub is just off Market Square, next to the Norman church. No food – just one bar and three rooms where you can enjoy your drink, crisp and nut. A talking pub and very, very busy. Boddingtons Bitter, Charles Wells Bombadier and rotating guests.

OPEN: 11–11
Real Ale
No children – a child free zone. Dogs on leads.
All wheelchair facilities.

UPPERMILL

Cross Keys   Tel: 01457 874626

Off Church Road, Uppermill, Saddleworth, Nr Oldham OL3 6LW
Lees. Philip Kay, tenant.

Don't think this is just a pub at the centre of the local community: it is the meeting place for every interest group in the vicinity. Monday night clog dancing, gun club every other Sunday, bridge school Monday and Friday evening; also Saturday lunchtimes. It is the headquarters of the local mountain rescue team and they sponsor the Road Running and Fell Races in August. After all that you need good sustaining bar food: steak, kidney and mushroom pie or breaded haddock stuffed with prawns and cheese are two of the most popular dishes. Lees ales and a choice of malt whiskies. Seats outside on the terrace amongst the flowers. If anyone has the time to look, there is a lovely view and – if you have the energy – good walks.

THE QUIET PINT

OPEN: 11–11
Real Ale.
Children in side rooms. Dogs in Butler's Room!
Clog Dancing Mon & Folk Wed evenings.

WALLASEY

Cheshire Cheese   Tel: 0151 6383152

2, Wallasey Village Road, Wallasey, Merseyside.
Greenalls. Pete Fehiley, manager.

At the heart of Merseyside, surrounded by miles of sandy beaches. Beer has been sold on this site for hundreds of years, but the Cheshire Cheese only dates back to the Victorian era. One large lounge, divided up into three distinct areas and a separate bar. The only food available is a roast at the weekend. Crisps and nuts the rest of the time. Seats in the beer garden, and a lovely walk to the promenade at New Brighton.

OPEN: 12–11
Real Ale
Children welcome. No dogs.
Wheelchair access.

WALLASEY

Magazine Hotel   Tel: 0151 639 3381

7 Magazine Brow, Wallasey, Merseyside LA5 1MP
Bass Taverns. Martin Venables, manager

Built on the banks of the river, this 18th century black and white pub dates back to the days when the sailing ships had to unload their gunpowder before being allowed to dock. The gunpowder was put into the magazine, 50 yards away – which is why the pub is so called. It was originally an hotel, but when the unloading of gunpowder ceased and the hotel trade died out, it survived by becoming a simple pub. It has one main bar and lots of small rooms full of beams and shiny brass. Home-made soups, steak and kidney pies, lasagne, mixed grills and daily specials. Food is served every lunchtime and Thursday and Friday evenings. Apart from those two days, evenings are devoted to the serious drinker. Draught Bass and one guest ale.

OPEN: 11–11; (12– 10.30 Sun).
Real Ale.
Children allowed. Dogs in garden.

WHARLES

Eagle & Child Tel: 01772 690312

Church Road, Wharles, Kirkham, Preston PR4 3SJ
Free House. Brian & Angel Tatham, licensees.

There's no food here and it is open only on weekday evenings. Strictly a drinking pub. No doubt there's a crisp or a nut to be found somewhere as in days of old, but really it's just a sensible, attractive, thatched country pub with interesting low beamed and cosy bars, old furniture and warming fires in winter. Boddingtons and three changing guest beers. Some seats outside.

OPEN: 7–11 (12–3. 7–11 Sat & Sun)
Real Ale. No food.
No dogs.

WHITEWELL

Inn at Whitewell Tel: 01200 448222

Forest of Bowland, Clitheroe, Lancs BB7 3AT
Free House. Richard Bowman, licensee.

Owned by the Queen, deep in the lovely rolling English countryside of the Forest of Bowland, next to the village church and overlooking the River Hodder, this 14th century building is an inn of many parts. As well as an hotel and pub it's a wine merchant and pictures are for sale in the picture gallery. Lots of magazines and guide books to read and a piano to play to while away the time. Traditional, well cooked bar food and a more adventurous restaurant menu are available. Interesting soups, game casseroles, lots of fish, including the popular Whitewell Gourmet Fish Pie, and roast fillet of beef for two. Grouse, partridge and pheasant in season. Marstons Pedigree and Boddingtons ales. Extensive, interesting wine list. View of the river from the restaurant and the seats in the garden.

OPEN: 11–3. 6–11.
Real Ale. Restaurant (not Sun lunchtime)
Children welcome. Dogs on leads.
Wheelchair access to pub.

L
LEICESTER WITH LINCOLN & NOTTINGHAM

COLEBY

Bell Tel: 01522 810240

Far Lane, Coleby, Lincs LN5 0AH
Pubmaster. Robert Pickles & Sara Roe, tenants.

This friendly, busy 18th century village pub has a comfortable beamed and panelled main bar with big log fires at either end, a restaurant and, nicely separated from them, a room with all the noisy bits, including satellite TV. Reasonably priced snacks in the bar and pool room. The restaurant menu is more extravagant: home-made leek and stilton soup, garlic mushrooms in basil and tomato sauce, boeuf Stroganoff, beef mushroom and guinness pie, chicken en croute, if you're really hungry a huge mixed grill and daily specials. Wednesday night is fish night, Thursday, vegetarian and Friday there will be live music, Sundays – breakfast with the Sunday papers. Flowers Original, Marstons Pedigree, Bass and Tetleys ales. Range of malt whiskies. Seats in the garden.

OPEN: 11–3. 7–11 (6–11 summer Sats)
Real Ale. Restaurant.
Children welcome. Dogs on leads.
Bedrooms (3 crown rated).
Jazz every Friday.

COLSTON BASSETT

Martins Arms Tel: 01949 81361

School Lane, Colston Bassett, Notts NG12 3FD
Free House. Lynne Strafford Bryan & Salvatore Inguanta, licensees.

First licensed 300 years ago, it was the squire's residence before that. A touch of bygone formality remains in the smart interiors and uniformed staff, but it is still a welcoming pub. The above average bar menu includes speciality sandwiches – you won't get a slice of processed ham or tired tomato here – we are into the offbeat and the different: tomato, Mozzarella, mixed leaves, red onion and basil, home cured gravidlax, cream cheese and a dill mustard dressing – and those are just a couple of sandwiches! Tiger prawns with basil and Thai spices, wrapped in filo pastry; chargrilled spicy Toulouse sausages served with a warm potato salad; rich game pie in a red wine sauce; interesting vegetarian dishes, and some original puds. Dining room menu too. Adnams, Bass, Fullers London Pride and Batemans XB are among the ales they keep. Interesting wine list. Tables outside in the large garden with views over National Trust parkland.

OPEN: 12–3. 6–11.
Real Ale. Restaurant (no food Sun eve)
Children in garden. No dogs.

GRANTHAM

Odd House   Tel: 01476 565293

4 Fletcher Street Grantham Lincs NG31 6BP
Free House. James McAuslan licensee.

Grantham is full of treasures, among them the 14th century church of St. Wulfram which has a library of chained books given to the church in 1598; one of the 83 volumes dates back to 1472. The Odd House is another little treasure, a small two bar drinking pub in an ancient city. Sustained by a crisp nut, John Smiths Bitter or one of the changing guest beers you are only two minutes walk from the bus or the railway station – you can start your journey suitably refreshed. A small garden at the side of the pub is an outside drinking area.

OPEN: 11–11 (11–10.30 Sun).
Real Ale
No children. Dogs welcome

GLOOSTON

Old Barn   Tel: 01858 545215

Glooston, Nr Market Harborough, Leics LE16 7ST
Free House. Charles Edmondson-Jones & Stewart Sturge, licensees

Situated on an old Roman road in the small hamlet of Glooston, this 16th century Old Barn Inn is hard to miss at the height of summer. Behind the hanging baskets even the windows are fringed with flowers. Down steps to the main bar which is behind the no-smoking restaurant. There is also a smaller bar at the front of the pub servicing the restaurant. Now that the new kitchen is up and running The Old Barn has a seasonal menu of the month. You could find fresh fish terrine, baked avocado served with a stilton sauce; roast leg of English lamb in a juniper and garlic sauce; braised Guinea Fowl and a choice of home-made puddings. In addition to the monthly menu there will be local game in season, chef's specials and a daily changing pudding. Always four ales on draught which could be – Bass or a Theakstons, Adnams, Batemans, Boddingtons, Burtonwood or Fullers etc; also, several European bottled beers and a choice of wines. Seats at the front of the pub and in the garden behind.

OPEN: N.B. evening opening only Mon–Fri 7–11. Sat 12–2.30. 7–11. Sun 12–3. (closed Sun eve)
Real Ale. Restaurant (not Sun eve).
Children if well behaved. Dogs on leads.
Bedrooms

HALTON HOLEGATE

Bell Inn   Tel: 01790 753242

Firsby Road, Halton Holegate, Lincs. PE23 5NY
Free House. John & Irene Clayton, licensees.

In the flat farming landscape of the Lincolnshire Fens, from Halton Holegate there is an uninterrupted view of the Boston Stump, the tower of St Botolph's church rising 272ft beside the river in Boston. Visible for miles across the fenland. The Bell and the wonderful carved bench ends in the church all date back to the early 16th century. One big bar in the pub, low beamed ceilings, inglenook fireplace and the ghost of a labrador dog. No-one knows for sure, but maybe he was a Lancaster Bomber pilot's pet who pined for his master when he failed to return. Interesting variety of food, both in the bar and restaurant: home-made fish soup, seafood au gratin served in a scallop shell, sandwiches, salads, lots of steaks, chicken Kiev, the Bell special steak, onion and mushroom pie in a rich Madeira sauce, lots more and also a vegetarian menu. Sunday roast. Batemans XB, Draught Bass, Boddingtons Bitter and occasional guests. Tables and chairs at the front of the pub.

OPEN: 12–3. 7–11. (12 –3ish. 7–10.30 Sun)
Real Ale. Restaurant.
Children in restaurant. Dogs on leads.
Car park.

HECKINGTON

Nags Head   Tel: 01529 460218

34 High Street, Heckington, Lincs NG34 9QZ
Wards. Bruce & Gina Pickworth, lease.

For some reason the Nags Head is a popular name in these parts; there are several in the vicinity. But don't be waylaid – this is the one you want. It's a 17th century coaching inn with the emphasis on food. It has a comfortable, two roomed bar with a coal fire, friendly landlord, and well presented bar food. This is what you may find on the blackboard: celery & cheese soup, garlic mushrooms on toast, warm smoked mackerel with horseradish , roast gammon and pineapple, fresh crab salad, grilled Sea Bass, sausage and smoked bacon quiche, sandwiches too, vegetarian dishes, home-made puds daily specials and a Sunday roast. Wards Best Bitter, Vaux Double Maxim and a changing guest bitter. Wines by the glass. Tables in the garden. Heckington has a very attractive 14th century church, and an interesting eight-sailed windmill, circa 1830 – the last in the country.

OPEN: 11–3. 5–11
Real Ale.
Children welcome. No dogs.
Quiz night Sun.
Bedrooms. Wheelchair access to part of the pub.

HOSE

Rose & Crown   Tel: 01949 60424

43, Bolton Lane, Hose, Nr. Melton Mowbray, Leics LE14 4JE
Free House. Carl & Carmel Routh, licensees.

One of the reasons you would beat a path to the door of the Rose & Crown is to sample the tremendous range of beers kept there – many from small breweries in the west and north of the country. Notice of the glories to come is given well in advance, but there have been beers from: Elgoods, Bushy's from the Isle of Man, Ushers, their very own Carl's Tipple, which is brewed specially for the pub by Butterknowle and about 5 others – there are eight handpumps. After all that you would want a roll or two (filled), soup of the day or deep fried camembert with a sweet/sour coulis, garlic mushrooms, fresh trout in rosemary sauce, fillet of pork with a wine and mushroom sauce, rack of lamb in a Madeira and ginger sauce, seafood salad and lots more; also vegetarian dishes. There is a printed menu, but most of it is daily inspiration on the blackboard. There is a non-smoking restaurant. Tables on the terrace at the back of the pub, also a paddock at the bottom of the car park where the children can be let loose.

OPEN: 12–2.30. 7–11
Real Ale. Restaurant.
Children in bar & eating area until 9 pm. Dogs in bar and garden water bowls provided. No Dogs in lounge or restaurant.
Car park.

HOSE

Black Horse   Tel: 01949 860336

21, Bolton Lane, Hose, Nr. Melton Mowbray, Leics. LE14 4JE.
Tynemill Group. Mike Aram, manager.

On the edge of the rich farmlands in the Vale of Belvoir, the Black Horse is a traditional busy village pub. Two bars – a flagstoned tap room, a lounge bar cum-snug and a small restaurant. The menu changes weekly but there could be melon, egg mayonnaise or prawn cocktail to start with, a range of steaks, the pub's very own way with a chicken – chicken sunrise – chicken breasts cooked in cornflakes with a sweet and sour sauce, rack of lamb with a red currant sauce, swordfish and a vegetarian dish or two. Six real ales: Everards Mild, John Smiths Bitter, Home Bitter and three guests. Seats in the garden.

OPEN: 12–2.30. 6.30–11. (12–3. 7–10.30. Sun)
Real Ale. Restaurant.
Children welcome. Dogs on leads.
Wheelchair access. Car park.

LAXTON

Dovecote Inn   Tel: 01777 871586

Moor House Road, Laxton, Newark, Notts. NG22 0NU
Free House. Stephen & Betty Shepherd, licensees.

Probably the only village retaining mediaeval strip cultivation: rotating the crops to keep soil fertility – three cropped, one fallow. If only EEC farming policy were so simple. Lots of different areas in the Dovecote, all the noisy bits in the pool room, the rest blissfully quiet. Home-cooked bar food: soup, sandwiches, ploughmans, a selection of vegetarian dishes, choice of salads, steak and kidney pie and interesting daily specials. Bass, Mansfield ales and Worthingtons. Tables on the small terrace. The village has a fine restored 12th century church.

OPEN: 12–3. 6.30–11 (12–3; 6.30–10.30 Sun)
Real Ale.
Children in eating area. Dogs on leads.

LEICESTER

Welford Place   Tel: 0116 2470758

9, Welford Place, Leicester LE1 6 ZH
Sam Smiths. Miss Sarah Hope, general manager.

Lucky Leicester, to be favoured by the inspiration behind Welford Place. Somewhere to meet your friends from 8 in the morning until 12 at night 365 days of the year. In the city centre, adjacent to the New Walk Centre and Phoenix Arts, Welford Place is a delightful Victorian building constructed in 1877. From breakfast to your post-theatre brandy, you will find a welcoming, friendly environment. As with its associated premises, the Wig & Mitre in Lincoln, there are menus for all times of the day from a leisurely lunch to a quick snack before an evening's entertainment. All day breakfast, a bowl of ratatouille with garlic bread, a fillet steak and tarragon mustard sandwich, pan fried King prawns with ratatouille and couscous are just a small selection of the delights here. Interesting puds to finish. Draught beers – Ruddles Best and County – a comprehensive wine list and an extensive selection of spirits, brandies and liqueurs served from 10.30 to 12 midnight. Room for everything – a cup of coffee or a function for 200 guests.

OPEN: 8–12 midnight, 365 days of the year.
Real Ale. Restaurant.
Children in eating area and restaurant. Dogs on leads.
Plenty of willing helpers for wheelchairs

LINCOLN

Wig & Mitre   Tel: 01522 535190

29 Steep Hill, Lincoln, LN2 1LU
Sam Smiths. Paul Vidic & Michael Hope, licensees.

More like a club than a pub, though still a pub, the Wig & Mitre has evolved into a meeting place, reading room, restaurant and, as they say themselves, "a haven of peace". Situated on the Pilgrim's Way just below the Cathedral, this inn dates back to the 14th century. Many of the original timbers were re-used when the old building was restored 20 years ago. "Food is in perpetual motion" throughout the day from an early breakfast to a sandwich and an à la carte menu; tea too, even breakfast in the afternoon if you so wish. The menu changes regularly but there will always be a "daily fish" and possibly sun dried tomato pasta with Parma ham, spring onions and Parmesan cheese; baked cheese soufflé or sirloin steak with cracked black peppercorms, brandy and cream, puddings and a piece of cheese too. Nothing is too much trouble. Wines (nearly 100 and many by the glass), ales and spirits are available from 11 in the morning until midnight. Sam Smiths ales on hand pump, and as you would expect, freshly squeezed orange juice (remember all those breakfasts) and coffee.

OPEN: 8–11. Food served continuously.
Real Ale. Restaurant.
Children in eating area & restaurant. Dogs on leads.

LOUGHBOROUGH

Swan in the Rushes   Tel: 01509 217014

21, The Rushes, Loughborough, Leics
Free House. Andrew Hambleton, licensee.

A solid, Victorian town pub with an excellent reputation for good quality, home-cooked bar food which complements its extensive range of European bottled beers and the six or more beers on hand pump. These could include Archers Golden, Marstons Pedigree, Boddingtons and a couple of guests. There is also a selection of farm ciders which change periodically. With all this on offer, it is not surprising the pub is very popular and can get crowded. Service does, nevertheless, remain friendly and efficient.

OPEN: 11–2.30. 5–11 (11–11 Fri & Sat).
Real Ale. No food Sat & Sun eves.
Children in dining room. Dogs on leads.
Live music Sat.

NOTTINGHAM

Ye Olde Trip to Jerusalem   Tel: 0115 9473171

Brewhouse Yard, Castle Road, Nottingham NE1 6AD
Hardys & Hansons. Patrick Dare, manager.

Reputed to be the oldest pub in England – although others do claim a similar distinction, Ye Olde Trip does, nevertheless, have a lot more to interest historians than its age. It was built into the rock below the castle and was, at one time, its brewhouse. The present building was probably rebuilt on the site of the original inn during the 17th century. Previously named "The Pilgrim," it was the meeting point for crusaders before they sailed to deal with the heathen hordes. Architecturally of interest, the panelled rooms have alcoves cut into the rock, and the cellars are in rock caves. An impressive part-panelled, part rockface, high-ceilinged bar upstairs is open only during very busy periods, and is worth seeing if at all possible. Traditional, sustaining bar food, daily specials plus a good choice of vegetarian dishes. Hardy and Hansons have introduced a "cellarman's cask" range of ales which changes every two months. Seats outside in the courtyard.

OPEN: 11–11. (12–10.30 Sun)
Real Ale. Lunchtime meals & snacks.(11–3)
No children. No dogs.
N.B. Ye Olde Trip will be closed in October 1996 for three months. When it re-opens, meals will be served all day until early evening.

OLD DALBY

Crown   Tel: 01664 823134

Debdale Hill, Old Dalby, Nr Melton Mowbray, Leics LE14 3LF
Free House. Lynne Strafford, Bryan & Jack Inguanta, licensees.

A converted farmhouse, still with its charming, rambling rooms, the Crown is now the focus for those discerning people who want to combine good food with the relaxed ambience found in a friendly country pub. The food here has the reputation of being really home-made. You can, if you're lucky, follow the herbs in from the garden. Even the bread is kneaded "in-house", so you know you are in the company of people who really care about their food: grilled smoked salmon sausage with a herb cream sauce; boneless quail, filled with a chicken, wild mushroom and tarragon mousse; Crown ploughmans, several vegetarian dishes, sandwiches and filled baguettes. There is also a dining room menu. A wide range of ales is on offer, amongst which could be Kimberly Bitter, Woodfordes Wherry and Timothy Taylors Landlord. Choice of malt whiskies and a good wine list. Tables on the terrace overlooking the large garden. There is also a petanque pitch.

OPEN: 12–3. 6–11.
Real Ale. Restaurant (not Sun eve).
Children welcome away from bar. No dogs.
Wheelchair access.

OSGATHORPE

Royal Oak Inn   Tel: 01530 222443

20 Main Street, Osgathorpe, Leicestershire LE12 9OA
Free House. Alfie & Valerie Jacobs, licensees.

Osgathorpe is a small village nestling in a valley on the edge of Charnwood Forest, once densely wooded as far as the eye could see, now open heath with rocky outcrops and the occasional clump of ancient trees. The Royal Oak, built as a farmhouse in the 18th century, is an attractive popular local, open only evenings and Sundays. Low beamed ceilings, big open fireplace with horsebrasses decorating the walls. Three lounges, one of which has music – so you have been warned. Only crisps and nuts to go with the beer: Marstons Pedigree, M & B Mild and Worthingtons Best Bitter. A terrace to sit on and a lovely garden to sit in.

OPEN: 7–11. Mon–Sat. (12–3. 7–10.30 Sun.)
Real Ale.
Children welcome. Dogs on leads.

SPRINGTHORPE

The New Inn   Tel: 01427 838254

16 Hill Road, Springthorpe, Nr Gainsborough, Lincs DN21 5PY
Free House. Michael Nelson, licensee.

A popular village local enjoying an enviable position – near the parish church and overlooking the village green. Originally a row a brick cottages, it was converted late last century. Now you have a comfortable lounge, public bar and a small dining room – packed for Sunday roast lunch. (Must book). There is a printed menù listing standard dishes, from beef burgers and steaks to scampi and roast duckling. Four or five daily specials on the blackboard. Batemans XXX, Marstons Pedigree, Youngers Scotch Bitter (Keg) and guest beers. The village green belongs to the village so if you want to sit there to enjoy your pint it's either on the grass or on one of the public benches. However, there is a small garden at the back of the pub.

OPEN: 12–2. 7–11 (7–10.30 Sun)
Real Ale
Children welcome. Dogs on leads.
Car park.

STAMFORD

George of Stamford   Tel: 01780 55171

71 High Street, St Martins, Stamford, Lincs PE9 2LB}
Free House. Ivo Vanocci & Chris Pitman, licensees.

Undeniably handsome, the George, with its fine Georgian façade, belies its great age. There are parts of a Norman hospice incorporated in the fabric of this famous old coaching inn, which was built by Lord Burghley in the 16th century. On the York to London road, the London and York bars – which face each other just inside the George – were the waiting rooms for the up and down coaches that stopped here each day. It is still a focal point for the local community, whether dining, or enjoying a glass of wine or pint of ale in the comfortable bar. There is a lunchtime buffet in the garden room where you could have a Caesar salad, or poached escalope of salmon, char-grilled lambs liver, open Danish sandwich or toasted club sandwich, something from the cold buffet, some pasta dishes, even fish and chips; also an extensive menu of excellent bar food and a restaurant menu. Adnams ales, a considerable wine list and all the other niceties you associate with a well run establishment – freshly squeezed orange juice, good coffee and afternoon teas. There is a very attractive cobbled courtyard at the rear of the creeper-covered George, filled with tables and chairs amid flowering tubs and hanging baskets.

OPEN: 11–11.
Real Ale. Restaurant (two)
Children welcome. Dogs in garden.
Bedrooms. Wheelchair access.

STRETTON

Ram Jam Inn   Tel: 01780 418776

Great North Road, Oakham, Leics. LE15 7QX
Free House. Tim Hart, licensee.

They admit that this is more a restaurant than a pub, although from the outside it looks very much like a traditional old coaching inn. Food is served all day from an interesting varied bar menu. Fresh fish daily and a roast every Sunday. From the Bistro menu there could be home-made pea a mint soup, duck and green peppercorn terrine, char-grilled marinated chicken breast served on a bed of couscous, a Greek vegetarian platter and home-made puds. You could choose an "instant lunch" of two courses: filled, toasted granary baps or sandwiches; other favourites prepared to order. Only one bar, but a comfortable lounge for lounging and a no-smoking restaurant. Ruddles County and Best plus a variety of bottled beers. Good wines. There are seats on the terrace behind the pub.

OPEN: 7am–11pm.
Real Ale. Restaurant.
Children welcome. No dogs.
Wheelchair access throughout pub.

THORPE LANGTON

Bakers Arms   Tel: 01858 545201

Main Street, Thorpe Langton, Leics LE16 7TS
Free House. Kate Hubbard, licensee and manageress.

Only open weekday evenings and for Saturday and Sunday lunch. North of the A6 you'll find lots of little Langtons. Take a left turn off the B 6047 for this one – just a small quiet village with a very popular, convivial pub, which over the last six years has built up an excellent reputation for fine food and a knowledgeable wine list. Thatched, mostly 18th century, it has been extended and refurbished – the envy of many. There is a contantly changing menu – all on blackboards – so it is a case of, go and see what is inspiring the chef. That said, you do have to book. They do still serve a pint or two – Tetleys and Draught Burton Ale. The pub piano is brought to the fore on Friday evenings, so if you don't appreciate a little night music, you know when to avoid it.

OPEN: Tues–Sat. 6.30–11. (12–2 Sat & Sun lunches) Closed Monday and

Sunday evenings.
Real Ale
No children during the evenings. No dogs.

UFFORD

Olde White Hart   Tel: 01780 740250

Main Street, Ufford, Lincolnshire PE9 3BH
Youngers. Andrew Haigh, tenant.

This is a pretty 17th century pub in a large attractive garden, so there's plenty of space to wander in, and to camp if you have brought your tent. There is also a terrace on which you can sit in summer. Popular with walkers and cyclists. The pub has two comfortable bars and a recently refurbished snug. Lunchtime snacks include a variety of exotic dishes which change from week to week. The usual sandwiches, maybe stuffed pancakes or rump steak with a garlic sauce, daily specials, and on Sunday there is a roast lunch and hot beef rolls. Theakstons Best, XB and Old Peculiar. Guest beers and lots of imported bottled beers. Wines by the glass and farm cider.

OPEN: 11–2.30. (3 Sat) 6–11
Real Ale. No food Sun eve or Mon.
Children in eating areas. Dogs on leads.
Live music Sun evenings.

WELLOW

Olde Red Lion   Tel: 01623 861000

Eakring Road, Wellow, Newark, Notts. NG22 OEG.
Free House. John & Carol Henshaw, licensees.

Wellow has an interesting history: pre Saxon, it was a fortified village surrounded by a moat, the remaining earthworks are now protected. The parish church is 12th century and Wellow is only one of three villages in the country to have a permanent Maypole which is still used. The 17th century Red Lion, was originally a one room ale house and a row of farm cottages. Good substantial, reliable pub food: filled rolls or sandwiches, breaded mushrooms with a garlic dip, smoked salmon terrine, grilled steaks or gammon with various sauces, steak and kidney pie, lasagne, a number of fish dishes, supreme of chicken with a chasseur sauce, vegetarian dishes and a children's menu. A micro brewery – The Maypole Brewery – in the village brews Lion's Pride specially for the pub. John Smiths, Courage Directors, Ruddles County and guest beers. Picnic tables outside in the garden.

OPEN: 11.30–3. 5.30–11. (11–11 Sat and Sun).
Real Ale.
Children welcome. No dogs.

WEST LEAKE

Star Inn   Tel: 01509 852233

Melton Lane, West Leake, Nr Loughborough, Leics
Gibbs Mew. Linda Collin, licensee.

There are fine views across beautiful countryside from this lovely old coaching inn. Inside the beamed bars are comfortably furnished and in winter they have open log fires. A happy mix of drinkers and diners make it lively, cheerful and friendly. Food is home-cooked and the menu changes daily. There could be soup, mushrooms in cream and garlic sauce, paté, roast leg of pork, chicken chasseur and a choice of puddings. Salisbury Best Bitter, Bass and Theakstons ales. Over a dozen malt whiskies. Seats and tables outside during the summer.

OPEN: 11–3. 6–11.
Real Ale.
Children in family room. Dogs on leads.

BARKING AND DAGENHAM

THE BARKING DOG
61 Station Parade, Barking

THE LORD DENMAN
270-272 Heathway, Dagenham

BARNET

THE MOON UNDER WATER
148 High Street, Barnet

THE WHITE LION OF MORTIMER
3 York Parade, West Hendon
Broadway NW9

THE RAILWAY BELL
13 East Barnet Road, New Barnet

THE MOON UNDER WATER
10 Varley Parade, Colindale NW9

*THE TALLY HO
749 High Road, North Finchley N12

THE BLACKING BOTTLE
122-126 High Street, Edgware

BEXLEY

THE WRONG 'UN
234-236 The Broadway, Bexleyheath

BRENT

J J MOON'S
553 Kingsbury Road, Kingsbury NW9

THE OUTSIDE INN
312-314 Neasden Lane, Neasden
NW10

J J MOON'S
397 High Road, Wembley

THE COLISEUM
Manor Park Road, Harlesden NW10

BROMLEY

THE MOON AND STARS
164-166 High Street, Penge SE20

THE HARVEST MOON
141-143 High Street, Orpington

THE SOVEREIGN OF THE SEAS
109-111 Queensway, Petts Wood

CAMDEN

THE MAN IN THE MOON
40-42 Chalk Farm Road, Camden NW1

THE BEATEN DOCKET
50-56 Cricklewood Broadway,
Cricklewood NW2

THE THREE HORSESHOES
28 Heath Street, Hampstead NW3

CITY OF LONDON

HAMILTON HALL
Liverpool Street Station EC2

CROYDON

THE GEORGE
17-21 George Street, Croydon

THE MOON UNDER WATER
1327 London Road, Norbury SW16

THE FOXLEY HATCH
8-9 Russell Hill Parade,
Russell Hill Road, Purley

EALING

THE RED LION AND PINEAPPLE
281 High Street, Acton W3

ENFIELD

THE MOON UNDER WATER
115-117 Chase Side, Enfield

THE WHOLE HOG
430-434 Green Lanes, Palmers Green
N13

THE HALF MOON
749 Green Lanes, Winchmore Hill N21

THE BANKER'S DRAFT
36-38 Friern Barnet Road,
New Southgate N11

THE LAMB
52-54 Church Street, Edmonton N9

THE NEW CROWN
80-84 Chase Side, Southgate

EPPING FOREST

THE LAST POST
227 High Road, Loughton

GREENWICH

THE BANKER'S DRAFT
80 High Street, Eltham SE9

HACKNEY

THE ROCHESTER CASTLE
145 High Street, Stoke Newington N16

HAMMERSMITH

THE MOON ON THE GREEN
172-174 Uxbridge Road,
Shepherds Bush W12

HARINGEY

THE OLD SUFFOLK PUNCH
10-12 Grand Parade, Green Lanes,
Harringay N4

THE NEW MOON
413 Lordship Lane, Tottenham N17

THE ELBOW ROOM
503-505 High Street, Tottenham N17

THE TOLL GATE
26-30 Turnpike Lane, Hornsey N8

THE ELBOW ROOM
22 Topsfield Parade, Tottenham Lane,
Crouch End N8

THE GATE HOUSE
1 North Hill, Highgate N6

HARROW

J J MOON'S
3 Shaftesbury Parade,
Shaftesbury Circle, South Harrow

THE MOON ON THE HILL
373-375 Station Road, Harrow

THE NEW MOON
25-26 Kenton Park Parade,
Kenton Road, Harrow

THE MOON AND SIXPENCE
250 Uxbridge Road, Pinner

THE SARSEN STONE
32 High Street, Wealdstone

J J MOON'S
20 The Broadwalk, Pinner Road,
North Harrow

THE VILLAGE INN
402-408 Rayners Lane, Pinner

THE MAN IN THE MOON
1 Buckingham Parade, Stanmore

HAVERING

J J MOON'S
46-62 High Street, Hornchurch

THE MOON AND STARS
99-103 South Street, Romford

HERTFORDSHIRE

THE HART AND SPOOL
148 Shenley Road, Borehamwood

THE MOON UNDER WATER
44, High Street, Watford

THE CROSS KEYS
2 Chequer Street, St. Albans

HILLINGDON

J J MOON'S
12 Victoria Road, Ruislip Manor

THE MOON UNDER WATER
10-11 Broadway Parade,
Coldharbour Lane, Hayes

J J MOON'S
Terminal Four, (Airside),
Heathrow Airport, Hounslow

WETHERSPOONS
Terminal Four, (Landside),
Heathrow Airport, Hounslow

THE MOON AND SIXPENCE
1250-1256 Uxbridge Road,
Hayes End

THE SYLVAN MOON
27 Green Lane, Northwood

THE GOOD YARN
132 High Street, Uxbridge

HOUNSLOW

THE MOON UNDER WATER
84-86 Staines Road, Hounslow

J J MOON'S
80-82 Chiswick High Road, Chiswick W4

THE MOON ON THE SQUARE
Unit 30, The Centre, Feltham

ISLINGTON

THE CORONET
338-346 Holloway Road, London N7

THE DOG
17-19 Archway Road, Archway N19

179 UPPER STREET
179 Upper Street, Islington N1

THE WHITE LION OF MORTIMER
125-127 Stroud Green Road,
Stroud Green N4

THE MASQUE HAUNT
168-172 Old Street EC2

KENT

THE PAPER MOON
55 High Street, Dartford

LAMBETH

THE CROWN AND SCEPTRE
2a Streatham Hill SW2

THE BEEHIVE
407-409 Brixton Road, Brixton SW9

LEWISHAM

THE TIGER'S HEAD
350 Bromley Road, Catford SE6

THE BIRD IN HAND
35 Dartmouth Road, Forest Hill SE23

MERTON

THE WHITE LION OF MORTIMER
223 London Road, Mitcham

WETHERSPOONS
33 Aberconway Road, Morden

THE WIBBAS DOWN INN
6-12 Gladstone Road, Wimbledon

NEWHAM

THE MILLER'S WELL
419-421 Barking Road, East Ham E6

EXTENSIVE RANGE OF CASK-CONDITIONED ALES • LARGE NON

OON PUB GUIDE

THE GOLDENGROVE
146-148 The Grove, Stratford E15

REDBRIDGE

THE NEW FAIRLOP OAK
Fencepiece Road, Barkingside

THE GEORGE
High Street, Wanstead E11

THE GREAT SPOON OF ILFORD
114-116 Cranbrook Road, Ilford

RICHMOND UPON THAMES

THE MOON UNDER WATER
53-57 London Road, Twickenham

SOUTHWARK

*THE FOX ON THE HILL
149 Denmark Hill SE5

SURREY

THE REGENT
19 Church Street, Walton-on Thames

SUTTON

THE WHISPERING MOON
25 Ross Parade, Woodcote Road,
Wallington

THE MOON ON THE HILL
5-9 Hill Road, Sutton

WETHERSPOONS
553-556 London Road, North Cheam

TOWER HAMLETS

THE CAMDEN'S HEAD
456 Bethnal Green Road,
Bethnal Green E2

WALTHAM FOREST

THE DRUM
557-559 Lea Bridge Road, Leyton E10

WANDSWORTH

J J MOON'S
56a High Street, Tooting SW17

THE MOON UNDER WATER
194 Balham High Road, Balham SW12

THE SPOTTED DOG
72 Garratt Lane, Arndale Centre,
Wandsworth SW18

THE RAILWAY
202 Upper Richmond Road, Putney SW15

THE GRID INN
22 Replingham Road,
Southfields SW18

WESTMINSTER

THE MOON UNDER WATER
28 Leicester Square WC2

WETHERSPOONS
Victoria Station SW1

THE MOON AND SIXPENCE
185 Wardour Street W1

THE LORD MOON OF THE MALL
16-18 Whitehall SW1

OUTSIDE M25

AVON

THE COMMERCIAL ROOMS
43-45 Corn Street, Bristol

THE BERKELEY
15-19 Queens Road, Clifton, Bristol

BERKSHIRE

*THE OLD MANOR
Church Road, Bracknell

THE MONK'S RETREAT
163 Friar Street, Reading

THE MOON UNDER WATER
86-88 High Street, Slough

BUCKINGHAMSHIRE

THE LAST POST
77 The Broadway, Chesham

THE FALCON
9 Cornmarket, High Wycombe

WETHERSPOONS
201 Midsummer Boulevard, Bouverie
Square, Milton Keynes

CAMBRIDGESHIRE

THE COLLEGE ARMS
40 The Broadway, Peterborough

CHESHIRE

WETHERSPOONS
78-92 Foregate Street, Chester

DERBYSHIRE

THE STANDING ORDER
28-32 Irongate, Derby

DEVON

THE IMPERIAL
New North Road, Exeter

DORSET

THE MOON IN THE SQUARE
4-8 Exeter Road, The Square,
Bournemouth

EAST SUSSEX

CLIFTONVILLE INN
98-101 George Street, Hove

ESSEX

THE ELMS
1060 London Road, Leigh-on-Sea

THE LAST POST
Weston Road, Southend-on-Sea

THE PLAYHOUSE
4 St. John Street, Colchester

THE MOON ON THE SQUARE
1-15 Market Square, Basildon

GLOUCESTERSHIRE

THE REGAL
Kings Square, Gloucester

GREATER MANCHESTER

THE MOON UNDER WATER
68-74 Deansgate, Manchester

WETHERSPOONS
49 Piccadilly, Manchester

THE ASH TREE
Main Street, Wellington Road,
Ashton-Under-Lyne

GWENT

WETHERSPOONS
Unit 10-12 The Cambrian Centre,
Newport

HAMPSHIRE

THE STANDING ORDER
20 High Street, Southampton

WETHERSPOONS
2 Guildhall Walk, Portsmouth

HEREFORD AND WORCESTER

THE GOLDEN CROSS HOTEL
20 High Street, Bromsgrove

KENT

THE MUGGLETON INN
8-9 High Street, Maidstone

LANCASHIRE

THE POSTAL ORDER
15 Darwen Street, Blackburn

THE GREYFRIAR
114 Friargate, Preston

LEICESTERSHIRE

THE LAST PLANTAGENET
107 Granby Street, Leicester

LINCOLNSHIRE

THE TOLLEMACHE INN
St. Peters Hill
28 Catherines Road, Grantham

MERSEYSIDE

WETHERSPOONS
20 Lord Street, Southport

WETHERSPOONS
Units 1,2 & 3 Charlotte Row,
Great Charlotte Street, Liverpool

NORFOLK

THE BELL HOTEL
5 Orford Hill, Norwich

THE TROLL CART
7-9 Regent Road, Great Yarmouth

NORTHAMPTONSHIRE

THE MOON ON THE SQUARE
The Parade, Market Place,
Northampton

OXFORDSHIRE

THE EXCHANGE
49-50 High Street, Banbury

SUFFOLK

THE WOLF
88-89 St John Street, Bury St Edmunds

SURREY

WETHERSPOONS
51-57 Chertsey Road, Woking

THE SUN
17 London Road, Redhill

WEST GLAMORGAN

THE POTTER'S WHEEL
86 The Kingsway, Swansea

WEST MIDLANDS

THE BENJAMIN SATCHWELL
112-114 The Parade, Leamington Spa

THE FIGURE OF EIGHT
236-238 Broad Street, Birmingham

THE FULL MOON
58-60 High Street, Dudley

THE MOON UNDER WATER
53-55 Lichfield Street, Wolverhampton

THE SQUARE PEG
Units 1, 2 & 3 Temple Court,
115 Corporation Street, Birmingham

WEST SUSSEX

THE RED LION
North Terminal, International
Departures Lounge, Gatwick Airport
(Airside)

THE JUBILEE OAK
6 Grand Parade, High Street, Crawley

THE HATTERS INN
2-10 Queensway, Bognor Regis

WILTSHIRE

THE SAVOY
38-40 Regent Street, Swindon

YORKSHIRE

THE BANKERS DRAFT
1-3 Market Place, Sheffield

THE RHINOCEROS
35-37 Bridgegate, Rotherham

SMOKING AREAS • EXCELLENT ALL-DAY FOOD • OPEN 7 DAYS

M
MIDLANDS

ALCESTER

The Hollybush Hotel   Tel:01789 762482

Henley Street, Alcester, Warwickshire B49 5QX
Free House. Marion & Walter Hobbis, licensees

Near a Roman settlement and at the junction of two Roman roads and two
rivers, the Alne and the Arrow, Alcester is an ancient market town with an
attractive mix of Tudor and Georgian buildings. Opposite the 17th century
Town Hall and near the church, the Hollybush is a fine 'proper' pub, where
you are made to feel at home, and the locals talk to visitors. A choice of
crisps and a nut or two, otherwise liquid refreshment only: Adnams
Broadside, M&B Brew X1 and Mild. Benches in the small garden at the back
of the pub.

OPEN: 11–3. 7.30–11.(12–2.30. 7–10.30. Sun)
Real Ale
No Children. No dogs.
Wheelchair access.

BRIERLEY HILL

Vine   Tel: 01384 78293

10 Delph Road, Brierley Hill, W. Midlands DY5 2TN
Bathams. Melvin Wood, manager.

Not a million miles from Dudley and the Zoo, this is a region that was noted
for the production of crystal glass. Several local museums in the area tell the
story of the glassmaker's art from Roman times to the present day. The Vine
is known locally as The Bull and Bladder from the stained glass Bull's Head
and the freely interpreted bunch of grapes decorating the front window.
Plenty of room in this bustling pub. Not quite a permanent beer line to the
brewery, but as it is next door there could well be! Popular, well made and

reasonably priced lunchtime snacks, sandwiches and lots of salads. Bathams Bitter and Mild on hand pump, also Delf Strong Ale in winter.

OPEN: 12–11.
Real Ale. Lunchtime snacks (not Sun)
Children in own room. Dogs on leads.
Live music Sun & Mon: Blues/Jazz/Folk.

CHAPEL BRAMPTON

The Brampton Halt   Tel: 01604 842676

Pitsford Road, Chapel Brampton NN6 8BL
Free House. Roger Thom, licensee.

Find the old railway line, the railway station and here you are. Only one bar in what used to be the Station Master's house. The weigh-bridge is still in the old goods yard – now used as a car park. Open for only two years, it has an extensive bar menu, and has become quite food orientated. "It wasn't intended to be that way", said Roger Thom, "but that's the way it's gone." Everything is home-cooked. All dishes are listed on the blackboards. Crown of melon with raspberry sorbet to start with, home-made vegetable soup, whitebait or grilled sardines; your main dish could be: grilled plaice, lamb chops in redcurrant sauce, chicken Kiev, rump steak, wild trout or steak and kidney pie. Lots of puds. Fullers London Pride, Draught Bass, Adnams Bitter, Everards Old Original and the occasional guests. Large garden. A preservation society is trying to open the old railway line which used to link Northampton and Market Harborough. So with any luck, those wonderful steam trains will be running through the station again.

OPEN: 11.30–3. 5–11 (12–3. 7–11 Sun)
Real Ale
Children welcome. Dogs in garden only.

CRICK

Red Lion   Tel: 01788 822342

52 Main Road, Crick, Northants NN6 7TX
Free House. Tom & Mary Marks, lease.

Always useful to know of a stopping place if you have to travel on motorways (M1 junction 18). In winter this comfortable thatched pub has log

237

fires in the low ceilinged bar, and in summer, you can relax on the terrace at the back of the pub and admire the floral display. Reasonably priced lunchtime snacks – seventeen hot dishes to choose from – some changing daily, sandwiches and ploughmans. Steaks, chicken Kiev, trout, lamb cutlets and moussaka and over 10 vegetarian dishes are among those available on the evening menu. Websters Yorkshire, Wadworths 6X, Ruddles Best and Morlands Old Speckled Hen.

OPEN: 11.30–2.30. 6.30–11.
Real Ale. No food Sun eves.
Children in family room lunchtime only. Dogs on leads.

DORRIDGE

Railway Inn Tel: 01564 77353

Grange Road, Solihull, West Midlands B93 8QA
Bass Lease. Philip (Joe) Watson, licensee.

On the outskirts of Solihull, the Railway Inn has the village to one side and green fields on the other. A small, friendly unspoilt village pub, it has just a public and lounge bar. The bar menu ranges from a sandwich to a T-bone steak. Draught Bass, M&B Mild, Brew X1, Highgate Mild and a selection of guest beers. Seats in the garden,

OPEN: 11–11 Wed. Fri. Sat. (11–2.30. 4.30–11 Mon. Tues. Thurs. 12–10.30 Sun)
Real Ale
Children only at meal times. No Dogs.

EARLSDON

Royal Oak Tel: 01203 674140

Earlsdon Street, Earlsdon, Coventry CV5 6EJ
Free House. Ray Evitts, licensee.

Since taking over this pub, the landlord has made it immensely popular with those who appreciate good beer served in pleasing, unfussy, friendly surroundings. Large wooden communal tables and comfortable chairs. Waiter service in the rear bar. House rules are rigorously applied – no dogs, no music, no noisy, rowdy behaviour and no food! Ansells ales, Bass, Tetley, draught Guinness and guest beers.

OPEN: 12–2.30. 5–11.(12–2.30. 7–10.30 Sun).
Real Ale. No food.
No dogs.

FIVEWAYS

Case is Altered   Tel: 01926 484206

Case Lane, Fiveways, Hatton, Nr Warwick CV35 7JD (N.of Warwick)
Free House. Mrs Gwen Jones, licensee.

Down a country lane about three miles from Warwick, this is a basic, old-fashioned pub in the best possible sense. The bar is beamed, has a red tiled floor, old wooden tables and chairs and log fires during the winter. Popular with locals, and at weekends with walkers and cyclists. No food, but probably a crisp or nut. Ansells Ales, Sam Smiths and Flowers Original.

OPEN: 11.30–2.30. 6–11.
Real Ale. No food.
No dogs.
Wheelchair access.

FOTHERINGHAY

Falcon Inn   Tel: 018326 254

Fotheringhay, Nr Oundle, Northants PE8 5HZ
Free House. Alan Stewart, licensee.

A busy, lively, friendly, informal village pub with a reputation for good value, imaginative food, at lunchtime and in the evening. All the dishes are home-made so they are restricted in number. It is advisable to book to ensure that the particular dish you have chosen hasn't run out. Usual bar staples, ranging from sandwiches, ploughmans to salmon fish cakes. The menus change daily but there could be melon with Parma ham, egg mayonnaise, quails eggs with smoked salmon, spinach and mushroom lasagne, chicken in a red wine sauce or even wild boar in a nutmeg and orange sauce, grills, salads and a choice of puds. Greene King, Adnams, Elgoods Cambridge, Nethergate and Ruddles County. Tables in the garden. A grassy mound marks the site of Fotheringhay Castle in which Mary Queen of Scots was executed in 1587.

OPEN: 10–3. 6–11 (7–11 Mon winter).

Real Ale. Restaurant (not Mon)
Children in eating area and restaurant. Dogs in tap room.

LAPWORTH

Navigation Inn

Tel: 01564 783337

Old Warwick Road, Lapworth, Warwicks
M & B (Bass). Andrew Kimber, lease.

A busy friendly canalside pub which, though popular all year, comes into its own during warm summer days when you can sit on the lawn and watch the water flow by. Appetising bar food: filled rolls, lasagne, beef Guinness and mushroom pie, steaks, curries, etc. Anything can be going on in the garden, from a barbecue to visiting Morris dances, or a theatre company. Draught Bass, M&B Mild Brew X1 and changing guest beer. Farm ciders during the summer. There are tables on the lawn which runs down to the water's edge.

OPEN: 11–2.30. 5.30–11. (all day summer Saturdays)
Real Ale.
Children in eating area before 9 pm. Dogs on leads .
Occasional Morris Dancing/folk music.

NEWBOLD ON STOUR

White Hart Inn

Tel: 01789 450205

Stratford Road, Nr Stratford on Avon
M & B (Bass). Mr & Mrs J Cruttwell, lease.

There is a juke box in the public bar but if you chat a lot in the main bar you may not hear it. A popular local, offering a good selection of reasonably priced food. It gets very busy on Friday and Saturday evenings. You should book if you want to have a Sunday lunch. Home-made soups, ploughmans, braised lamb in wine and herbs, poached salmon in cream herb sauce and paella. Bass and Worthingtons Best on hand pump. Seats outside at the front of the pub amid the flowers.

OPEN: 11–2.30 (3 Sat). 6–11.
Real Ale. Restaurant (no food Sun eve).
Children welcome. Dogs on leads.

OUNDLE

Ship Inn   Tel: 01832 273918

West Street, Oundle, Northants PE8 4EF
Free House. Frank Langbridge, licensee.

Heavily beamed bars, one with a blazing fire and one panelled snug which is no-smoking. Choice of bar food, ranges from soups, sandwiches, ploughmans, salads, steak & kidney pie, lasagne to curries. Only pies on Sundays. A busy, popular pub. Tetleys, Wadworths 6X, Murphys, Marstons Pedigree, Bass and a guest beer.

OPEN: 11–3. 6–11 (11–11 Sat). N.B. The juke box, or whatever in the public bar, can be heard in the rest of the pub.
Real Ale.
Children welcome. Dogs on leads.
Bedrooms.
Live music Fri or Sat.

PITSFORD

The Griffin   Tel: 01675 481205

25 High Street, Pitsford, Northants NN7 9ND
Free House. Mr & Mrs A Worthington, licensees.

This stone-built pub, about three miles north of Northampton, takes its name from the heraldic emblem of the Earls of Strafford who, during the 18th century, were Lords of the Manor for both Boughton and Pitsford and created a wonderful Gothic folly in nearby Boughton Park. Popular during the early evening with local doctors, lawyers, accountants and farmers having a pre-dinner drink before wending their way home. This gives the Griffin a 'clubby' atmosphere in the early evening. Friendly and relaxing, the Pitsford Young Farmers Club and, of course, many local people use it too. Only bar snacks are served. Theakstons Best Bitter, XB and Old Peculiar on hand pump.

OPEN: 12–2.30. 6–11.
Real Ale. No food Monday lunchtime.
No children. Dogs in bar only.

SHIPSTON-ON-STOUR

The White Bear   Tel: 01608 661558

High Street, Shipston-on-Stour, Warwickshire CU36 1AJ
Bass M&B lease. John Saunders, licensee.

This is an area of undulating countryside with rushing streams, where according to the map, you are either in, on, or under a marsh, river, or edge. Overlooking the town square, the White Bear is a comfortable small hotel. The same imaginative menu is available in both the bar and restaurant. Bar snacks vary from home-made soup, sandwiches, quiche and steaks to grilled fish there is also a regularly changing specials board. Draught Bass and M&B range of beers, Marstons Pedigree is the guest. Good short wine list with some wines by the glass. The pub has a small garden, also tables and chairs beyond the car park.

OPEN: 11–3. 6–11. Mon–Fri. (11–11 Sat. 12–3. 7–10.30 Sun.)
Real Ale. Restaurant.
Children welcome. Dogs on leads.
Car park. Wheelchair access.
Ten letting rooms.

SHIPSTON-ON-STOUR

The Horseshoe   Tel: 01608 661225

Church Street, Shipston-on-Stour, Warwickshire CV36 4AP
Will Youngers. Roger Figures, licensee.

Among the pretty houses, right in the centre of Shipston, the Horseshoe, dating back to the 17th century, is low ceilinged, well beamed, with panelling in both the lounge and public bars. Bar food ranges from home-made soup and sandwiches to a mixed grill. Currently the most popular dish from the restaurant à la carte menu is a leg of lamb for two. Gosh, I'm quite impressed. These Midlanders must be very hearty eaters or the lambs are very small. All Youngers ales with Tetleys Bitter as the guest. Seating for 40 on the terrace, so you should be able to find somewhere to rest your pint pot.

OPEN: 11–3. 7–11. (11–11. Sat. 12–10.30 Sun.)
Real Ale. Restaurant.
Children welcome. Dogs on leads, except in restaurant.

SHUSTOKE

Griffin Inn Tel: 01675 481205

Nr Coleshill, Birmingham B46 2LB (at Furnace End E of Shustoke)
Own Brew. Michael Pugh & Sydney Wedge, licensees.

An old-fashioned, 300 year old village pub with its own small brewery set up in what used to be a coffin shop. There is a large, beamed bar and a roomy conservatory where children are allowed. Good choice of bar food ranges from sandwiches, various fish dishes, steak & kidney pie to steaks. There are a dozen or so hand pumps for a wide choice of beer – the guests changing every couple of days. The Griffin's own bitter has been christened, and the first-named, M Reg GTI reflects the motoring interest of the landlord. Not sure what interest Gravediggers' Mild indicates, something to do with the coffins, no doubt. The Sunbeam Alpine Tiger Club meets monthly. Seats outside in the garden and on the terrace.

OPEN: 12–2.30. 7–11.
Real Ale. Lunchtime meals & snacks (not Sun).
Children in conservatory. Dogs on leads.

WOOTTON WAWEN

Bulls Head Tel: 01564 792511

Stratford Road, Wootton Wawen, Warwickshire, B95 6BD.
(On the A3400, Birmingham to Stratford-on-Avon road).
Free House. John Willmott, licensee.

Over 300 years old, this large, handsome, heavily timbered, black & white inn is proving increasingly popular since becoming a free house. Inside are attractive beamed bars and a restaurant. They have an imaginative à la carte menu; the speciality of the house are the fresh fish and seafood dishes. Marstons Pedigree, Morlands Old Speckled Hen, Wadworths 6X, Fullers London Pride, a good selection of wines. Seats in the lovely garden or on the vine covered terrace.

OPEN: 12–3. 6–11.
Real Ale. Restaurant.
Well behaved children. No dogs.

N

NORFOLK

BLAKENEY

Kings Arms   Tel: 01263 740341

Westgate Street, Blakeney, Norfolk
Free House. Howard & Marjorie Davies, licensees

On the North Norfolk coast, Blakeney is a yachting centre with a main street of brick and flint houses. Near the quay and in the bracing sea air of one of East Anglia's most picturesque villages, the 18th century Kings Arms – once three fishermen's cottages – is among the most popular pubs in the area. It is simply furnished and the walls of the bars are decorated with lots of photographs of the licensees' theatrical careers and original paintings by local artists. A wide range of bar food is available: ploughmans, sandwiches, filled jacket potatoes, local crabs and other fish, steaks, vegetarian dishes and daily specials. A shorter menu is available during weekday and weekend afternoons. There are two no-smoking areas in the pub. Norwich, Webster and Ruddles Bitters plus the local Woodfordes Wherry. Fosters and Carlsberg lagers. Seats on the terrace at the front of the pub and in the large garden. There is also a separate children's area.

OPEN: 11–11.
Real Ale.
Children welcome. Dogs on leads.
Self-catering flatlets. N.B. There is a newly built extension with four new en-suite bedrooms and a large dining area which leads into the garden. All disabled facilities available.

BLAKENEY

White Horse   Tel: 01263 740574

4 High Street, Blakeney NR25 7AL
Free House. Daniel Rees, licensee.

Really a small hotel with one good size bar. Not far from the harbour and the

244

bracing sea air, this is a popular spot in the holiday season. Good sustaining pub fare: home-made soups (some fishy ones, as you would expect), sandwiches, salads, steak and kidney pie, more fish and daily specials. Good home-made puds. Adnams Southwold Bitter, Flowers Original, Best and Guinness. Well chosen wine list. Seats in the sunny courtyard.

OPEN: 11–3. 6–11
Real Ale. Restaurant.
Children in restaurant.

BLICKLING

Buckinghamshire Arms   Tel: 01263 732133

Blickling, Nr Aylsham, Norfolk NR11 6NF (off B1354 N of Aylsham)
Free House. Miss Pip Wilkinson, licensee.

Once the servants' quarters of Blickling Hall – which now belongs to the National Trust – this 17th century listed building has three pleasant and comfortable bars, all with open fires. If you are lucky enough to stay here, you get a wonderful view of floodlit Blickling Hall from two of the bedrooms. Good selection of barfood: home-made soups, sandwiches, ploughmans, game pies, baked gammon and home-made puds. Adnams Best, Broadside, Sam Smiths OB, and Woodfordes Wherry, plus a good selection of wines. There are picnic tables on the lawn. You can walk through Blickling Park all year round, and Blickling Hall, a 17th century Jacobean moated house, set in formal gardens is worth a visit.

OPEN: 11–3. 6–11.
Real Ale. Restaurant.
Children in Restaurant. No dogs.
Bedrooms.

BROCKDISH

Greyhound   Tel: 01379 668775

The Street, Brockdish, Diss, Norfolk IP21 4JY
Free House. John A Crowson, licensee.

Very near the Suffolk border. The Greyhound, a 17th century coaching inn, still has the original coach entrance into what used to be the old stable yard – now the car park. Drive through here, and the bar is on your right. Good pub grub with a difference; Heather, the landlord's wife, is famous for her pies – she is an award winning cook. There are usually six real ales on offer; Woodfordes Wherry, which has just won the National Championship, the house beer which is from a micro-brewery called Buffy's, and four others. Seats in the flowery garden.

OPEN: Not usually open lunchtimes Mon–Thurs. Telephone to make sure.
12–2 Fri, Sat & Sun. 7–11 (7–10.30 Sun.)
Real Ale
No children. No dogs – they have their own.
N.B. The music you hear is probably the local folk group having a practice session in one of the rooms.

BURNHAM MARKET

Hoste Arms   Tel: 01328 738257

The Green, Burnham Market, Norfolk. PE31 8HD
Free House. Paul Whittome, licensees.

A handsome seventeenth century hotel, The Hoste Arms overlooks the green in the beautiful Georgian village of Burnham Market, in the heart of Nelson's Norfolk. Inside there are two very welcoming bars, one of which has a grand piano the landlord will play when he's in the mood – usually when there's live jazz on Friday evenings. The bar menu, at lunchtime and in the evening, is served in the two panelled dining rooms and the conservatory, and could include: baked salmon on spinach pasta with roasted red peppers, half a dozen Burnham oysters, pot roasted breast of chicken with dauphinoise potatoes, home-cooked ham and daily specials from the blackboard. In the evening, the restaurant, which is partly non-smoking, serves an à la carte menu. Woodfordes Wherry, Ruddles and Websters, and a guest beer. You can sit and enjoy your drink in the garden or at the front of the pub among the flower tubs.

OPEN: 11–11. (11–3. 6–11 winter)
Real Ale. Restaurant.
Children welcome. Dogs on leads.
Bedrooms.
Live Jazz Fri.

BURNHAM THORPE

Lord Nelson   Tel: 01328 738241

Walsingham Road, Kings Lynn P31 8HN
Greene King. Lucy Stafford, lease.

Why the Lord Nelson? Well, he was born 300 yards away in 1758; just before he sailed away to fight the Battle of Trafalgar, he held a party in this old pub, then called the Plough. Built over 350 years ago, the re-named Lord Nelson has three rooms – one no smoking – but no bar. Beer is served by a waiter who draws the beer from the barrels in the cellar, which is actually on the same level as the main rooms. Usual bar menu and a daily changing specials board, which could feature lemon sole, salmon or shark steaks. Greene King, IPA and Mild also Woodfordes Nelson's Revenge. All the real ales are gravity fed from the barrel. The parish Church of All Saints has some Nelsonian momentoes, including a lecturn and crucifix made from timbers from his flagship, The Victory. Burnham Thorpe is a small village near the coastal path and the beach.

OPEN: 11–3. 6–11.(12–3. 7–10.30 Sun.)
Real Ale
Children welcome. Dogs on leads.
Wheelchair facilities.

COLKIRK

Crown   Tel: 01328 862172

Crown Road, Colkirk, Fakenham, Norfolk NR21 7AA
Greene King. P Whitmore, tenant.

A straightforward village pub, friendly and comfortable, serving good, interesting food without pretention. Cosy fires in the public and lounge bar. There is also a dining room. Menu includes soup, hot herby mushrooms, chef's paté of the day, ham and cheese pancake, Scotch beef, lots of fresh fish, home-made casseroles, curries and salads. Good puds too. The specials board might include: braised steak in cream and garlic sauce, pan-fried loin of pork with Cumberland sauce, fresh skate wing provençale and a vegetarian spicy bean casserole. Around 50 wines to choose from, either by the bottle or the glass. Greene King Abbot and Rayments ales. Tables outside, at the back of the pub.

OPEN: 11–2.30. 6–11.

Real Ale.
Children in lounge & dining area. Dogs on leads.
Reasonable wheelchair access.

ERPINGHAM

Saracens Head   Tel: 01263 768909

Wolterton, Nr Erpingham, Norfolk, off A140 Nr Wolterton Hall.
Free House. Robert Dawson-Smith, licensee.

You need a good map to find the Saracens Head, but persevere, the hunt
is worth it. The secret is to find Wolterton Hall; the pub is not far away. When
you get there you'll find interesting, unusual snacks and a selection of main
dishes which change for both lunch and dinner; Monday to Friday there is
a special, very reasonable, two-course lunch with, I quote, "no chips, peas
or fried scampi." Also a special "Two choice" Sunday supper. Feast nights
are held throughout the year: a Mediterranean feast night, for example. You
can even organize your own if you are so inclined. The everyday changing-
menu could include: baked eggs and smoked salmon and cream, fennel
mayonnaise and salad, sautéed wild mushrooms and ham in a sherry sauce,
mussels in cider and cream – and those are just the snacks! Chicken breasts
simmered in white wine, butter and cream, braised local pigeons with prunes
and Marsala, fresh Scottish salmon poached in cider and apples and lovely
puddings. Think of some more interesting dishes and they will probably be
on the dinner menu. Seats in the delightful courtyard and the walled garden.
There is even a special evening garden menu. Adnams ales and several
guest beers; a good choice of wines.

OPEN: 11–3. 6–11.
Real Ale.
Well behaved children welcome. No dogs.
Bedrooms.
Wheelchair access.

HEDENHAM

Mermaid   Tel: 01508 482480

Norwich Road, Hedenham NR35 2LB
Free House. Jackie Sweeney, licensee.

One big bar with low ceilings and a big open fire. A typical 15th century

248

country pub. Bar snacks only, of the ploughmans variety, to go with the beers: Greene King IPA, Draught Bass, Adnams Extra and Best Bitter. Plenty of places to sit in the large garden.

OPEN: 12–3. 6–11. (12–3. 7–10.30. Sun.)
Real Ale
Children welcome. Dogs on leads.

KINGS LYNN

Duke's Head Hotel   Tel: 01553 774996

Tuesday Market Place, Kings Lynn PE30 1JS
Free House. Nigel Dobbing, general manager.

This is one of those places you can't possibly miss. Not only is it painted pink, it is also rather large. Built in 1683 to replace the demolished 16th century Griffin Inn, it was named the Duke's Head in honour of the Duke of York, who later became James II. The main entrance was originally an open carriage way, enabling the coaches to drive into the stable yard. The place you are making for in the Duke's Head is the panelled Lynn Bar. There you will find an interesting bar menu and a good selection of beers – Woodfordes Nelsons Revenge, Great Eastern, Draught Bass and Adnams Draught Bitter. If you want to a reasonably priced two course lunch – a duo of fish mousses and chef's steak and mushroom pie for example – you will have to listen to musak; only the bar and cocktail bar are quiet.

OPEN: 11–3. 6–11. (12–3. 7–10.30. Sun.)
Real Ale Two Restaurants
Children to stay. No dogs.
Car park.

MUNDFORD

Crown Hotel   Tel: 01842 878233

Crown Street, Mundford, Thetford IP26 5HD
Free House. Barry Walker, licensee.

On the square of a quiet village, near the Forestry Commission's coniferous woodlands of Breckland. There's a dearth of pubs around here, so make for the Crown which has kitchens and restaurant upstairs, beamed lounge bar with a big open fire and public bar, with even more beams, on the ground floor. Interesting bar food includes imaginative home-made soups, sandwiches, warm salads, always a fish or chicken dish, and steak. Daily specials could include oven-baked lamb with peppers and onions, sauté of chicken in a smoked cheese and ham sauce or tuna steak. Good puds too. Sam Smiths, Woodfordes Wherry, Theakstons, Websters Green Label and a guest beer. House wines and a fair list of malt whiskies.

OPEN: 11–11. (11–10.30 Sun.)
Real Ale. Restaurant.
Children welcome. Dogs on leads.
Wheelchair access.

NORWICH

The Plasterers Arms   Tel: 01603 627357

43 Cowgate,(off Magdalen St.), Norwich. NR3 1SZ
Adnams. Allan Kerrigan, tenant.

Within the City walls, it's near Anglia TV's studios and half a mile from Norwich Cathedral – between the spiritual and the temporal. Built last century, the Plasterers Arms was a free house until Adnams bought it in 1992, however the landlord still runs it in a traditional way. No pretentious food, "just traditional home-cooking and anything out of the chip pan, if you want it!" says the landlord, "but of course you can have scampi, burgers and stuff like that." Also five vegetarian dishes, roasts and puds. Full Adnams range when available, plus two permanent guests: Burton Ale and Tetley Bitter plus Crones natural cider. (very potent).

OPEN: 11–11 (12–2. 7–10.30 Sun).
Real Ale.
No children. Dogs on leads.

NORWICH

The Bell Hotel   Tel: 01603 63001

5 Orford Hill, Norwich, Norfolk NR1 3QB
Wetherspoons. Ross Sterling & Linda Murray, managers.

It used to be an hotel, then Wetherspoons took over, re-arranged the inside, installed the mod-cons and created two bars – upstairs and downstairs. Full menu available all day. This is standard in all Wetherspoon outlets, changing three times a year. Every day at the Bell you have four different daily specials – no gastronomic fantasies, just good honest fare to go with the cask conditioned beers. Youngers Scotch Bitter, Courage Directors, Theakston Best, a local regional beer and guest beers from small breweries.

OPEN: 11–11 (12–10.30 Sun)
Real Ale
Children between 12–7 o'clock. No dogs policy. Guide dogs only.
All wheelchair facilities.

REEDHAM

Ferry Inn Tel: 01493 700429

Reedham Ferry, Norwich, Norfolk NR13 3HA
Free House. David Archer, licensee.

As the name implies, this pub has rather watery connections. The ferry plying to and fro across the river belongs to the pub and is able to carry three cars. They also have a launching ramp for boats up to 35 ft long. After all that excitement you can either anchor yourself in the bar or on the terrace to enjoy all that the pub has to offer. There is a wide range of dishes: freshly prepared sandwiches, ploughmans, fresh fish and home-made pies, a changing seasonal menu using local produce, a children's menu and a selection of vegetarian dishes. Woodfordes Wherry, Adnams Best and Broadside plus guest beers. Also country wines.

OPEN: 11–3. 6.30–11 (11–2.30. 7–11 winter).
Real Ale. Restaurant.
Children until 9 pm. Dogs on leads.
The Ferry Inn has a touring and camping park.

SHERINGHAM

Windham Arms Tel: 01263 822609

15–17, Windham Street, Sheringham.
Free House. Robert Davis, licensee.

Near the sea-front, which you can't see as another pub is in the way! (Not one of ours). But now you know the sea is there, you can clutch your pint, find space on the sea wall, sit, and watch the nautical goings-on. Built of brick and flint in the middle of the last century, this is an attractive old place where you get a bar menu at lunchtime and a restaurant menu in the evening. A variety of dishes are listed on the blackboard – plaice and lemon sole on the bone, steaks, lasagne – all served with fresh vegetables. Greene King IPA, Abbot, Woodfordes Wherry, Great Eastern and Draught Bass. Large terrace to drink on if you get fed up with the sea view.

OPEN: 11–11 (12–10.30 Sun)
Real Ale.
Children welcome. Dogs on leads.

SNETTISHAM

Rose & Crown Inn   Tel: 01485 541382

Old Church Road, Snettisham, Norfolk
Free House. Anthony Goodrich, licensee.

Find the pretty hanging baskets and you have found the Rose & Crown. A rambling, beamed old pub, with big fireplaces and three bars. Very popular with families as it is geared up to accommodate children and keep them happy. Well served bar food in ample proportions: home-made soup of the day, pan fried garlic mushrooms, best pork and herb sausages with onion gravy and bubble and squeak, lamb casserole, served with herb dumplings, a choice of vegetarian dishes and grills. From the specials board upi might choose baked fillet of cod with a herb crust and cucumber cream, navarin of lamb in a puff pastry case with basil, or a caramelised sirloin steak with a French mustard sauce. Children's menu and a selection of barbecue dishes. Greene King Abbot, Adnams, Bass and guest beers on hand pump. Seats on the terrace and in the walled garden. Family room, and a well equipped children's play area outside.

OPEN: 11–11.
Real Ale. Restaurant. N.B. music in restaurant when very quiet
Children in own room & eating areas. No dogs.
En-suite Bedrooms.

STIFFKEY

Red Lion   Tel: 01328 830552

Wells Road, Stiffkey, Wells next Sea, Norfolk NR23 1AJ
Free House. Adrienne Cooke, licensee.

This white brick and flint building was re-opened in 1990 after having been closed down, along with other village pubs, by one of the big national brewers during the 60's. Situated in the village which has a partly ruined Elizabethan Hall and an interesting church with 15th century brasses, The Red Lion is now a busy, jolly place. It is furnished with pine tables and settles and serves good, home-cooked food. The blackboard menu is changeable but there are always generously filled sandwiches, a paté, ploughmans, fresh local fish, mussels, lobster, crab and seasonal local game pie. Woodfordes Wherry, Abbot and guest beers. Wines from Adnams. Seats on the terrace.

OPEN: 11–3. 6–11 (7–11 out of season)
Real Ale. Restaurant (closed Sun).
Children welcome. Dogs on leads.
Wheelchair access is limited.

STOW BARDOLPH

Hare Arms   Tel: 01366 38229

Stow Bardolph, Norfolk PE34 3HT
Greene King. Trish & David McManus, tenants.

A nice old country pub, very much part of the village, busy and friendly. It has a large comfortable bar, adjacent to the conservatory. A wide variety of food is served throughout the week. Bar food could include sandwiches, soups and home-made paté. The bar favourites at the moment are half a guinea fowl in a Madeira sauce with grapes, lamb steak in a recurrant and rosemary sauce, salmon fillet with prawn and brandy sauce, and pork steak in green peppercorn, brandy and cream sauce. The restaurant menu is more extensive. All the dishes are home-cooked, using local seasonal produce, local game, fresh fish, lamb and beef. Imaginative puds. Greene King ales. Good selection of wines. Tables in the garden among the peacocks and the other feathery residents.

OPEN: 11–2.30. 6–11.
Real Ale. Restaurant (not Sun eves)
Children in Conservatory. No dogs.

CHRISTMAS

Pub opening times at Christmas can vary. Some don't open at all. A few open all day, while others open at mid-day only. If you plan to visit one at Christmas, check by calling them on the telephone.

THORNHAM

Lifeboat Inn
Tel: 01485 512236

Ship Lane, Thornham, Norfolk PE36 6LT
Free House. Charles & Angie Coker, owners & licensees.

Favoured by smugglers in the 16th century, it's now a charming, rambling inn and restaurant. Low beamed ceilings, quarry tiled floors, old oak furniture, blazing fires in winter and tempting home-cooked food. The bar menu ranges from soup, ploughmans, smoked chicken and mango salad, open sandwiches, stuffed Thornham mushrooms, game pie, Brancaster mussels, to Lifeboat fish pie. Daily specials on the blackboard. The dishes go up a notch on the extensive restaurant menu. Greene King ales, Adnams, Woodfordes Wherry and guest beers. Good range of wines. Not far from the sandy Thornham beach, there are lots of wonderful walks nearby.

OPEN: 11–11.
Real Ale. Restaurant.
Children welcome. Dogs on leads.
Bedrooms.
Live music occasionally.
Wheelchair access to all parts of the pub.

UPPER SHERINGHAM

Red Lion
Tel: 01263 825408

Holt Road, Upper Sheringham, Norfolk NR26 8AD
Free House. Chris Taylor, licensee.

Over 300 years old, these flint cottages have only fairly recently been converted into the village pub. With two attractive bars, the Red Lion has become popular for its reliable, tasty home-cooked food. The blackboard menu changes frequently, but there could be Stilton stuffed flat mushrooms, home-made cream of mushroom and celery soup, fresh lemon sole with a crab sauce, vegetable pasta bake with honey and mushroom sauce served with salad. diced pork with cider, apple and thyme, wild rabbit casserole and home-made treacle tart for afters. Special three-course Wednesday suppers. Sunday roasts. This is another 'chip-free' zone. Greene King IPA and Woodfordes Wherry. Adnams Broadside is the usual summer guest ale. Over 60 malt whiskies to try. After all that you can gather yourself together in the sunny walled garden, or go an see the old sail-powered Sheringham lifeboat kept in a shed by the shore.

OPEN: 11–3. 7–11 (pub quiz Sun eves winter).
Real Ale.
Children in eating area. Dogs on leads.
Bedrooms.
Wheelchair access possible, willing helpers on hand.

WARHAM ALL SAINTS

Three Horseshoes   Tel: 01328 710547

The Street, Warham All Saints, Norfolk NR23 1NL
Free House. Iain Salmon, licensee.

Within this pretty village of flint cottages you will find the 18th century Three
Horseshoes. The village pub, still with its gas lighting and stone floors,
retains the atmosphere of the 1920s, though one has to emphasise that the
attitude to pub food has taken a great leap forward. There's a good choice
of home-cooked bar food based on fresh, local produce. As well as assorted
sandwiches, filled rolls and ploughmans, there could be farm terrine, Norfolk
potted herrings, Stilton mushroom bake, a gamekeeper's pie, a marshman's
medley fish pie or a vegetable cottage garden bake. A daily selection on the
blackboard complements the printed menu. All dishes are cooked to order.
Half portions too for those of us with smaller appetites – such a good idea.
No chips either. Greene King IPA and Abbot, plus guest ales. House wines.
Tables on the grass outside. Lots of things to see in Wareham – St Mary's
church still has its original Georgian box pews and pulpit. Wareham camp
an iron age fort is not far away, and Warham Marsh is one of Europe's largest
salt marshes. If you feel energetic, you can join the Norfolk coastal path for
a brisk walk.

OPEN: 11–3. 6–11.
Real Ale. No-smoking restaurant
Children in eating area. Dogs on leads.
Bedrooms.
Occasional live music Sat evenings.
Wheelchair access to all areas.

N
NORTHUMBRIA

BERWICK-UPON-TWEED

The Free Trade   Tel: 01289 306498

75 Castlegate, Berwick-upon-Tweed, Northumberland TD15 1LF
Free House. Edward Collins, licensee.

An unchanging Victorian drinking pub in an ancient border town. Fought over many times by the Scots and English between the 12th and 15th centuries, Berwick changed hands 13 times before finally becoming part of England in 1482. The Free Trade in Castlegate – beyond the Elizabethan walls, and not far from the railway station –is a place for liquid refreshment only. A crisp and nut perhaps, certainly biscuits for the dog. An old fashioned bar with a pool table for the youngsters. The landlord says he can stock any beer he likes, but Vaux Lorimers Scotch Ale is permanent.

OPEN: 11–11. 12–10.30 Sun. Those are the real ones – flexible opening hours here!
Real Ale
Children if well behaved. Dogs very welcome, biscuits provided.

BLANCHLAND

Lord Crewe Arms   Tel: 01434 675251

Blanchland, Nr Consett, County Durham DH8 9SP (Nr. Derwent Reservoir)
Free House. A Todd, Peter Gingell, Ian Press, licensees.

Someone should write about the most haunted pubs in the country – this one has a tragic ghost. She's the sister of a Jacobite, Tom Forster, (whose family originally lived here), and still haunts the building, asking people to deliver a message to her long-dead brother. The flower be-decked Lord Crewe Arms was formerly part of the 13th century Blanchland Abbey, which, until the dissolution of the monastaries, dominated the surrounding area. Much remains of its historic past, and the layout of the 18th century village follows virtually the same boundary lines as the destroyed Abbey. The cloister garden is still evident and is now listed as an ancient monument. After that history lesson and having made your way to the Crypt Bar, you will find a good choice of bar food: wild boar and pheasant pie, grilled salmon and potato fish cakes, baked Gnocci Romain with buttered German style noodles and ratatouille, lots of fillings for the rolls, daily specials and home-made cakes for afternoon tea. There is a different evening bar menu and they do Sunday lunches. Vaux ales, brewed in Sunderland. Seats in the enclosed garden. NB: there is sometimes music in the restaurant but not the bar.

OPEN: 11–3. 6–11.
Real Ale. Evening restaurant. Also Sun lunch.
Children welcome.
Bedrooms.

CORBRIDGE ON TYNE

Angel Inn   Tel: 01434 632119

Corbridge on Tyne, Northumberland NE45 5LA
Scottish & Newcastle. Mandy McIntosh Reid, manageress.

Founded in Saxon times, the village is situated on one of the country's best salmon rivers, and the Angel Inn – originally the Head Inn – is the oldest building in the village. An important posting stop, the weekly mail coach would deliver the Newcastle paper which the landlord would then read out to the villagers. Now the different demands of the 20th century have again made it a desirable, popular stopping place, providing all you could wish for in the way of food, drink and hospitality. The bar menu changes daily; monthly, in the no-smoking restaurant. Good, substantial dishes using fresh local produce: fresh pasta with smoked chicken and cream, home-made lasagne, Tynedale rabbit with a herb and cream sauce, Craster crab salad or North Sea cod in batter. From the à la carte menu there could be a Northumbrian forest terrine with kumquats and Cumberland glaze, fillet of Cheviot lamb on a red wine glaze, venison noisettes on a white wine glaze with pink peppercorns and beetroot; home-made puds to finish. Theakstons ales and Youngers on draught. Choice of wines.

OPEN: 12–2.55. 5–11. Teas: 3–5.
Real Ale. Restaurant.
Children welcome. Dogs on leads.

COTHERSTONE

Fox & Hounds   Tel: 01833 650241

Cotherstone, Co. Durham DL12 9PF (on B6277)
Free House. Michael & May Carlisle, licensees.

Not far from Barnard Castle, the Fox and Hounds is surrounded by some wonderfully empty countryside. We forget how lucky we are to have all that space "up north". Overlooking the village green, this 18th century pub has a reputation for serving good, imaginative food. Well worth a stop, not only for the food, but for the setting. Attractive beamed bars, winter fires, and well kept ales. Varied bar menu – all home-made, children's dishes and a Sunday roast. John Smiths Bitter and regional ales. A choice of over 50 wines. Good walks nearby.

OPEN: 11.30–2.30. 6.30–11.
Real Ale. Restaurant.
Children in Restaurant. No dogs.
Bedrooms.

CRASTER

Jolly Fisherman   Tel: 01665 476461

Craster, Alnwick, Northumberland NE66 3TR
Vaux. William & Muriel Silk, licensees.

An attractive unspoilt fishing village noted for its Kippers. The only pub in the village, so it's understandably popular. Full of local fishermen, lifeboatmen, landbased locals and those travelling through. Situated above the harbour, with views of the rocky coastline – this is a wild and rugged part of the country. No surprise when we say that seafood sandwiches are favourites here: local crab, oak smoked salmon, prawn – other simple dishes too. Home-made crab soup with fresh cream and whisky and a choice of two other soups. Ales are Vaux Samson Bitter, Double Maxim and Lorimers Best Scotch, also Wards Thorne Best Bitter. Seats in the garden. The nearby ruins of the 14th century Dunstanburgh Castle, perched 100' above the shore, can only be reached by walking along the coastal path.

OPEN: 11–3. 6–11.
Real Ale. Snacks only.
Children welcome. Dogs on leads.
Wheelchair access.

DIPTON MILL

Dipton Mill Inn   Tel: 01434 606577

Dipton Mill Road, Nr Hexham, Northumberland NE46 1YA
Free House. Geoff Brooker, licensee.

Dipton Mill Inn, with a few cottages for company, is in peaceful countryside
two miles from Hexham. The Inn, originally a 17th century farm-house, and
the cottages next to it, were extended about a hundred years ago into what
you see today. A small pub, with only one main bar – and off this, a room
which houses the bar billiards table. Hot food is served at lunchtime and also
in the early evening during the summer. A typical menu is soup, beef in ale
pie, chicken breast in a sherry sauce, always salads and sandwiches, a
choice of savoury flans and a selection of puddings. Ales are mainly from the
local brewery where they brew three beers: Shire bitter, Devil's Water and
Whapweasel. (Whapweasel is named after a burn on the fells), also
Theakstons Best. Very beautiful countryside. The old mill stream runs
through the garden, and another stream runs alongside the pub. Seats in the
attractive garden. You are in good walking country.

OPEN: 12–2.30. 6–11.
Real Ale. Lunchtime meals and snacks.
Children in Games Room. No dogs.

DURHAM

Shakespear Tavern   Tel: 0191 3869709

Saddler Street, Durham City DH1 3NU.
Newcastle/ Courage. Mrs Jean Brannon, manager.

The Shakespear Tavern is in the heart of this ancient city; near the Castle,
Cathedral and the oldest of the University's colleges. Very friendly, popular
and full of character – apart from the television set above the door – the pub
has remained unchanged since the 1950's. Our researcher says it is much
as he remembers it from when he was a student at Durham University in
1951. He found the noise from the television annoying but there is a quiet
lounge and a snug bar – the only one left in the city still with the original 18th
century panelling – behind the main bar. No meals, just a selection of
sandwiches and toasties. Theakstons XB, Best Bitter, Marstons Pedigree,
McEwans Best Scotch, 80/-, Newcastle Exhibition, John Smiths Extra
Smooth, McEwans Lager and Brakspears Lager.

THE QUIET PINT

OPEN: 11–11. (7–10.30 Sun. sometimes 3–10.30)
Real Ale
Children welcome. Dogs on leads

EGGLESCLIFFE

Pot and Glass   Tel: 01642 651009

Church Road, Egglescliffe, Cleveland TS16 9DP
Century Inns PLC. Bill Taylor, tenant.

Find the 11th century church and next to it is the 17th century Pot and Glass
– in a cul-de-sac. The landlord says, not surprisingly, "there is really no
passing trade." As the pub looks out onto the churchyard you could say they
have all passed on! This is a charming village pub in a lovely setting, with a
public bar, lounge and small side room for meetings and private parties. Low
ceilings, beams and panelled walls but no open fires. There used be, but the
pub being small you either nearly roasted to death, or froze on the fringes.
Lunchtime food only: home-made steak pies, lasagne, fish and chips and a
scampi or two. Well kept Draught Bass, Stones BB and Worthington BB. The
owners of the pub send out a list of the available guest beers and the
landlord chooses from that. These could be something from Ruddles,
Saddlers or Hartleys. Just a small garden where you'll have to sit if you take
your dog.

OPEN: 12–3.30. 5.30–11 (12–4.30. 5.30–10.30 Sun)
Real Ale
Children welcome in side room until 9pm. Dogs in garden.

FALSTONE

Blackcock Inn   Tel: 01434 240200

Falstone, Northumberland NA48 1AA (8 miles west of Bellingham)
Free House. Tom and Alex Richards, licensees.

This one's on the edge of the Kielder Forest's 145,000 acres of pine, spruce
and larch, through which are lots of nature trails and marked tracks. The
village is remote and in an area once fought over by the Scots and English.
The Blackcock Inn, originally a 16th century fortified farm house, has been
added to over the years. Warm, cosy and unspoilt, the bar is part of the
original house. Just the sort of place where you want good, filling, lunchtime
bar food: jacket potatoes with a variety of fillings, filled Yorkshire puddings

(steak and kidney or pork and mushroom), fish and chips and home-made puds. In the evening there is a five page restaurant menu: chicken and Stilton roulade, chicken Sabra cooked in wine and orange juice, steaks, venison and beef pie (game-keepers pie), venison with prunes, smoked duck and quite a selection of fish dishes. Boddingtons Bitter, Buchanans Bitter and Whitbreads Castle Eden. Guest beers too – 438 have been on offer at the Blackcock over the last three years, mostly from the smaller breweries.

OPEN: 11–3. 6–11. (12–3. 7–10.30 Sun)
Real Ale. Restaurant.
Children only in pool room and restaurant with an adult – out by 9.30.
Dogs on leads.
Car park. Stairlift to the bedrooms. Wheelchair access.

GREAT WHITTINGTON

Queen's Head   Tel: 01434 672267

Great Whittington, Northumberland NE19 2HP
Free House. Ian Scott, licensee.

Great Whittington is really a Little Whittington – a small village of about 160 inhabitants near Hadrian's wall. You can combine a bit of sightseeing, a bracing walk and then a good lunch at the Queen's Head. Lunch first probably. This is really more of a restaurant but there are two comfortable beamed bars, both with log fires. A bistro blackboard menu features in the bar: lamb's liver with bacon and onion, breast of chicken with broccoli, goujons of fresh haddock or salmon with a lemon and dill sauce; an à la carte menu in the restaurant. There is a choice of over 30 wines to go with the food. Hambleton Bitter, Durham Brewery Magus, Own Queen's Head Bitter and Courage Directors are the beers. There are picnic tables in the garden.

OPEN: 12–2.30. 6–11 (12–3. 7–10.30. Sun)
Real Ale. Restaurant.
Well behaved children at lunchtime only. Dogs in garden.
Car park. Wheelchair access.

THE QUIET PINT

HALTWHISTLE

Milecastle   Tel: 01434 320682

Military Road, Nr Haltwhistle, Northumberland NE49 9NN
Free House. Ralph & Margaret Payne, licensees.

On the southern edge of the Northumberland National Park, the fairly remote Milecastle Inn is a welcome sight for anyone at the end of a thirsty hike across the hills and moors where Emperor Hadrian built his wall and measured out each mile of it with a small fort – or "milecastle". The Inn has a small snug interior with a good winter fire, a short, well chosen menu, plus well-kept ales. Filling home-made soups, hearty pies, lots of game (in season), quite a list of "dishes of the day," and local ales from the Hexham Brewery. Malt whiskies and a good wine list. Seats outside at the front of the pub and in the enclosed garden at the back. Muddy walking boots outside only – where the pub starts you stop – unless in socks.

OPEN: 12–2.30. 6.30–11.
Real Ale. Restaurant (closed Sun, Mon, Tues evenings).
Children over five if eating. No dogs.

HEDLEY ON THE HILL

Feathers   Tel: 01661 843607

Stocksfield, Northumberland NE43 7SW
Free House. Marina Atkinson, licensees.

I know this information is at the end, but I want to emphasise that this pub is not open during the day except at weekends and Bank Holidays. We have all done it – turned up at the right place at the wrong time. Sandwiches usually available weekday evenings but the food at weekends would appear to be ample compensation for the lack of it during the week. Interesting home-made soups, a three cheese ploughmans, fennel and courgette au gratin, crab and mushroom ramekin, smoked salmon and spinach pasta, croissant filled with locally smoked chicken breast and brie, Greek lamb casserole with spices in red wine, tomatoes and aubergines, creamy chicken casserole in white wine with tarragon, mushrooms and asparagus plus vegetarian dishes, children's meals and good puddings. Local ales – Mordues Worky Ticket and Radgie Gadgie, Durham Magus from the Durham Brewery and Butterknowle Bitter and Consiliation could be among the guests; Boddingtons always available. A choice of 30 malt whiskies.

262

OPEN: 6–11 weekdays. 12–3. 6–11 Sat. Daytime opening weekday Bank Holidays only.
Real Ale. Weekend meals. Evening sandwiches.
Children in eating area and family room till 8.30. Dogs on leads.
Folk night twice a month.

HOLWICK

Strathmore Arms   Tel: 01833 640362

Holwick, Middleton-in-Teesdale DL12 ONJ
Free House. Mrs Lynn Hawdon, licensee.

In the hills above Middleton-in-Teesdale, this splendid pub is on a narrow lane which leads no-where in particular. Inside, it has an attractive bar with a roaring log fire on cold days. Behind the main bar is a comfortable snug. The landlady is very jolly and gives her visitors a hearty welcome. Nothing is too much trouble for either her, or her staff. The bar menu offers home-made soup, corn on the cob, grilled local trout, Cumberland sausages, steak and kidney pie, gammon and eggs – all served with fresh vegetables, and for vegetarians – a nut roast. (Our researcher, who is on a special diet, says they miraculously produced a meal especially for him). A warning for those having the minestrone – don't order a main course until you've seen the size of the soup plate! Filling is a word that springs to mind. Theakstons XB, Ruddles Bitter, Middleton Brewery Ales also Hedgerow wines and mead. The bar has an old but well kept piano. Friday night is live music night; singers, guitarists – they all have a go. If things seem to be getting too noisy they are sent to the function room upstairs.

OPEN 12–11. (12–10.30 Sun)
Real Ale
Children welcome until 9.30. Dogs on leads.

MATFEN

Black Bull   Tel: 01661 886330

Matfen, Newcastle-upon-Tyne NE20 0RT (off B6318 NE Corbridge)
Free House. Colin & Michelle Scott, licensees.

Another pub which is more of a "dining pub" – nothing wrong with that as there is still the well-frequented bar for just a drink, snack and chat. In summer, this is a pub you can't miss. Find the wonderful floral display and somewhere behind it you will find this attractive pub, which was awarded "Best Pub – Northumbria in Bloom," for two years running. Nicely presented bar food: soups, duck liver paté, herb pancake filled with spiced prawns, home-made steak and mushroom pie cooked in ale, honey-glazed chicken with toasted almonds and various salads. There is also an extensive, changing, restaurant menu. Part of the restaurant is no-smoking. Theakstons Best and several guest ales. Seats outside at the front of the pub among the flowers.

OPEN: 11–3. 6–11 (11–11 Sat)
Real Ale. Restaurant.
Children in eating area. No dogs.
Bedrooms. Wheelchair access.

NEW YORK

Shiremoor Farm   Tel: 0191 2576302

Middle Engine Lane, New York, Northshields, Tyne & Wear NE29 8DZ
Sir John Fitzgerald Ltd. M W Garrett & C W Kerridge, licensees.

This is a lovely place, which was developed from renovated old farm buildings. Without losing any of the character, they have been turned into a well appointed pub and restaurant catering for everyone – not only someone wanting a pint and bar snack, but also for the family who want high chairs, bottle warmers etc. For the grown ups, there is the traditional bar menu, with the addition of more interesting dishes: roast duck julienne, breast of chicken in garlic and brandy sauce, beef stroganoff, steaks, daily specials and home-made puddings. Theakstons Best and Old Peculiar, Stones Best, Butterknowle Conciliation and guest beers. Tables on the grass by the farm courtyard among the flowers.

OPEN: 11–11.
Real Ale. Restaurant. (Food all day Sunday).
Children in eating areas. No dogs.

NEWCASTLE-UPON-TYNE

Crown Posada   Tel: 0191 2321269

31 The Side, Newcastle-upon-Tyne, NE1 3JD
Free House. Malcolm McPherson, manager.

An interesting old city centre pub which leans architecturally towards the

Victorian with its stained glass mirrors, tulip lamps and painted ceilings. One long bar, with a snug to one side, serves lunchtime sandwiches and snacks. The ales are: Theakstons Best, Boddingtons Bitter, Butterknowle Conciliation Ale, Jennings and guest beers. If you want to catch up on the day's events the daily papers are kept in the snug for you to read.

OPEN: 11–11 (Sat: 11–4. 7–11)
Real Ale. Lunchtime snacks (not Sun).
No children. Dogs on leads if well behaved.

NEWCASTLE-UPON-TYNE

Tap & Spile   Tel: 0191 276 1440

33–37 Shields Road, Byker, Newcastle-upon-Tyne NE6 1DJ
Pubmaster. Mr & Mrs J & P.W. Bland, managers.

They keep quite a selection of beers here, so this is the place to come if you want to try a few of the more unusual ales. Lunchtime sandwiches, crisps and nuts too no doubt. More a chap's place this I think – so if you want quiet and a good pint, the Tap & Spile is the place to be. Five regulars: Marstons Pedigree, Ruddles Best, Thwaites Craftsman, Jennings Cumberland, Hadrians Gladiator and up to nine changing guests. Westons farm cider and some country wines.

OPEN: 12–3. 6–11 (all day Fri & Sat).
Real Ale.
Dogs on leads.
Live Jazz Mon.

NEWTON ON THE MOOR

Cook & Barker Inn   Tel: 01665 575234

Newton on the Moor, Felton, Morpeth, Northumberland NE65 9JY
Free House. Lynn & Phil Farmer, licensees.

High above sea level, and with wonderful views of the Northumbrian coast, this is a good place to stop if you're travelling on the A1. All the locals have probably beaten a path here anyway. A good, solid, stone village pub, which has been updated and re-organised. Now you have a large beamed bar for drinks and snacks, plus a stone-walled restaurant in what was the forge. Good soups, beef with ginger and spring onions, hot beef and onion

265

sandwiches, lamb's liver with vegetables, warm salad of woodpigeon with hedgerow berries, smoked salmon cake with a chive and vermouth sauce, mixed grills, steaks, and home-made puddings. For the vegetarian, a freshly baked croissant filled with creamy garlic mushrooms. Courage Directors, Ruddles Best Bitter, Theakstons Best and XB plus Boddingtons – all on hand pump. Seats in the garden.

OPEN: 11–3. 6–11.
Real Ale. Evening Restaurant.
Children in eating area. No dogs.
Bedrooms. Wheelchair access to restaurant.

ROMALDKIRK

Rose & Crown Hotel   Tel: 01833 650213

Romaldkirk, Barnard Castle, Co. Durham DL12 9EB
Free House. Christopher & Alison Davy, licensees.

This is a fine old 18th century coaching inn with an interior which reflects its age. Beamed, panelled, polished and attractive, with the bonus of interesting and imaginative menus in the bar, and a no- smoking restaurant. Bread will be home-made, as are the chutneys and pickled onions accompanying the ploughmans. Regional cheeses, meat from the local butcher, game from the surrounding moors and fish from the East Coast ports. Even the ice cream is home-made. Very good value daily lunchtime specials. Morlands Old Speckled Hen, Theakstons Best and Old Peculiar on hand-pump. Varied wine list – half bottles, and by the glass. Tables outside overlooking the village green.

OPEN: 11–3. 5.30–11.
Real Ale. No-smoking restaurant (not Sun eves).
Children welcome. Dogs on leads.
Bedrooms.

SHOTLEY BRIDGE

Manor House Inn   Tel: 01207 255268

Carterway Heads, Shotley Bridge, Consett, Northumberland DH8 9LY
(A68 between Corbridge & Consett)
Free House. Mr A J Pell, licensee.

On the A68 between Corbridge and Consett – on the tourist route to the

Derwent Reservoir. This is a long, stone-built village pub with rather unfortunate modern windows. However we are not judging a pub by architectural mistakes, only by what goes on inside. A friendly, efficient, well-run pub with an interesting blackboard menu. Food could include: leek and courgette soup with French bread, smoked chicken and brie croissants, moules marinières, baked sea trout and steaks. Home-made puddings. Butterknowle Bitter, Westons Beamish and three guest ales. Seats in the garden (wind permitting!).

OPEN: 11–3; 6–11
Real Ale.
Well behaved children welcome. Dogs in small bar only.

STOCKTON-ON-TEES

The Masham   Tel: 01642 580414

79 Hartburn Village, Stockton-on-Tees, Cleveland TS18 5DR Bass. Dennis & John Eddy, tenant and manager. Hartburn village, a tree-lined backwater off the Darlington road, is attached to Stockton-on-Tees, but it is difficult for strangers to tell where one ends and the other begins. The pub, small and friendly, is a popular local meeting place. It has a bar, and bar area, three small rooms, and a garden at the back. Meals are not served, but sandwiches are available every day. Bass and a guest beer (usually Black Sheep) on hand pump, are particularly well kept. House entertainment, (apart from the customers), is a TV in one of the small rooms for the big sporting events – rugby, cricket, etc; you can't hear the TV anywhere else in the pub – but the customers sometimes get carried away with enthusiasm! Seats and tables on the paved area in the garden. There is also a secluded children's play area.

OPEN: 11–11.
Real Ale. Sandwiches only.
Children in family room. Dogs on leads.

STOCKTON-ON-TEES

Cricketers Arms   Tel: 01642 675468

2 Portrack Lane, Stockton-on-Tees, Cleveland TS18 2HG
Whitbread. Victor Newton, tenant.

Off Maritime Road this is a friendly street corner pub. Just a lounge and

public bar. Traditional bar food served in the lounge bar. Whitbreads Trophy
Bitter, Best Scotch – no guest beers.

OPEN: 11–11. (12–3. 7–10.30 Sun)
Real Ale
Children lunchtimes on Sundays only. Dogs in the bar, not on the seats!
Car park. Wheelchair access.

TWEEDMOUTH

Rob Roy   Tel: 01289 306428

Dock Road, Tweedmouth, Berwick-on-Tweed, Northumberland.
Free House. Keith & Julie Wilson, licensees.

On the South bank of the River Tweed, only a mile from the A1. The landlord,
Keith Wilson, has a story to warm the cockles of your heart. (Apt really: this
is a fish restaurant/pub). Some time ago the sound system broke down and
repairs were delayed. So many people said how much they appreciated the
quiet during the silent era, that Keith Wilson decided to do away with the
musak for ever. Just what we want to hear. The Rob Roy is a place strong
on fish. Indeed it's called a 'Seafood Restaurant with a Bar'. The bar menu
offers: soup of the day, freshly made sandwiches, Lindisfarne oysters, salad
of sweet pickled herrings, peppered farmhouse paté with Melba toast, North
Sea scallops in a cream and fennel sauce, monkfish in garlic butter and lots
more. Sea Bass fillet from the restaurant menu, grilled Dover sole, tournedos
of beef in a cream and green peppercorn sauce, or a warm salad of North
Sea scallops with bacon and mushrooms. Puds too. They only serve wild
salmon; fresh during the season, otherwise frozen in preference to farmed
fish. The à la carte menu is changed regularly depending on the fresh fish,
shellfish and game available; wild Tweed salmon and sea trout during the
season and lobsters and crabs if the weather is favourable. Sounds a place
to be treasured.

OPEN: 11.30–2.30. 6.30–11. (12–2.30. 7–10.30. Sun) Closed Tuesday.
Keg Beers and wines only. Restaurant.
No dogs.

WARENFORD

Warenford Lodge Tel: 01668 213453

Warenford, Belford, Northumberland NE70 7HY
Free House. Raymond Matthewman, licensee.

Stone-built, with mullioned windows, this is another pub with no obvious pub sign and with every appearance of being someone's private house; however, unless everyone has decided to walk, you will see a lot of parked cars, which means you're where you want to be. A very popular place to eat – you do have to book to be sure of a table in the evening . Lots of fishy dishes which could include: Northumbrian fish soup, marinated seafood salad , grilled herbed mussels and Lindisfarne oysters. Also on the menu: garlic snails, lamb and spinach lasagne, Warenford pigeon pie, baked sea wolf, tagliatelle with a tomato and porcini mushroom sauce – or you could just have a steak. Home-made puddings and a choice of ice creams. Newcastle Exhibition and McEwans Scottish ales plus a varied wine list.

OPEN: 7–11 (Sat & Sun 12–2. 7–11).
Real Ale. Evening Restaurant & weekend snacks & meals. Not Mondays except Bank Holidays.
Children in Restaurant. No dogs.
A few steps for wheelchairs, but there are willing helpers.

OXFORD

BINFIELD HEATH

Bottle & Glass   Tel: 01491 575755

Harpsden Road, Binfield Heath, Henley-on-Thames, Oxon RG9 4JT
Brakspears. Mike & Anne Robinson, tenants.

Between Henley-on-Thames and Reading, this 15th century thatched pub
has flagged floors, antique tables, settles and large log fires during the
winter. An interesting choice of traditional food, all prepared and cooked "in
house" from fresh ingredients: paté, Cumberland sausages, rump steak,
mussels in garlic, fresh fish, lunchtime sandwiches and other dishes. The
house specialities change from day to day. There is a large garden with 24
tables with their own thatched canopies to protect you from the noon-day
sun. Brakspears ales on hand pump and a good choice of malt whiskies.

OPEN: 11–3. 6–11
Real Ale. No food Sun eves.
No children. Dogs on leads Sundays only.
Wheelchair access to pub.

BLEWBURY

Red Lion   Tel: 011235 850403

Chapel Lane. Nottingham Fee, Blewbury, Didcot, OX11 9PQ.
Brakspears. Roger Smith, tenant.

This is a 17th century half-timbered pub in a pretty and peaceful village
luckily by-passed by the A417. Some time ago the regulars had a
competition to 'name the bars'. They get quite crowded at times, so they
decided on 'The Ankle Tap' and 'The Elbow Room'. Even the landlord thinks
them quite bizarre. (A Mrs Tapp used to live there, so that could explain one
of them). Just so you know, you can book a table in the Elbow Room, but
not in the Ankle Tap! Menus are on the blackboard and they specialise in

fish: sea-food soup, mussels, sea-bass and lobster also chicken in a curry and tarragon sauce, or pork with apricots. The menus change regularly. Brakspears Ordinary, Special and Old. Boddingtons is the guest beer. Seats in the garden.

OPEN: 11–2.30. 6–11 (11–11 Sat)
Real Ale. Restaurant.
Children in eating areas only. Dogs in the garden.
Full wheelchair facilities.

BLOXHAM

Elephant & Castle	Tel: 01295 720383

Bloxham, Nr. Banbury, Oxfordshire OX15 4LZ
Hook Norton. Charles Finch, tenant.

You just have to look at a Cotswold stone pub and its wonderful warm colour to get the impression of a friendly welcome. Two bars: one a simply furnished public bar, the other a more comfortable lounge – both with good winter log fires. There are seats in the flower-filled courtyard where there is a summer barbecue on Saturday evenings and Sunday lunchtimes. Hook Norton ales with a changing monthly guest beer from small independent breweries. Good choice of malt whiskies.

OPEN: 10–3. 6–11 (5–11 Sat).
Real Ale. Restaurant. Bar Food lunchtimes only (not Sun)
Children in restaurant. Dogs on leads.

BLOXHAM

Red Lion Inn	Tel: 01295 720352

High Street, Bloxham, Oxon. OX15 4LX
Free House. Paul & Carol Cooper, licensees.

In the middle of the village, opposite the Church the 18th century beamed, panelled and polished Red Lion won the 'Cherwell in Bloom Competition' for the best floral display by an hotel or pub in 1995, so you know the garden here is something special – and the food. The landlord likes to be running a 'pub doing good food, rather than a restaurant serving mediocre food.' Pasta and vegetarian dishes, broccoli and mushroom mornay, spinach and cheddar cannelloni, duck, pork, gammon, daily specials and a roast on Sunday. Once a month they have a Fish Day – and a Speciality Day with dishes from different parts of the world. Adnams Southwold and Wadworths 6X are the regular beers and there are two regularly changing guest beers. They try not to repeat any beers during the year. Plenty of room to sit and admire the floral displays in the half acre of garden, which is also good for children to play in.

OPEN: 11.30–2.30. 7–11. (11.30–3 Sat & Sun. 7–10.30 Sun)
Real Ale.
Children to eat only. Dogs in the garden.
Car park.

BURCOT

Chequers   Tel: 01865 407771

Abingdon Road, Burcot, Oxon OX14 3DP
Free House. Mary & Michael Weeks, licensees.

A charming thatched pub, dating back in part to 1550, with comfortable, unspoilt beamed bars. There is a no-smoking area called the Gallery, with an interesting collection of paintings. The blackboard menu changes daily and all the food is home-made including the bread. Chicken liver and herb paté, garlic mushrooms with melted cheese, Granny Motts real steak & kidney puddings, bacon and brocolli bake, seafood pie, vegetarian dishes, salads, different ploughmans, steaks, not forgetting puddings and home-made ice-cream. Attractive, flowery garden for summer lounging. Ruddles County, Ushers Best and guest beers on hand pump. A 6ft grand piano is kept at concert pitch and some very talented pianists queue up to play on Friday and Saturday evenings.

OPEN: 11–2.30. 6–11.
Real Ale. Restaurant. No meals or snacks Sun eves.
Children in eating area. No dogs.
Evening Fri/Sat pianist.
Purpose built access for wheelchairs to all essential parts of pub.

BURFORD

Angel   Tel: 01993 822438

14 Witney Street, Burford, Oxon
Free House. John Harrington, licensee.

Ideally placed for an exploration of the Cotswolds, the stone-built Angel, with its pretty walled garden, has become more of a restaurant pub since John Harrington took over and installed a French Chef. The menu is now à la carte and changes every three to four weeks. Typical fare would include vichychoisse, ravioli, scallops, mille feuilles of salmon, pan-fried chicken breasts, lasagne, roast rack of lamb or lemon sole. Bar snacks are served lunchtime only. Marstons Pedigree, Morlands Original, Draught Bass and a guest beer on hand pump. Seats in the lovely sheltered garden.

OPEN: 11–2.30 (11–3 Sat). 6.30–11. Closed Sun evening Nov–Mar.
Real Ale. Restaurant.
Children in garden but not in bar, none under 14 in the restaurant. Dogs in garden.
Bedrooms

BURFORD

Lamb   Tel: 01993 823155

Sheep Street, Burford, Oxon OX18 3LR
Free House. Richard de Wolf, licensee.

A glorious example of a Cotswold inn, with honey-coloured stone walls covered in climbing roses and benches outside from where you can watch the world go by and enjoy your drink. Inside there are flagged floors, log fires, comfortably furnished bars and a pretty pillared restaurant. A courtyard and an attractive walled garden are behind the inn. Bar lunches: soups, ploughmans, filled pancakes, paté, and curries. Restaurant meals in the evening. Wadworths IPA, 6X and Hook Norton Best Bitter on hand pump plus Old Timer in winter.

OPEN: 11–2.30. 6–11.
Real Ale. Restaurant open eves; bar food lunchtimes.
Children welcome. Dogs on leads.
Bedrooms

BURFORD

Mermaid Inn   Tel: 01993 822193

High Street, Burford, Oxon OX18 4QF
Morlands. John Titcombe, lease.

Another handsome Cotswold pub, 600 years old, with a long bar and two restaurants, the upstairs one for smokers, the one downstairs in the dining conservatory for non-smokers. Food is served all day and includes filled baguettes, Cumberland sausages with fried onion on garlic bread, omelettes, home-cooked ham and salads. Morlands ales on hand pump. There are tables on the very wide pavement in front of the pub.

OPEN: 10–11 (11–11 Suns & Winter)
Real Ale. Restaurants.
Children in restaurant (not small children). No dogs.
Pianist Fri & Sat evenings.

CLIFTON

Duke of Cumberlands Head   Tel: 018693 38534

Clifton, Nr Deddington, Oxon OX15 0PE
Free House. Nick Huntington, licensee.

Thatched. Built in 1580. Beamed, with huge fireplaces and a comfortable lounge bar, it offers the added bonus of a French restaurant and a constantly changing blackboard menu in the bar. Dishes vary but they could be garlic mushrooms, salade niçoise, good home-made soup and a fish dish. Roast Sunday lunch. Good range of wines by the glass. Tables outside in the garden. Adnams, Wadworths 6X, Hook Norton, Hampshires King Alfred and guest ales from Easter throughout the summer.

OPEN: 12–3.00. 6.30–11.
Real Ale. Restaurant (not Sun or Mon eves). No bar food Sun eves.
Children until 9 pm. Dogs on leads.
Bedrooms.

CLIFTON HAMPDEN

Plough   Tel: 01865 407811

Clifton Hampden, Nr Abingdon, Oxon OX14 3EG
Courage. Yuksel Bektas, lease.

A lovely 16th century thatched pub which is completely non- smoking. If you want a quick puff, go out into the car park. Food is served throughout the day. Run in the best traditions of a public house, what the customer wants, when he wants it, he will get it. The landlord, Mr Bektas (in tails and white gloves) believes in service. In good food too. No frozen food vans out the back here. One menu throughout the pub, informally in the bar, and more formally in the restaurant. The menu could include a variety of smoked fish, a pasta dish or two, salmon in mustard and white wine sauce and home-made puddings. Wonderful coffee (several varieties). Courage Best, Ruddles County and Websters ales and a good wine list. A special place this.

OPEN: 11–11.
Real Ale. Restaurant (no-smoking). Food served all day.
Children welcome. Guide dogs only.

FINSTOCK

Plough Inn   Tel: 01993 868333

The Bottom, Finstock, Oxon OX7 3BY
Free House. Keith Ewers, licensee.

Now run by the Ewers brothers – one shows at Crufts – there are lots of doggy artefacts around, and their own dog. Dog visitors are welcome in the garden (on a lead) or in the public bar. Thatched, with a cosy beamed bar, a log-burning stove in the big inglenook fireplace, comfortable furnishings and a no-smoking dining room. Their speciality is a steak & kidney pie with red wine/Guinness and a crusty top, but the menus are changing all the time. Bar food could include grilled bass, quiche, vegetarian pie, steaks and home-baked ham. Hook Norton Best and Old Hooky, Boddingtons, Adnams Broadside and guest beers. Farm ciders, choice of wines and a range of malt whiskies. Tables outside in the garden.

OPEN: 12–3. 6–11. All day Sat.
Real Ale. Restaurant.
Children welcome. Dogs on leads.
One bedroom.

HAILEY

King William IV   Tel: 01491 686675

Hailey, Nr Ipsden, Wallingford, Oxon OX10 6AD
Brakspears. Brian Penney, tenant.

A small old-fashioned family-run pub. No fancy meals, just good honest bar food: ploughmans, pasties, filled rolls, soup at lunchtime, (only filled rolls available in the evening). Seats outside at the back with a view of the rolling countryside, and where there is a fascinating collection of old farm machinery. Keeping in the mood, you can hitch a lift on a horse and cart which plies between the pub and Nettlebed. Brakspears ales drawn from casks in front of the customers. Farm ciders.

OPEN: 11–2.30. 6–11.
Real Ale.
Children in eating area lunchtimes. No dogs.

HOOK NORTON (nr)

Gate Hangs High   Tel: 01608 737387

Banbury Road, Nr Hook Norton, Oxon OX15 5DS
Hook Norton. Stuart Rust, tenant.

A toll once had to be paid on cattle and horses passing through this gate, but not on geese. To give the birds unimpeded passage, it was hung high enough for them to pass under, whilst stopping the larger animals – and that is how the pub got its name, or so the landlord believes. In the middle of nowhere, (well, about a mile north of the village), but nevertheless very popular, the pub has no restaurant, just a room with tables, and a bar. There is a variety of home-made bar food with changing daily specials. Also an evening blackboard menu. Hook Norton Ales and a guest beer, a good choice of wine and selection of malt whiskies. There are seats in the garden. The Hook Norton brewery isn't far away and well worth a visit.

OPEN: 11.30–3. 6.30–11.
Real Ale. Restaurant. No meals or snacks Sun eves.
Children in eating area & restaurant. Dogs on leads.

ISLIP

Swan Inn   Tel: 01865 372590

Lower Street, Islip, Kidlington, Oxon OX5 2SB
Morrells. Mr Michael Watkins, tenant

A small pub by the River Ray, a tributary of the Cherwell. Family-run, friendly, with no machines of any kind, only good beer and conversation, also a reputation for well-cooked bar food. In the winter they specialise in a variety of home-made pies which could be pheasant, rabbit, duck, or venison. Home-baked ham. Their ham egg and chips is very popular. Lots of summer salads, smoked salmon roulade, and savoury flans. Morrells Varsity Bitter, Graduate and College Ale. Seats on the verandah at the front of the pub.

OPEN: 11–2.30 (11–3 Sun). 6–11.
Real Ale. No food Sun & Mon eves.
Children welcome. Dogs on leads.

MOULSFORD

Beetle & Wedge   Tel: 01491 651381

Ferry Lane, Moulsford, Oxon OX10 9JF
Free House. Richard & Kate Smith, licensees.

You are in "Wind of the Willows" country here and if you are looking for a very civilised day by the river, this is the place to be. Very elegant, it has nevertheless, an informal boathouse bar with traditional real ales, and a charcoal fire on which a selection of dishes are grilled – whole Dover sole, escalope of salmon Hollandaise, sirloin steak Bearnaise. Vichysoisse and other soups in the Boathouse Bar, along with smoked Toulouse sausage with warm potato salad, sautéed spicey squid with cucumber, tomato and spring onions, salad of lambs kidneys, button mushrooms and bacon, seared scallops with fennel and cucumber salad, much more, plus amazing puds. In good weather the boathouse bar moves onto the terrace, just a few feet from the river. There are also tables by the jetty. Lunch is served by the Water Garden on fine, summer days. Only the finest, fresh, local produce is used in this very appealing riverside hotel. Wadworth 6X, Adnams and Badger Tanglefoot on hand pump. Extensive wine list. For the truly energetic who want to work up an appetite for lunch – rowing boats are for hire nearby.

OPEN: 11.30–2.30. 6–11. N.B.You must reserve a table if you want to eat – it is very popular.
Real Ale. Restaurants. One no-smoking.
Children welcome. No dogs.
Bedrooms. Wheelchair access.

MURCOTT

The Nut Tree   Tel: 01865 331253

Main Street, Nr Kidlington Oxon OX5 2RE
Free House. Gordon Evans, licensee.

Not only a duck pond and ducks, but also donkeys in the 6 acres surrounding the pub. "We've been here 20 years, so we've gathered a few animals on the way" said the landlord. Anyway, that's not the only reason you're here. You want to know about the pub. Behind the hanging baskets it's 15th century and thatched. A conservatory extension houses the restaurant and there is one lounge bar with low ceilings, oak beams, creaking floors, log fires and a ghost: a little girl about 11 or 12 years old in a smock and bonnet. She has been seen several times and it is thought she may have perished in a fire many years ago. The Nut Tree is also listed as one of the meeting places for the Otmoor Rioters who rioted against the Enclosures Act in the 1700's. That probably pushed up the beer sales! Back to the present day. There is an extensive menu from sandwiches, locally made sausages to beef Wellington and daily specials. Lots of fresh fish delivered three times a week from Billingsgate. Nothing is frozen except the scampi and all the meat is locally grown and killed. Six ales are available all the time: Hook Norton, Morrells Bitter, Chiltern Bitter, a Wychwood beer and other guests. A good range of wines and malt whiskies. Lots of seats outside in the attractive garden.

OPEN: 11–3. 6.30–11 (12–3. 7–10.30 Sun)
Real Ale. Restaurant.
Children in garden or conservatory, not in bar. Dogs in garden.

NUFFIELD

Crown   Tel: 01491 641335

Nuffield, Henley, Oxon RG9 5SJ
Brakspears. Ann & Gerry Bean, tenants.

Just the place to stop and recharge the batteries whilst walking the Ridgeway Path. Collapse on the seats at the front of the pub in summer or in the beamed bars with their roaring log fires in winter, ordering from the extensive menu of home-made bar food: soups, salads, sandwiches, paté, sausage and bean casserole, gammon steaks, steak & kidney pie, leek tart, vegetarian dishes, daily specials and home-made puds. The only thing that isn't home-made is the bread. Brakspears ales on hand pump and a good choice of wines.

OPEN: 11–2.30. 6–11.
Real Ale.
Children in family room, lunchtimes only. Dogs on leads.
Wheelchair access to pub only.

THE QUIET PINT

OXFORD
Turf Tavern
Tel: 01865 243235

4 Bath Place, off Holywell Street, Oxford, OX1 3SU
Whitbread. Trevor Walter, manager.

Set in an attractive courtyard in the middle of Oxford, the pub has two comfortable, low-beamed rooms, and is well known for always having between 20 and 30 different guest ales on offer – even though it is a Whitbread pub. The uncomplicated bar menu lists baps with various fillings, both hot and cold, roasts, steak & mushroom and other pies, and a vegetarian dish or two. Seats in the courtyards. The ales change all the time; there is also the occasional beer festival. Country wines and farm cider are also available, plus mulled wine in winter.

OPEN: 11–11
Real Ale.
Children in one bar only. Guide dogs only.

OXFORD
Rose and Crown
Tel: 01865 510551

North Parade Avenue, Oxford OX2 6LX
Sycamore Taverns. Andrew and Deborah Hall, tenants.

If you go up the Banbury Road, North Parade is on your left; up the Woodstock Road it's on your right. Either way, you get to this old fashioned local built in the mid 19th century. It has three rooms with a bar in two of them, a proper pub piano (in tune) and a friendly, popular landlord. Substantial pub menu: a hot dish of the day, pasta, fresh fish – usually trout – rump steak, filled baked potatoes, omelettes, filled baguettes, ploughmans, sandwiches and a roast on Sunday. Ind Coope ABC, BB and Burton Ale. Large courtyard at the back of the pub, with a retractable awning and big heaters which means it can be used all year.

OPEN: 10.30–3. 5–11. (12–3. 6–10.30 Sun)
Real Ale
Children, weekend lunchtime only. No dogs.

OXFORD
Kings Arms Tel: 01865 242369

Holywell Street, Oxford OX1 3SP
Youngs. David Kyffin, tenant.

Right in the middle of things. Surrounded by colleges and near the University library buildings and Blackwells bookshop. The Kings Arms is an old coaching inn with several different bars and a no-smoking dining room. Popular with members of the University, locals (they're the ones still proping the bar up in the vacations), and cosmopolitan visitors. Very busy at lunchtime, but service is fast. Food ranges from predictable pub grub – home-made soups, sandwiches, filled rolls and an "Oxford ploughmans" featuring an award winning local blue cheese – to a Kings Arms pie made with chicken and mushrooms cooked in Youngs oatmeal stout. Special vegetarian dishes too. Youngs range of ales, Wadworths 6X, Wheatbeer, over 20 malt whiskies and a choice of over 20 wines by the glass, including champagne. Tables outside in summer so you can enjoy watching Oxford on the move.

OPEN: 10.30–11 (12–10.30 Sun)
Real Ale
Children and dogs welcome if accompanied by well behaved people!

RAMSDEN
Royal Oak Tel: 01993 868213

High Street, Ramsden, OX7 3AU
Free House. John Oldham, licensee.

The chef is the owner and licensee rolled into one in this comfortable, unassuming 17th century old coaching inn off the Witney/Charlbury road. Akeman Street, the old Roman road, connecting Bicester and Cirencester runs through Ramsden. One way or another people have been travelling through here for an awfully long time! The Royal Oak is known for the excellence of its food. A lunchtime bar menu lists sandwiches, ploughmans, lasagne, pie of the week and a vegetarian dish or two. Otherwise you have a choice of a dish from either the printed or blackboard menus: leg of lamb steak in a port and red currant sauce, chicken in red wine, fillet of salmon with sorrel sauce, venison and daily specials. Home-made puds too.Three cask conditioned ales on all the time: Hook Norton BB and two guests. Good wine list. Seats in the sunny courtyard between the pub and three converted holiday cottages.

THE QUIET PINT

OPEN: 11.30–2.30. 6.30–11.(12–3. 7–10.30. Sun)
Real Ale. Restaurant.
Children welcome. Dogs on leads.
Wheelchair access.
Three holiday cottages.

ROKE

Home Sweet Home Tel: 01491 838249

Roke, Nr Wallingford, Oxon OX10 6JD
Free House. Jill Madle, Peter & Irene Mountford

Certainly someone's home in the past, as this was originally a row of
cottages. It's now a smart pub with two beamed bars, one of which leads
into the restaurant. Quite an extensive choice of food throughout the pub –
the sandwiches have lots of different fillings. There is a wide range of salads
and substantial dishes may be chosen from the changing blackboard menu.
A more elaborate menu is available in the evening restaurant. Brakspears
Bitter and Eldridge Pope ales. There is a pretty garden with picnic tables at
the front of the pub.

OPEN: 11–3. 5.30–11.
Real Ale. Restaurant.
Well behaved children welcome. Dogs on leads only in the bar.

SHENINGTON

Bell Inn Tel: 01295 670274

Shenington, Nr Banbury, Oxon OX15 6NQ
Free House. Jennifer Dixon, licensee.

Very much the local, probably since it was built in 1722 on the edge of the
village green. A well beamed traditional interior with some pine panelling and
good log fires. There is a changing blackboard menu, all the food is home-
cooked using the best local seasonal produce. Good soups, quiches,
salmon in cucumber sauce, mushrooms in creamy paprika, celery and nut
bake and puds. Boddingtons, Hook Norton and Flowers ales. A good wine
list. Tables at the front of the pub overlooking the village green.

OPEN: 12–2.30. 7–11. (12–3. 6.30–11 Sat).
Real Ale. Restaurant.
Children welcome. Dogs on leads
Bedrooms.

SHIPTON-UNDER-WYCHWOOD
Lamb   Tel: 01993 830465

High Street, Shipton-under-Wychwood, Oxon OX7 6DQ
Free House. Michael & Jennifer Eastwick, licensees

Situated on the outskirts of the village, this attractive old honey-coloured, stone-walled, Cotswold Inn with stone-tiled roof, has been catering for the traveller for several hundred years and continues to be as popular as ever. There is a good cold buffet, home-made soups and other traditional bar dishes. In the evening the blackboard menu offers a more extensive range of food: local game in season, fresh fish from Cornwall, the ducks from Minster Lovell and carefully-chosen beef and lamb. The home-made fruit pies are said to be excellent. There are "wine-of-the-week" suggestions on the blackboard; also a good wine list. Hook Norton, Wadworths 6X, cider and Guinness on draught. There are tables in the garden.

OPEN: 11–11.
Real Ale. Restaurant (not Sun eves).
No children. Well behaved dogs on leads.
Bedrooms. No wheelchair access.

SHIPTON-UNDER-WYCHWOOD
Shaven Crown Hotel   Tel: 01993 830330

High Street, Shipton-under-Wychwood, Oxon OX7 6BA
Free House. Trevor & Mary Brookes, licensees

Originally a hospice for nearby Bruern Abbey, the 14th century Shaven Crown was built around a medieval courtyard garden and is an attractive place to sit and enjoy a drink and meal on a summer's day. The comfortable beamed bar, with a log fire in winter, offers a wide range of bar snacks: smoked haddock mousse, whitebait, salmon, cod and dill fishcakes, curried prawns, steak sandwich, home-baked ham, venison sausages braised in red wine and vegetarian dishes. Puddings too. There is a more extensive menu in the evening restaurant: pancakes filled with salmon & spinach in white wine sauce, deep-fried Camembert, Normandy pheasant, chicken with apricot stuffing and fennel sauce, fish dishes, steaks and more puddings. Hook Norton ale and guest beers. The wine list varies from week to week. Those architecturally minded among you, do try to see the medieval hall, now the Residents' Lounge, with its double-collar braced roof, still in perfect condition after six hundred years.

THE QUIET PINT

OPEN: 12–2.30. 7–11.
Real Ale. Restaurant.
Children welcome but not under 5 in evening restaurant. Dogs on lead, not in hotel rooms.
Wheelchair access to part of Hotel and WC's, but not bedrooms.
Bedrooms.

SOUTH STOKE

Perch & Pike Inn
Tel: 01491 872415

South Stoke, Oxon RG8 0JS
Brakspear. Michael & Jill Robinson, tenants.

On the Ridgeway between Goring and Wallingford, this is an attractive and popular small flint-built pub. Log fires in winter, always fresh flowers and candles on the table in the evening. Proper napkins, too, if you are eating. The menus are unusual and varied, changing every couple of weeks: interesting summer salads, imaginative hot dishes and mouth-watering sweets. The specials change daily, the beef is Aberdeen Angus and everything is fresh, seasonal and home-cooked. Brakspears ales, wines by the glass. Seats outside in the pretty garden which is within walking distance of the river.

OPEN: 12–2.30. 6–11.
Real Ale. Restaurant. No meals or snacks Sun eves.
Children in eating area. Dogs on leads.
Stables available.

STEEPLE ASTON

Red Lion
Tel: 018693 40225

South Street, Steeple Aston, Oxon OX6 3RY
Free House. Colin Mead, licensee.

It isn't often, when writing about a pub, that you can say "this is the place for a decent glass of wine". The landlord is very keen on his wines and in consequence keeps an interesting, inimitable cellar. Bar food is limited to lunchtimes only: home-made soups, ploughmans with local cheeses, sandwiches, winter hotpots and summer salads. There's a more ambitious and creative menu in the evening restaurant. Hook Norton Bitter and guest beers only. Over 100 wines are kept and there are regular wine-tastings and promotions. Seats on the sunny terrace at the front of the pub amid the flowers.

OPEN: 11–3. 6–11.
Real Ale. Evening restaurant (closed Sun & Mon). Lunchtime meals & snacks (not Sun).
Children in restaurant. Dogs on leads

SULGRAVE

Star Inn Tel: 01295 760389

Manor Road, Sulgrave, OX17 2SA
Hook Norton Brewery. Andrew Willerton, tenant.

"Great Beer, Great Food, Lousy Service!" The pub said it – not me. They also boast `George the Skeleton', so if he's still waiting for lunch there might be a grain of truth in it! Our researcher says not.... he thought it `an above average pub, a very civilised establishment.' Originally an old farmhouse, this pub is a comfortable, well beamed place with open fireplaces and flagstones, decorated with some interesting artefacts dating back to pre-war days. All the food is freshly cooked and promptly served. Lots of dishes on the blackboard menu from a wide variety of hors d'oevres and filling sandwiches to a mixed grill. Sunday roasts, and good puds. Hook Norton range of ales, Symonds Scrumpy Jack and good house wines. Seats in the delightful garden and on the terrace.

OPEN: 11–2.30. 6–11. (12–3. 7–10.30 Sun)
Real Ale. Restaurant.
No children. Dogs on leads.
Car park.
Three en-suite bedrooms.

SWINBROOK

Swan Inn Tel: 01993 822165

Swinbrook, Nr Burford, Oxon OX18 4DY
Free House. H V Collins & C Y Collins, licensees

Not far from the River Windrush, you will find the wisteria covered 16th century Swan Inn. It has only a small bar, but it is very popular with walkers and locals. Traditionally furnished, with stone-flagged floors and winter fires. Home-cooked bar food and a more ambitious evening menu. Home-made steak and kidney pie and braised venison in ale are two popular lunchtime dishes, and pigeon breasts with paté and Brie in a puff pastry case, or poussin stuffed with spinach and stilton in the evening. Bass, Morlands Bitter and cider from Hereford. Benches outside – muddy boots outside too.

OPEN: 11.30–2.30. 6–11.
Real Ale. No food Sun eve.
No children. No dogs. No dirty boots in dining room.
Wheelchair access to pub only.

TOOT BALDON

Crown Inn   Tel: 01865 343240

Toot Baldon, Nr Nuneham, Courtenay, Oxon OX44 9NG
Free House. Liz & Neil Kennedy, licensees

Busy, friendly, this is a country pub with good home-cooked food. There is a small eating area with only 30 seats so it is best to book if possible, to make sure of a table – or just get there early. A good choice of bar food: home-made soup, giant prawns cooked with garlic, wine and herbs, Oxfordshire sausage, vegetarian pasta, crusty fillet steak roll,steaks – always a ploughmans and a choice of sandwiches, also changing and quite exciting specials on the blackboard menu: e.g. salmon steak with fresh herbs, or pork chop topped with blue cheese in a cider sauce. Ales vary, but currently Morlands Original, Old Speckled Hen, Adnams Broadside and Mansfield Bitter. Seats outside on the terrace where there is a barbecue in summer.

OPEN: 11–3. 6.30–11.
Real Ale. Restaurant. No meals or snacks Mon eve.
Children welcome. Dogs on leads.
Wheelchair access.

WYTHAM

White Hart   Tel: 01865 244372

Wytham, Nr Oxford, Oxon OX2 8QA
Ind Coope. Louise Tran, licensee.

An attractive, creeper-covered pub in the pretty, thatched village of Wytham (the whole of which is owned by Oxford University). It has a flagstone floor and a part-panelled bar with open fires. Bar food includes a huge choice of salads, filled baked potatoes, lots of fish dishes – swordfish, halibut, tuna and others. Most of the food is prepared to order. Daily specials and some vegetarian dishes. There is a barbecue during all opening hours Tuesday to Sunday, weather permitting of course. Ind Coope Burton, ABC, Tetleys and one guest beer. Seats in the very lovely walled garden.

OPEN: 11–3. 5.30–11. (11–11 Sat. 12–11 Sun)
Real Ale.
Children welcome. No dogs.

S
SOMERSET

BARRINGTON

Royal Oak Tel: 01460 53455

Barrington, Somerset TA19 0JD
Free House. Terence Jarvis, licensee.

Near Barrington Court, a fine example of a Tudor Manor House, the Royal Oak, an old stone-built village pub serves the villages of Barrington and Puckington. Well beamed inside, it has a lounge, public bar and a function room upstairs, which can be used as an overflow. Quite an extensive menu with a number of fish dishes, steaks and the usual bar food. The six real ales are changed fairly frequently; when one barrel runs dry a new beer takes its place. Variety is the key. To work it all off there is a popular skittle alley.

OPEN: 12–3. 6.30–11 (11–11 Sat. 12–4. 7–10.30 Sun)
Real Ale.
Children welcome.

BATH

Francis Hotel Tel: 01225 424257

Queen Square, Bath, Somerset BA1 2HH
Free House. Peter J. Lister, General Manager.

Dating back to the early 18th century, the elegant frontage of The Francis forms part of Queen Square. Designed by John Wood the Yorkshire born architect, this was one of the first squares to be built in what was then the medieval town of Bath. The comfortable Roman Bar at The Francis is the ideal place to stop, draw breath, have a snack, refresh yourself with a glass of something before getting back on the tourist route. Lots of imaginative dishes to choose from: home-made soup of the day, freshly baked baguettes filled with smoked salmon and cucumber, potted spiced crab and prawns, French onion tart with leaf salad, a four egg omelette with five different fillings, millefeuille of beef fillet with oyster mushrooms, and more besides. Bass, Draught Guinness, Worthington Cream Flow, and some lagers. Naturally enough, there is a good choice of wines.

OPEN: 11.30 –2.30. 5–11. (11–11 Fri & Sat. 12–3. 7–10.30 Sun)
Real Ale. Restaurant.
Children welcome. No Dogs.

BATH

Old Green Tree   No telephone.

12 Green Street, Bath, Somerset.
Free House. Nick Luke, licensee.

Small, very popular town pub with three panelled rooms, one of them no-smoking. No music or machines, just a delightful, chatty pub. It can get very crowded, particularly at lunchtime, which is the only time food is available. The short menu includes well filled rolls, good sized ploughmans, pasta dishes, a Thai chicken curry that has become a firm favourite, salads, and daily specials of freshly cooked seasonal dishes, supplemented by "Nick's Quirks" (listed on blackboards). The five ales come from local breweries and the choice varies considerably. There are also a number of unusual wines. Pimms is served during the summer and hot punch in winter.

OPEN: 11–11 (closed Sun morning)
Real Ale. Lunchtime meals & snacks (not Sun)
Children over 10 if eating lunchtime only. No dogs.

BATH

Star Inn   Tel: 01225 425072

23 The Vineyards, Bath BA1 5NA
Bass. Peter Heindorff, licensee/manager.

A 200 year old classic town pub near Guinea Lane. Inside there are several small interconnecting rooms: a snug, the glass room – like a public bar with panelling partitions – lounge and public bar. Only filled rolls available, but you are really here for the beer. Exceptionally well kept Draught Bass and Wickwars Brand Oak Bitter, served in jugs from the cask.

OPEN: 12–2.30. 5.30–11
Real Ale
No children. Dogs welcome.

BRISTOL

Highbury Vaults   Tel: 0117 9733203

164 St Michael's Hill, Kingsdown, Bristol BS2 8DE
Smiles. Bradd Francis, manager.

Being near the university, this pub is understandably very popular in term time. Fundamentally a Georgian building with a late Victorian/Edwardian interior. It has a small front bar and a bigger bar at the back. Reasonably priced traditional bar food which changes daily. All the dishes are freshly cooked and might include: spinach and mushroom lasagne, pork and apples in cider and lamb and rosemary casserole. No fried food and no chips with anything here! The main ales stocked come from Smiles, with three guest ales changing each week, including London Pride, Adnams Broadside, Bishops Finger, Barn Owl, Double Dragon and many more. In summer they have a weekend barbecue in the pub courtyard.

OPEN: 12–11.
Real Ale. No food Sat/Sun eves.
No dogs. Children only in the front bar.

BRISTOL

The Commercial Rooms   Tel: 01179 279681

43–45 Corn Street, Bristol BS1 1HT.
Wetherspoons, Andy & Heather Harvey, managers.

A Grade II listed building, the Commercial Rooms is, as you would expect, in the heart of the city's commercial centre. Built in 1809 as a meeting place for merchants to discuss business and used for auctions by the then thriving coffee trade. In the 1920's The Commercial Rooms had 1,000 members but when it finally closed in 1994 the number had fallen to less than 300. Lovingly restored by Wetherspoons, it has a striking interior with a 25 foot glazed skylight supported by twelve figures. The Grand Coffee room, with an island bar, is now the main drinking area. Two no-smoking rooms are to be found at the end of the bar. Six cask conditioned beers at all times – Youngers Scotch Bitter, Courage Directors, Theakston Best, XB, Wadworths 6X and a local regional beer. Guest beers from the smaller breweries. Reliable bar food, with a choice of daily specials, is served all day.

OPEN: 11–11
Real Ale.
No Children. No Dogs, except guide dogs.

BRISTOL

The Naval Volunteer Tel: 0117 929 1763

18 King Street, Bristol, BS1 4EF
Greenalls. Rod MacDonald, manager.

Among the oldest unspoilt ale houses in Bristol. Others are older, but they have all been developed. Three bars, open fires and low ceilings; the tall chap with the slight stoop is the landlord! Traditional pub grub – all home made. Steak and ale pie, Cornish pasties, Cumberland sausages, a filled roll or two. The regular beers are Draught Bass and Smiles Best, but there are up to 10 guest beers in summer and up to 20 in winter.

OPEN: 11–11
Real Ale.
Dogs very welcome.

BRISTOL

Prince of Wales Tel: 01179 245552

5, Gloucester Road, Bishopston, Bristol. BS7 8AA
Courage. Bob Mason, leaseholder.

The city of Bristol dates back to Norman times and grew up around the harbour on the River Avon. Although heavily damaged during the War, it still has some glorious Georgian terraces, a Cathedral with a Norman Chapter House and fine Victorian buildings. The Prince of Wales – with the hanging baskets – was created out of three cottages. Now one large room, the original panelling still remains on what was the lounge bar side. Comfortable and welcoming, there is a typical pub menu with some daily specials. Courage range of beers with Butcombe Bitter as a permanent guest. Seats in the courtyard at the back of the pub.

OPEN: 11–2.30. 5.30–11. 11–11 Sat.
Real Ale
Children Sunday lunchtime only. No Dogs.

THE QUIET PINT

CHARD

Bell & Crown   Tel: 01460 62470

Combe Street, Crimchard, Chard, Som TA20 1JP.
Free House. Ron Montague, licensee.

On the outskirts of Chard, the highest town in Somerset, this old building
has been a public house since early last century. No-one knows anything
about the origins of the three cottages that became the Bell & Crown, as the
deeds were lost in a fire. This popular local, still with the old gas lighting,
serves good reliable pub food: sandwiches, sausage egg and chips, steak
– that sort of thing. Ushers Spring Fever, Shepherd Neame Best Bitter,
Caledonian 80/-, and this is a special treat – Cottage's Southern Bitter –
delivered either by steam lorry or horse drawn dray. Worth being there on
delivery day.

OPEN: 11–3 (not Monday) 7–11 No food Sun. and Mon. nights
Real Ale
Children at mealtimes. Dogs on leads.

COMBE HAY

Wheatsheaf   Tel: 01225 833504

Combe Hay, Nr Bath, Somerset BA2 7EG
Free House. M G Taylor, licensee.

Unless you have a reason for exploring the lovely countryside surrounding
the city of Bath, you wouldn't usually venture along the narrow, twisting,
wonderfully overgrown lanes that lead from one hidden village to the next.
Clinging to the side of the hill in this charming village, the Wheatsheaf is
one good reason for venturing forth. On a clear day the views from the pub
garden are of the English countryside at its best. Inside are cosy, low-
ceilinged rooms, country furnishings, a big log fire in winter and a huge
blackboard menu. Interesting, imaginative choice of dishes including some
familiar bar snacks. The specials board might include: king prawns in garlic
butter, venison in red wine sauce, game in season and several fish dishes
inluding crab and lobster. Home made puddings too. There is also a full à
la carte menu. Courage Best and Wadworths 6X. Seats in the garden.

OPEN: 11–3. 6.30–10.30 (Fri & Sat 11).
Real Ale. Restaurant.
Children in eating areas. Dogs on leads.
Wheelchair access to pub.

COMBE St NICHOLAS

Green Dragon   Tel: 01460 63311

Combe St Nicholas, Nr Chard, Somerset.
Free House. Jim & Lin Barker, licensees.

A short step away from the village green, this is a friendly, family run pub. The Thatch Bar is used as dining area and a lounge bar; it is also a no-smoking area – if you want a quick drag, go to the other end of the pub. A full range of food is available including soups, garlic bread to go with the soup – or anything else – sandwiches, steak pies, ham, egg and chips, all sorts of steaks, vegetarian dishes and daily specials. Flowers 6X and a guest beer. Huge car park. A couple of picnic tables outside on a "strip of grass".

OPEN: 11–2.30. 6–11 (7–10.30 Sun) 11–11 Sat.
Real Ale
Children if well behaved. Dogs in public bar.

COMPTON MARTIN

Ring O'Bells   Tel: 01761 221284

Compton Martin, Nr Bath, Somerset BS18 6JE
Free House. Roger Owen, licensee.

Close to the Mendip Hills and Chew Valley Lake, this village pub is popular with walkers and locals alike. Stone walls, flagstoned floors and big log fires make it wonderfully inviting in winter. Usual sandwiches, ploughmans, grills and lasagne plus imaginative specials. A roast lunch is available on Sundays. Bass, Wadworths 6X and Butcombe Bitter plus a guest ale. Local cider on draught. Seats in the garden amid the apple trees – there is also a play area for children.

OPEN: 11.30–3. 6–11.
Real Ale. Restaurant (not Sun eves).
Children in family room. Dubious about dogs.

CRANMORE

Strode Arms   Tel: 01749 880450

Cranmore, Nr Shepton Mallet, Somerset BA4 4QT
Free House. Rodney & Dora Phelps, licensee.

Originally a 14th century farmhouse, then a coaching inn, now the village pub. Situated opposite the duck pond and not far from the East Somerset Railway, it houses an interesting collection of railway memorabilia. Country furnishings, big log fires in winter and a smart restaurant. Bar food includes the usual range of sandwiches, ploughmans, filled baked potatoes, venison sausages, the very popular egg mayonnaise Strode, fish dishes plus five daily specials on the blackboard, and four or five delicious puds which could include apple dumplings and Dora's 'sticky toffee pudding'. Marstons Pedigree, Wadworths 6X and Flowers IPA. Farm cider. Seats on the terrace at the front of the pub overlooking the village pond.

OPEN: 11.30–2.30. 6.30–11. Closed Sun eve Oct–Feb.
Real Ale. Restaurant.
Children in restaurant. Dogs in bar on leads.
Wheelchair access.

CROSCOMBE

Bull Terrier   Tel: 01749 343658

Croscombe, Nr Wells, Somerset BA4 4QJ
Free House. Barry Vidler, licensee.

There's a Medieval Cross next to this old building, originally the priory and home of the Abbot of Glastonbury. First licensed early in the 17th century, it has three bars: the lounge – called the "Inglenook" – which still has its original beamed ceiling – the "Snug" and the "Common Bar"; also a family room. Home-made food, ranges from ploughmans and vegetarian dishes to specials like turkey, ham and mushroom pie, home-made steak and kidney pie or ginger chicken with noodles. Good puddings. Varying ales, but mainly Bull Terrier Best Bitter brewed for the pub; also Butcombe Bitter, Greene King Abbot, Theakstons XB and Smiles Best. Local cider and a good wine list. The walled garden backs onto the village church and – continuing the ecclesiastical theme – a footpath from the village leads to the Bishop's Palace in Wells.

OPEN: 12–2.30. 7–11 (closed Mon winter)
Real Ale. No food winter Sun eves or all day Mon.
Children in family room. Dogs if they like the look of them.
Bedrooms.
Wheelchair access to pub.

DUNSTER

Luttrell Arms   Tel: 01643 821555

High Street, Dunster, Somerset TA24 6SG
Free House (Forte). Mrs M Coffey, manager.

Built in the 15th century, the Luttrell Arms was originally the guesthouse for
the monks of Cleeve Abbey. They created a Gothic hall with a wonderful
hammer beam roof, a window of exceptional size for the time and a truly
immense fireplace. Originally "The Ship", it was renamed the Luttrell Arms
in 1779 – a gesture of respect for the Luttrells, owners of Dunster Castle. An
historic, medieval village; the high street dominated by a 16th century yarn
market, built when Dutch craftsmen arrived to take advantage of the areas
prosperous cloth weaving industry. It was probably the Dutch who were
responsible for the ornate moulded plasterwork found in the Luttrell Arms.
Now an elegant, well run hotel, there is nevertheless a good pubby
atmosphere in the timbered back bar. They serve good traditional bar food
at lunchtime in the old kitchen next to the Gothic Hall, this includes the
chef's home-made pie of the day. Daily specials are on the blackboard in the
bar: puds on the blackboard in the Old Kitchen. More formal meals are
served in the Luttrell Restaurant. Flowers IPA, Bass and John Smiths plus
the local Exmoor ale. Extensive wine list. Good walks and lots of places to
explore.

OPEN: 10.30–11.
Real Ale. Restaurant.
Children in eating areas. Dogs on leads.

EXFORD

Crown Hotel   Tel: 01643 831554

Exford, Somerset TA24 7PP
Free House. Mike Bradley, licensee.

In the picturesque heart of the Exmoor National Park, the 17th century

Crown, with its later additions, offers elegant accommodation as well as an informal public bar atmosphere. Here they serve freshly prepared, imaginative bar meals and pints of traditional ale. The blackboard menu changes frequently. In the separate restaurant there are well chosen seasonal menus, the most popular dishes being game and fish. There is also a carefully selected wine list. Brakspear Bitter and Flowers Original on hand pump.

OPEN: 11–2.30. 6–11 (12–3. 7–10.30 Sun)
Real Ale. Restaurant.
Children welcome. Dogs on leads.
Bedrooms

FAULKLAND

Tuckers Grave   Tel: 01373 834230

Faulkland, Nr Bath, Somerset BA3 5XF
Free House. Ivan & Glenda Swift, licensees.

Poor Tucker, hanged himself at a nearby farm back in the mists of time and was buried at the crossroads where this old stone pub now stands. Think of a pub that has been serving the small local community for centuries and you have a picture of this unspoilt little place. Casks of Bass and Butcombe Bitter; also Cheddar Valley cider. A skittle alley for fun, seats in the garden for relaxation and a ploughmans or sandwich for lunchtime sustenance.

OPEN: 11.30–3. 6–11.
Real Ale.
Children welcome. No dogs.

HUISH EPISCOPI

Rose & Crown   Tel: 01458 250494

Huish Episcopi, Langport, Somerset. TA10 9PU
Free House. Mrs Eileen Pittard, licensee.

Very much an old fashioned pub, unspoilt by modern "improvements". In the same family for over 120 years, this is one of our national treasures. Also known as Eli's after Grandfather Eli Scott. You'll find " Eli" in brackets on the Inn sign. The heart of the pub is the flagstoned central still room. No bar, you just go into the still room and they'll draw your beer, cider or stout from the cask. Our informant tells us that "the Guinness was very good, the old lady serving me took ages drawing it into the glass – as they do in Ireland. Perhaps that's why it tasted better". The floor of the large room is 2ft higher than the rest of the pub. Until about 20 years ago flooding was a regular occurrence; the extra 2ft at least kept your feet dry. There are still winter floods, but away from the pub. This is a very welcoming place. Food is good simple fare: soup, sandwiches, plain or toasted, ploughmans, beef lasagne, a vegetarian dish or two and daily specials. Always Bass and Boddingtons and three guest ales. Julian Temperley's Borough Hill Cider, (he also makes Somerset Cider Royal Brandy). Tables in the garden; children have a separate play area. Good walks nearby.

OPEN: 11.30–2.30. 5.30–11 (all day Fri & Sat).
Real Ale
Children Welcome. Dogs allowed.

KELSTON

Old Crown   Tel: 01225 423023

Bath Road, Kelston, Nr Bath, Somerset BA1 9AQ
Free House. Michael Steele, licensee.

On the old Bath to Bristol road you might be forgiven for thinking that time has stood still if you arrive at night and find candle-light flickering inside the pub. Traditionally furnished, with polished flagstone floors, it has two bars and two small, attractive dining rooms – lunchtime bar food and an evening restaurant for serious eating. Well kept ales include Bass, Butcombe, Wadworths 6X and Smiles Best. Tables under the fruit trees in the orchard at the back. The car park is on the opposite side of the busy road.

OPEN: 11.30–2.30. 5–11. Restaurant (not Sun) Thurs, Fri & Sat eves.
Lunchtime meals & snacks (not Sun).
No children. Dogs on leads.

LITTON

Kings Arms   Tel: 01761 241301

Litton, Somerset BA3 4PW
Free House. Neil Sinclair, licensee.

No music, no one-armed bandits, no juke box. Bliss. An unpretentious, picture-book, 15th century Mendip pub, filled with friendly conversation.

THE QUIET PINT

Quite an extensive menu: ploughmans, smoked mackerel, whitebait, garlic crevettes, crispy sweetcorn and more to start with; then a choice of fish platters: River Chew, Punters, Fishermans or American platters, six different fish dishes, salad snacks and even a slimline platter or sandwiches. Our informant says the beers are beautifully kept and served at near room temperature. Bass, Courage Best and Wadworths 6X.

OPEN: 11–2.30. 6–11
Real Ale
Children in own room. No Dogs.

LUXBOROUGH

Royal Oak   Tel: 01984 640319

Luxborough, Nr Dunster, Exmoor National Park, Somerset TA23 0SH
Free House. Kevan Draper & Rose Draper, licensees.

Situated by a stream – at the bottom of a valley near the Exmoor National Park at Dunkery Beacon – is about as idyllic as you can get. Add a 14th century thatched country pub with heavily beamed bars complete with flagged floors, inglenook fireplaces, and an assortment of country furniture, a recently added "own brewery" and what more could you want, but the well kept local ales and good, hearty country cooking? The choice ranges from sandwiches to rabbit stew or roast wild boar. There is a specials board which may have game pies, fish dishes or venison. Sunday lunches. Cotleigh Tawny, Exmoor Gold, Thatchers Cheddar Valley, Flowers IPA are among the ales you may find; also Rich's Farmhouse Cider. Good list of wines by the bottle and a few by the glass. Seats outside in the garden.

OPEN: 11–2.30. 6–11 (6.30–11 winter).
Real Ale. Restaurant.
Children in dining room and rear bar. Dogs in bar.
Folk Music Friday.
Additional en-suite bedrooms will be ready in 1997.

MONTACUTE

Kings Arms Inn   Tel: 01935 822513

Bishopston, Montacute, Somerset TA15 6UU
Free House. Jonathan & Karen Arthur, licensees.

A handsome 16th century inn, once a staging post where the horses were changed before the long pull up Ham Hill on the main road from Plymouth to London. Now a popular beauty spot with tremendous views to the Mendips and Quantocks to the north, and the Dorset hills to the south. In the centre of the village, the Kings Arms is a popular meeting place for locals and visitors alike. More room for everyone since the next door cottage was incorporated into the hotel. Big log fires in winter. Bar food includes an impressive cold buffet and daily hot dishes plus sandwiches and soup. There is a new chef, so expect an interesting menu in both the bar and the restaurant. No smoking in all the dining areas. Wadworths 6X, Draught Bass and Tanglewood. Farmhouse cider and good wine list. Montacute House, owned by the National Trust, is worth a visit. There is a lovely orchard for families at the rear of the pub.

OPEN: 11–2.30. 6–11.
Real Ale. Restaurant.
Children in eating areas. No dogs.
Bedrooms. Wheelchair access

OLDBURY ON SEVERN

Anchor   Tel: 01454 413331

Church Road, Oldbury on Severn, BS12 1QA
Free House. Alex de la Torre, licensee.

In a quiet village not far from the river and tidal flats of the Severn Estuary, the Anchor Pub – with its beamed bar, window seats, traditional furnishings and big log fires – is a welcome haven if you are walking the area in a bracing westerly. The bar food – all cooked by the landlord – uses lots of local produce and changes daily in both the bar and restaurant. Favourite dishes include fresh salmon in a white wine and cream sauce; snorkers – locally reared pork and garlic sausages cooked on the charcoal grill – and a raspberry crème brulée to finish. A selection of good cheeses, a plate of rare roast beef and locally produced sausages are always available. No chips; instead you have a choice of dauphinoise or "Don Quixote" potatoes. Bass from the cask, Black Sheep, Butcombe Bitter, Theakstons Best Bitter and Old Peculiar on hand pump. Seats outside in the attractive garden.

OPEN: 11.30–2.30. 6.30–11 (11.30–3. 6–11 Sat).
Real Ale. Restaurant.
Children in restaurant. Dogs on leads.
Occasional live entertainment.
Wheelchair access.

PITNEY

Halfway House

Tel: 01458 252513

Pitney, Nr.Langport, Somerset TA10 9AB
Free House, Mr & Mrs John Lichfield, owners, licensees.

No music, no fruit machines, no juke box . A friendly old village pub with log fires – except in summer – flagstone floors and simply furnished. CAMRA Somerset Pub of the year 1995; South West England Pub of the year 1996 and Gt. Britain National Pub of the Year. About eight real ales, mostly from small local breweries – Bridgwater Sunbeam, Oakhill Best Bitter, Teignworthy Reel Ale and many more. Home-made curries are the speciality of the house. There is a garden for you to enjoy, and as the landlord says, "we ought to be in the book". Too right. Here he is.

OPEN: 11.30–2.30. 5.30–11.
Real Ale
Dogs and their walkers welcome.

PORLOCK

Ship Inn

Tel: 01643 862507

High Street, Porlock, Somerset TA24 8QD
Free House. Judy Robinson, licensee.

Porlock village, set in a natural bowl, is surrounded by wooded hills and has spectacular views. At the bottom of Porlock Hill sits the partially-thatched, 13th century Ship Inn. Originally a coaching inn it was mentioned in Lorna Doone and is where Southey and Coleridge used to meet for a stimulating drag on the cannabis and write poetry. Inside, it's heavily beamed, flagstoned and traditionally furnished. They serve well-chosen bar food – familiar favourites: soups, ploughmans, paté and local sausages also venison cooked in red wine, Exmoor lamb cooked with apricots, mint and redcurrant jelly and Somerset pork cooked in cider. Daily specials and fresh fish when available. Children's menu. Cotleigh Old Buzzard in winter, Barn Owl in summer, Courage Best and a local guest beer. Steep garden at the back of the pub, with a children's play area. Not far from the sea and open moor.

OPEN: 10.30–3. 5.30–11.
Real Ale.
Children welcome away from bar. Dogs on leads.
Morris dancing & occasional folk. Bedrooms.

STANTON WICK

Carpenters Arms   Tel: 01761 490202

Stanton Wick, Nr Pensford, Bristol BS18 4BX
Free House. Nigel Pushman, licensee.

In a hamlet overlooking the Chew Valley, this stonebuilt pub was originally a row of miners' cottages. Lots of beams and warming fires inside. Two dining areas: the restaurant, and another, less formal one for bar meals. Well chosen bar food, with daily specials written on the blackboard. A more elaborate menu features in the restaurant. Bass, Butcombe Bitter, Wadworths 6X and Worthington Best. Ten wines by the glass and a well priced wine list. Seats in the flowery garden.

OPEN: 11–11.
Real Ale. Restaurant (not Sun eve)
Children welcome. Dogs on leads.
Occasional live pianist in restaurant
Bedrooms.

TAUNTON

Masons Arms   Tel: 01823 288916

Magdalene Street, Taunton
Free House. Jeremy Leyton, licensee.

Situated in the centre of this historic country town – the scene of bitter, bloody battles during the Civil War – the Masons Arms stands in the shadow of St. Mary Magdalene church. Originally the home of the local rent collector, it became a public house in 1855. This busy town pub serves a good selection of hot and cold food plus daily specials. Keeping food hot takes on a new meaning here. Forget the electric hot tray – they use hot stone trays on which they also cook your food. They are heated to a high temperature and your steak is then cooked in front of you. The landlord needs a supply of more stones, so if you know a man that can, you know who to tell. (Think they're really Japanese). Draught Bass and Exe Valley Dobs Best Bitter, plus four guest beers. No garden, but for the energetic among you, a newly decorated skittle alley awaits.

OPEN: 10–3. 5–11.
Real Ale
Dogs welcome. Children, rather not.
Holiday flat to rent.

THE QUIET PINT

WEST HUNTSPILL

Cross Ways Inn
Tel: 01278 783756

West Huntspill, Nr Highbridge, Somerset TA9 3RA
Free House. Michael Ronca & Tony Eyles, licensees.

On the A38 and 3 miles from Exit 22 on the M5, is not the usual way to introduce an easily accessible pub, but anyone travelling on boring motorways and wanting peace and quiet plus good food and a pint is usually desparate for this sort of information. The 17th century Cross Ways Inn has a low beamed, traditionally furnished interior, log fires and friendly, welcoming atmosphere. Extensive menu with something for everyone, including children's meals. Pub specials include a Mexican style pork, smoked sausage and bean stew, broccoli, chicken and ham mornay, ham and mushroom tagliatelle, moussaka and salad, a vegetable bake and curries. They have a Bistro Friday and Saturday nights when there is a two or three course dinner; the menu changes every week. Flowers IPA, Original and Royal Oak plus varying guest ales – could be Smiles Best, Butcombe Bitter, Bass or Oakhill. Choice of malt whiskies and Rich's farmhouse cider. Seats in the large garden among the fruit trees.

OPEN: 12–3. 5.30–11 (6–11 Sat)
Real Ale. Restaurant Fri & Sat only
Children welcome (except in main bar). Dogs on leads.
Occasional live music.
Three en suite bedrooms.

WINCANTON

Stags Head Inn
Tel: 01963 440393

Yarlington, Wincanton, Somerset BA9 8DG
Free House. Andy & Ann Sugg, licensees.

Without the inn sign hanging from the side of the pub and stag's horns fixed above the front door, you would hesitate even to think that this was a pub. At first glance it would seem to be a solid, stone built village house, with a long low garden wall and front gate. But inside this small and very friendly pub there are two bars with pine serving counters, traditional furnishings and wholesome varied bar food. There is an à la carte menu in the restaurant and special Sunday lunches. Butcombe Bitter, Castlemaine XXXX, Tetleys and Lowenbrau; also Inch's farm cider. Seats in the garden.

OPEN: 12–2.30. 7–11.
Real Ale. Restaurant (no food Monday).
No dogs.

WINSFORD

Royal Oak Inn   Tel: 01643 851455

Winsford, Exmoor National Park, Somerset TA24 7JE
Free House. Charles Steven. licensee.

In a picturesque village on the edge of the Exmoor National Park, among stone and thatched cottages, you will find the smart, cream-washed, thatched 12th century Royal Oak. Well it was 12th century but they had a disastrous fire last year closing them down for nine months, but all is well again and they are back in business. So shall we say, originally 12th century. Inside are still some fine oak beams, panelling and big open fires. Bar meals include home-made soup, sandwiches, ploughmans, seafood pancake, sirloin steak grilled with fried mushrooms and onions on toast, steak and kidney pie, chicken and leek pie, grilled steak, salmon or trout also daily specials such as chicken and apricot terrine, toad in the hole or broccoli and cauliflower cheese bake. Puds too. Everything is home-cooked, including the bread. A full menu is served in the elegant restaurant. Small select wine cellar. Four barrels of real ale in the bar and guest ales which change every few weeks. The River Winn, on which the Royal Oak has its own beat, runs through the village and fishing can be arranged.

OPEN: 11–2.30. 6–11.
Real Ale. Restaurant (not Sun eves)
Children welcome except in front bar. Dogs on leads.
Eight comfortable en suite bedrooms in the Inn, six more in the annexe.
Dogs can be accommodated too.

WITHAM FRIARY

Seymour Arms   Tel: 01749 850742

Witham Friary, Frome, Somerset BA11 5HS
Free House. Jean Douel, licensee.

Seven miles from Frome, off the B3092, this is an unspoilt old place, built as public house in 1857. Two rooms, stone flags on the floor, beer from the barrel served through a hatch, and no food. There is a garden to sit in to enjoy Ushers Best Bitter and Rich's Cider. The pub, surrounded by fields, has lovely views of the surrounding countryside from the garden. Good walks nearby.

OPEN: 11–3. 6–11
Real Ale. Real Cider. No food.
Dogs on leads.

WITHYPOOL

Royal Oak   Tel: 01643 831506

Withypool, Somerset, TA24 7QP
Free House. Michael Bradley, licensee.

Not a haunt of the anti-hunting brigade: stags' antlers and fox masks nailed to the walls make a very positive statement. Fishing memorabilia in another room. Filling, well-chosen and extensive bar snacks range from sandwiches and soups to steaks and a choice of fish in season. The blackboard menu is more adventurous and may offer you lamb casserole, poached salmon or half a crispy duck. Any 'special' fish dish is always popular. There's a table d'hote and an à la carte menu in the restaurant. Very busy, particularly on Sundays and in the hunting and shooting season. Flowers IPA, Castle Eden and Bentleys Yorkshire. Farm ciders and malt whiskies. Interesting wine list. Lots of walks, wonderful views, and if you're really keen, you can hunt, shoot or fish by arrangement.

OPEN: 11–2.30. 6–11.
Real Ale. Restaurant.
No children. Dogs on leads.

WE'RE NOT AGAINST ALL MUSIC

We are not against all music in pubs. Live music is totally acceptable and the pub piano is part of that tradition. Moreover, publicans nearly always announce an event giving those who want to avoid it a chance to drink elsewhere. What most QUIET PINT readers object to is having to compete against a constant barrage of background music to hear or be heard.

S
SUFFOLK

ALDEBURGH

Cross Keys   Tel: 01728 452637

Crabbe Street, Aldeburgh, Suffolk IP15 5BN
Adnams. G Prior, tenant.

The Cross Keys is in an idyllic situation at the height of summer: only the promenade separates the courtyard at the back of the pub from the beach. Sitting in the courtyard you can have a drink or a meal and watch the world go by. Inside, the two bars, each with a cosy stove to warm things up, are a refuge from the cold easterly winds which blow during the winter. Familiar bar food plus good open sandwiches, vegetarian dishes and lots of fish. Adnams Traditional ales. There are some interesting things to see in Aldeburgh. The church has a John Piper window commemorating Benjamin Britton, the founder of the Music Festival, and there's a half-timbered 16th century Moot Hall which is now a museum.

OPEN: 11–3. 6–11 (11–11 Sat).
Real Ale. No food winter Sun eves
Dogs on leads.

BLYFORD

Queens Head   Tel: 01502 478404

Southwold Road, Blyford IP19 9JY
Adnams. Tony Matthews, tenant.

Situated opposite the church, this old thatched pub is one to make a note of if you are wandering the lanes of Suffolk in the early morning, as they serve breakfast from 8.30. Inside it is heavily beamed, comfortable, with huge open fires during the winter. No music and no one-armed bandits either. A conversational pub. There is a good variety of lunchtime bar snacks, and a greater, more adventurous, selection of meals during the evening: chicken breast stuffed with leeks in a Stilton and wine sauce, rack of lamb with cranberry sauce, whole roast pheasant in burgundy, or slowly baked leg of lamb "Greek style," smothered in herbs and spices and fresh fish from Lowestoft. All Adnams ales. A no-smoking family room. Tables outside in the garden where there is an activity area for the children.

OPEN: 11–3. 6.30–11.
Real Ale. Restaurant.
Children in eating area & no-smoking restaurant. No dogs.
Wheelchair access is limited.

BRENT ELEIGH

The Cock   Tel: 01787 247371

Brent Eleigh, Sudbury CO10 9PB
Free House. Charles Lydford, licensee.

Postal addresses are so confusing. Brent Eleigh is a small village near Lavenham on the A1141 Lavenham-Hadleigh road – between the glories of Lavenham and the delights of Hadleigh. A favourite with the Anglia Press Agency reporters, so you know The Cock Inn is worth a visit. Journalists are very fussy about where they drink, and that is all you get here: well kept beer with a nut and a crisp as a side order. Two bars in this unspoilt, 15th century thatched building. A basic Suffolk drinking pub with large tables in each bar to take all the beer mugs. Greene King IPA and Abbot, Adnams Bitter and Mild – no guests. Seats in the small garden at the front of the pub.

OPEN: 12–3. 6–11 (12–3. 7–10.30 Sun)
Real Ale, no food.
Children – iffy – allowed Sundays in smaller bar. Dogs on leads.
Small car parks, front and back. Wheelchairs difficult, but help available.

CHILLESFORD

The Friars Inn, (known as The Froize)   Tel: 01394 450282

The Street, Chillesford, Near Woodbridge, Suffolk IP12 3PW
Free House. Mr Alistair & Mrs Joy Shaw, licensees

East of Chillesford, on a quiet country road between Woodbridge and Orford, the Froize is between the expanse of Tunstall forest to the north and the head of the Butley river – famous for its oysters – to the south. A popular local pub. Just one bar with a welcoming friendly atmosphere. Lots of exciting plans to expand the bar food areas; even so, there is a comprehensive menu. The speciality is local fish, with the addition of game in season. Adnams and Greene King, Mauldons fairly regularly, and many other guest beers. Good wine list.

OPEN: Summer all day opening Tues–Sun, and Bank Holiday Mondays. Otherwise closed Mondays all year. Winter. 11–3. 6–11. All day Sat and Sun. Lunch and supper served Tues to Friday inclusive.
Children welcome. Dogs on leads.

DUNWICH

Ship Inn   Tel: 01728 648219

St James' Street, Dunwich, Nr Saxmundham, Suffolk IP17 3DT
Free House. Stephen & Ann Marshlain, licensees.

Visiting Dunwich today, it is hard to believe that in Henry II's reign it had 15 religious establishments and a flourishing shipbuilding industry. The village you see today is all that remains of the prosperous medieval centre that was gradually washed away by the sea over the intervening centuries. The Ship Inn, originally the haunt of smugglers, has a comfortable bar with a wood-burning stove in a big fireplace, and plenty of fishing and nautical bric-a-brac distributed throughout the pub. As well as a dining room, it has a family conservatory. Bar snacks at lunchtime only. During the evening the restaurant menu applies throughout the pub. It is renowned for its own fish and chips, and many other fish dishes, but you can still get soups, pies, salads, ploughmans and good puddings. Adnams ales and Greene King Abbot. Seats on the terrace and in the sheltered garden.

OPEN: 11–3 (11–3.30 Sat). 6–11 (6.30–11 winter)
Real Ale. Evening Restaurant
Children not in bar. Dogs on leads.
Bedrooms.

EARL SOHAM

Victoria   Tel: 01728 685758

Earl Soham, Suffolk IP13 7RL
Own Brew. Clare & John Bjornson, licensees

A pub where the beer is brewed on the spot. Not only can you sample the goods on the premises, you can even take some home with you. Traditionally furnished, and with pine panelling, tiled floors, big open fires and pictures of our dear Queen Victoria. The pub is very popular and gets quite busy. It has a good selection of bar food, soups, curries, chilli, salads and vegetarian dishes plus a Sunday roast. The ales, from the Earl Soham Brewery, are called Victoria Bitter, Albert (strong), Jolabrugg (very strong), and Gannet which is a mild. Seats at the front of the pub and on the lawn at the back.

OPEN: 11.30–2.30. 5.30–11.
Real Ale.
No dogs. Folk music Tues & Fri eves.

EASTON

White Horse Inn   Tel: 01728 746456

The Street, Easton, Suffolk.
Pubmaster. Pip Smith, tenant.

Next to the church and overlooking the village green, the 16th century White Horse Inn is perhaps everyones idea of the perfect village pub. Public and lounge bar, a pool room that doubles as a function room, and a small restaurant serving good food – you can't do better than that. Here they specialise in home-made pies with three different fillings: steak and kidney; chicken and game or chicken and leek. All the food, including the bar menu, is listed on the blackboards. There could be fillet of pork in a mustard and cream sauce, trout in a brandy and prawn sauce, fillet of lamb in a mint and cream sauce, gammon and three kinds of stir fry. Flowers IPA and Original, also Kilkenny which is brewed by Guinness. Big beer garden at the back of the pub.

OPEN: 11–3. 6.30–11
Real Ale Restaurant
Children in eating areas. Dogs in bar only.
Wheelchair access.

GREAT GLEMHAM

Crown   Tel: 01728 663693

The Street, Great Glemham, Nr Saxmundham, Suffolk IP17 1DA
Free House. Roger Mason, licensee.

Between Framlingham and Saxmundham, deep in the lovely Suffolk countryside. Inside the pub is a large beamed bar which has two huge fireplaces filled with blazing logs during the winter. Lots of food available, ranging from filled rolls to lasagne, steak & kidney pie, vegetarian dishes, and a children's menu. Adnams ales and Bass. Choice of wines and a selection of malt whiskies. Tables on the lawn at the corner of the pub during the summer.

OPEN: 12–2.30. 7–11.
Real Ale. Restaurant (no meals or snacks Mon).
Children in restaurant. No dogs.
Bedrooms.

HORRINGER

Beehive   Tel: 01284 735260

The Street, Horringer, Suffolk IP29 5SD
Greene King. Gary & Dianne Kingshott, tenants.

In a very desirable location, sharing a boundary with glorious Ickworth Park, you'll find the pretty village of Horringer and the attractive, rambling, Beehive pub. Inside there are lots of low-beamed nooks and crannies – plenty of room in which to sit and sample the imaginative food. The printed menu changes about three times a year, but there could be home-made taramasalata with hot pitta bread, Beehive hors d'oeuvres, pancakes filled with flaked smoked haddock, cheese and cream, Cumberland sausages braised in a rich red wine, wide choice of fish dishes from the specials board and lots of home-made puddings. Greene King IPA and Abbot ales plus a short, interesting, wine list. Seats on the terrace at the back of the pub and also in the garden.

OPEN: 11.30–2.30. 7–11.
Real Ale. No food Sun evening
Children welcome. Dogs on leads.
Wheelchair access to pub only.

HOXNE

Swan   Tel: 01379 668275

Low Street, Hoxne, Suffolk IP21 5AS
Free House. Tony & Frances Thornton-Jones, licensees.

Very near here is the site of King Edmund's murder in 870 A.D. by the marauding Danes. His body was later buried on the site of the town named after him – Bury St Edmunds. Legend has it that part of the tree he was tied to before execution forms a section of the screen in a nearby church. The Swan, a little younger than the martyrdom, has its own ecclesiastical connections in that it was built by the Bishop of Norwich in the 15th century and much of the interior of The Swan dates back to that time. Better than average bar menu: seafood platter, lamb cutlets, filled pancakes, omelettes and grills. There is a specials board, among which courgette and rosemary soup, a selection of smoked fish, herby brie parcels, pork satay with peanut sauce, or pasta with cream, ham and mushroom sauce, are just a few of the dishes that may be on offer – good puds too. Greene King Abbot ale, Adnams Bitter, Old Ale and Tally Ho in winter. Well chosen wine list and a selection of wines by the glass. Seats outside in the large sheltered garden which boasts a croquet lawn for the mildly energetic.

OPEN: 12–2.30 (12–3 Sat). 5.30–11. (12–3. 7–10.30 Sun.)
Real Ale. Restaurant.
Children in eating area. Dogs on leads.

LAMARSH

Red Lion   Tel: 01787 227918

Bures, Lamarsh, Suffolk CO8 5EP
Free House. John & Angela O'Sullivan, licensees.

Particularly attractive on a summer's evening if you just want to sit and let time drift by, watch the river, look at the view and contemplate life. Built in the 14th century, it has lots of beams, pretty flowers inside and a friendly, helpful staff. The menu is very changeable, as it depends on what inspires the chef that day. Be assured that it will be imaginative, varied and well cooked. Courage Directors, Greene King IPA, John Smiths, Marstons Pedigree, Suffolk Ale and Wadworths 6X. Wines by the glass and a selection of malt whiskies. Life on the river can get very exciting when the young farmers hold their annual raft race on Whit Bank Holiday weekend.

OPEN: 11–3. 6–11. (11–11 Sats.)
Real Ale. Restaurant.
Children in eating area. Dogs in barn.
Occasional live music.

LAVENHAM

Swan Tel: 01787 247477

High Street, Lavenham, Suffolk CO10 9QA
Free House (Forte). M R Grange, licensee.

Wonderful Lavenham. An unspoilt, carefully preserved medieval town, with magnificent timbered houses and the church of St Peter and St Paul dominating the horizon. Dating back to the 14th century, the Swan, heavily beamed inside and out, with a minstrels' gallery in the no-smoking restaurant, is very much the smart hotel. At its heart though, is a small, friendly bar, still with its mementoes from the time when it was a local for the American 48th Bomber Group, stationed here during the last war. At lunchtime the favourite ham and turkey salad or filled baguettes, steak sandwiches and other bar snacks are served from a buffet in the the Lounge which overlooks the courtyard garden. John Smiths and Greene King IPA ales, a number of malt whiskies and cognacs. Seats in the garden courtyard.

OPEN: 11–3. 6–11.
Real Ale. Restaurant.
Children welcome. Dogs on leads in bar.
Pianist every night.
Bedrooms. Wheelchair access difficult, but there are willing helpers.

LAXFIELD

Kings Head Tel: 01986 798395

Gormans Lane, Laxfield, Nr Woodbridge, Suffolk IP13 8DG
Free House. Adrian Read, manager.

Laxfield, with its long wide village street and interesting half-timbered Guildhall, was the birthplace of William Dowsing, a fervent follower of Oliver Cromwell. "Destroyer" Dowsing was mainly responsible for the destruction of some of the most beautiful artefacts and interiors in our churches during the time of the Civil War. Bearing in mind the village's relationship with a follower of Oliver Cromwell, 'The King's Head' is aptly named. Low, thatched and unspoilt, nothing much has changed over the years; beer is still drawn from the cask in the tap room. Food though, has moved with the times. Popular, hearty bar food using the best local produce; a blackboard menu which could offer: home-made soups, pork with apricot dumplings, cod with a cheese and bacon crust, chicken pie, liver and bacon, all with fresh vegetables, and puds such as fruit crumbles, apple pie, lemon tart or

Ipswich almond pudding. Adnams Ales, Greene King Abbot and a couple of guest beers. Country wines and local cider. Seats in the sheltered garden where there is a croquet and bowling green.

OPEN: 11–3. 6–11. (12–3. 7–10.30. Sun).
Real Ale.
Children in eating area. Dogs on leads.
Occasional folk nights.
Wheelchair access to all parts of pub.

LEVINGTON

The Ship Inn   Tel: 01473 659573

Church Lane, Levington, Nr Ipswich, Suffolk IP10 0LQ
Pubmaster. William & Shirley Waite, tenants.

On the edge of an attractive village overlooking the River Orwell, popular with locals, townies and visiting yachtsmen, the pub has a decidedly nautical air. Prints, pictures, nets and even a compass under the counter. Is that to check where you are? Simple, well chosen bar food: ploughmans, quiche, sausages in cider sauce, lots of salads and a vegetarian dish or two. Daily specials offering more substantial dishes and good puds. Flowers Original, Tolly Cobbold Bitter, Bass, Wadworths 6X and Greene King IPA drawn from the cask. Country wines and some wines by the glass. Seats in front of the pub overlook fields and the river.

OPEN: 11.30–3. 6–11.
Real Ale. Restaurant.
No children under 14. No dogs.
Folk music first Tues in month.

ORFORD

Jolly Sailor   Tel: 01394 450243

Quay Street, Orford, Nr Woodbridge, Suffolk IP12 2NU
Adnams. Philip Attwood, tenant.

Orford is at the end of the road, so to speak – any further and you would have to become a sailor, jolly or otherwise, as you would be in, or on, the River Or. An old smugglers' inn, the Jolly Sailor is reputed to be built out of the timbers of ships wrecked nearby. Inside, there are several small rooms, warmed by a big stove in winter. Well chosen bar food, local fish and chips, home-cooked ham, omelettes and ploughmans. The dining room is no-smoking. Adnams range of ales. There are tables in the large garden.

OPEN: 11.30–2.30. 7–11.
Real Ale.
Dogs on leads in middle bar.
Bedrooms.

PIN MILL

Butt & Oyster   Tel: 01473 780764

Pin Mill, Nr Chelmondiston, Ipswich, Suffolk IPN 1JW
Pubmaster. Dick & Brenda Mainwaring, tenants.

Overlooking the River Orwell and originally a bargemans' retreat, this classic 17th century riverside pub is still popular with sailors and landlubbers alike, including film crews. It used to be the 'done thing' to sail here for lunch – probably still is. If so, what better place to be than sitting at one of the tables on terra firma watching the negotiation from yacht to dinghy and vice versa after a good lunch. Traditional bar food with a selection of blackboard specials. The ploughmans is very generous and there will be a vegetarian dish or two. Tolly Original Bitter and Mild.

OPEN: 11–11. (11–3. 7–11 winter)
Real Ale.
Children welcome away from main bar. No dogs.
Occasional piano & folk dancing.

RATTLESDEN

Brewers Arms   Tel: 01449 736377

Lower Road, Rattlesden, Nr Bury St Edmunds, Suffolk IP30 0RJ
Greene King. Ron Cole, tenant.

Deep in the country between Stowmarket and either Bury St Edmunds or Lavenham, depending really where in Suffolk you start from – you could say you were in the middle of the triangle. A jolly, popular, 16th century village pub with a reputation for imaginative, well-cooked food, it has a creative changing menu; nevertheless, a simple filled roll, bowl of soup and other bar snacks are always available. Greene King ales, quite a few local wines and

THE QUIET PINT

a choice of malt whiskies. There are seats in the pretty rose-filled garden which has a boules pitch. N.B As we went to press we heard that a new tenant is soon to be taking over the Brewers Arms. There is a chance that he will bring in the dreaded music – do let us know.

OPEN: 12–2.30 (12–3 Sat). 7–11.
Real Ale. Pub closed Sun & Mon evening, Last week June, 1st week July.
Well behaved children. Dogs in one bar & garden.
Jazz Thurs eve.

SNAPE

The Crown   Tel: 01728 688324

Bridge Road, Snape IP17 1SL
Adnams. Paul Maylott, tenant.

"No music, no slot machines, a near perfect interior. The Crown deserves several stars in your Quiet Pint" – read the postcard from one of our readers. So it does. This is a fine rambling old building, lots of nooks and crannies, low, beamed ceilings, creaking floorboards and huge settles to settle in. One small bar but wherever you are in the Crown they serve interesting food. No sandwiches, but ploughmans, chicken and brandy paté, king prawns in garlic butter, marinated anchovies, warm smoked sprats, smoked duck breast salad, potato and cheese pancake, lobster, prawn and saffron tart, avocado and prawn salad also fillet steaks, whole plaice, chicken breasts with a mozarella cheese, basil and sun-dried tomato stuffing. Gosh! The menu changes every day, but this gives you some idea of what you could have. Apart from the prawns and chips, everything is as fresh as can be. Adnams Best Bitter and Adnams seasonal ales. `Unusually long and enterprising wine list for a pub.' It is the landlord's particular hobby. A big front garden to sit in.

OPEN: 11–3.6–11 (12–3.7–10.30 Sun)
Real Ale. Dining Room
No children. Well behaved dogs on leads.
Two double, one single room en-suite.
Wheelchair access. Lots of car parking space.

SNAPE

Golden Key   Tel: 01728 688510

Priory Road, Snape, Nr Saxmundham, Suffolk IP17 1SG
Adnams. Max & Susie Kissick-Jones, tenants.

Close to Snape Maltings and the site of the Aldeburgh Festival, you will find
this charming 15th century pub. It has a large main bar, divided into public
(tiled floor) bar and lounge (carpeted). Lots of sustaining, well prepared bar
food: home-made soups, paté, filled rolls, sausage and onion pie, smoked
haddock, quiche, fresh fish, steaks and roast on Sunday. Adnams ales, local
farm ciders and a choice of malt whiskies. Seats at the front of the pub, also
in the colourful garden at the back.

OPEN: 11–3. 6–11 (extensions during Aldeburgh Festival)
Real Ale.
Children in eating area. Dogs on leads.

SNAPE

Plough and Sail   Tel: 01728 688413

Riverside Centre, Snape Maltings
Free House. G. J. Goodenham, licensee.

Lots of things go on at the Maltings; not only the Aldeburgh Festival in
summer but antique fairs, concerts, television recording sessions and at the
Riverside Centre there are craft shops and garden shops. When you've
exhausted what's on offer, and yourself, time to call in at the Plough and Sail.
A choice of home-made soups, freshly made closed or open sandwiches,
home-made paté, salads and, as you would expect, plenty of fish dishes
plus everything you would find on a good restaurant menu. Adnams
Southwold Bitter, Broadside and Barley Mow in summer, Tally-Ho in winter.
Greene King Abbot an occasional guest beer. Good wine list, some by the
glass. Tables in the enclosed courtyard at the back of the pub.

OPEN: 11–3. 5.30–11 (12–3. 6.30–10.30. Sun. 7–10.30 winter)
Real Ale. Restaurant.
Children, not inside. Dogs on leads when not serving food.

SOUTHWOLD

Crown Hotel   Tel: 01502 722275

High Street, Southwold, Suffolk IP18 6DP
Adnams. Anne Simpson, manager.

Originally a posting inn, this very attractive Georgian hotel has been renamed three times during its lifetime. At first it was called the Nag's Head; after rebuilding in 1715 it became 'The New Swan' (not to be confused with The Old Swan in the marketplace); then in 1829 it took on a new identity and was called 'The Crown'. Now restored, it is very handsome – an elegant Georgian town house – combining pub, wine bar, restaurant and small hotel. It has an extensive wine list, imaginative weekly changing bar food and a restaurant where they serve a very reasonably priced three-course lunch. Flagship of the nearby Adnams Brewery – the ales are kept in the best condition. There is an impressive wine list, (they are wine merchants as well). Lots of wines by the glass, including classic vintages selected monthly. Do note the wonderful wrought iron inn sign attached to the front of The Crown Hotel.

OPEN: 10.30–3. 6–11 (closed first week Jan)
Real Ale. Restaurant.
Children in eating area & restaurant. Dogs in one bar.
Bedrooms.

STOKE BY NAYLAND (Nr Colchester)

Angel   Tel: 01206 263245

Polstead Street, Stoke by Nayland CO6 4SA
Free House. Peter Smith, licensee.

This attractively restored 16th century inn is at the main crossroads of the village situated in the heart of 'Constable country.' The casual drinker is still catered for in the small bar, but on the whole it is a serious eating pub. A blackboard menu operates throughout the bars and restaurant; the selection of reasonably priced dishes can change twice a day. As the Angel is hugely popular, it is best to book to be sure of a table. Lots of fish dishes: fresh dressed crab with home-made mayonnaise, steamed mussels in white wine, tomato and Feta cheese salad, brochette of scallops wrapped in bacon, honey glazed roast rack of lamb, roast ballotine of duckling with Cassis sauce, or vegetable filo parcels with fresh tomato coulis, local game in season, home-made steak & kidney puddings are just a selection and traditional Sunday roasts. Home-made puddings too. Greene King Abbot ale, Adnams Bitter, Greene King IPA and a guest bitter. Lots of interesting wines. Seats outside on the terrace.

OPEN: 11–2.30. 6–11.
Real Ale. Restaurant.
No children in the bar. No dogs.
Wheelchair access.

SUDBURY

The Angel   Tel: 01787 379038

Friar Street, Sudbury, Suffolk
Greene King. Brenda Rowe, tenant.

This pub has a literary past. Sudbury was 'Eatanswill' in Charles Dickens' Pickwick Papers, and The Angel was, well The Angel, – a mid-17th century building whose cellars date back to the 10th century. It's in the middle of Sudbury and is an attractive, low ceilinged, well beamed structure, creaking with the effort of it all, with not a right angle in the place. Lounge, public bar and snug. Varied bar snacks: sandwiches and ploughmans or poached salmon, haddock Royale, scampi, Cajun chicken, roast chicken, gammon steaks, a large vegetarian menu – "we serve anything" says the landlady. You can eat in the bar or the restaurant. Greene King related beers. Small, pretty patio.

OPEN: 11–11.30 (12–10.30 Sun)
Real Ale. Restaurant.
Children welcome. Plenty of dogs.

TOSTOCK

Gardeners Arms   Tel: 01359 270460

Church Road, Tostock, Nr Bury St Edmunds IP30 9PA
Greene King. Reg Ransome, tenant.

Situated near the village green this is a pleasant, beamey old pub serving well presented home-made bar food and well kept ales. The usual well tried selection of bar snacks and daily specials written on the beams of the pub: Thai King prawn green curry with stir fried vegetables on rice, lamb Balti, chicken and broccoli bake. Various vegetarian dishes . A greater variety of grills and other dishes are available during the evening, when it can get very busy. Greene King Abbot, IPA and seasonal beers. Seats in the attractive garden.

OPEN: 11.30–2.30 (11–2.30 Sat). 7–11.
Real Ale. Restaurant (not Sun lunch). No snacks Mon/Tues eves
Children in eating area of bar. Dogs on leads.

S
SURREY

ALBURY HEATH

King William IV   Tel: 01483 202685

Little London, Albury Heath, Guildford, Surrey GU5 9DB
Free House. Mike & Helen Davids, licensees.

Set in lovely walking country, this friendly little pub is a welcome stopping place for a quiet pint and a sandwich or two. Its rooms are small with flagstone floors, and in one there is a huge inglenook fireplace, with an equally huge log fire in the winter. Short, reasonably priced bar menu: ploughmans, pies, home-cooked ham and eggs and a Sunday roast. Every month they have a special fish evening. All the fish is brought in fresh from Billingsgate, and there is quite a variety to choose from. Boddingtons, Whitbreads Castle Eden and the local Hogs Back ales. Regularly changing guest beers. Seats in the pretty front garden.

OPEN: 11–3. 5.30–11.
Real Ale. Restaurant.
Children welcome. Dogs on leads.

BETCHWORTH

Dolphin Inn   Tel: 01737 842288

The Street, Betchworth, Surrey RH3 7DW
Youngs. George Campbell, manager

An unspoilt village pub dating back to the late 16th century. The Dolphin has beams, flagstone floors and panelled walls. Near excellent walking country, it is understandably popular and gets very busy. Interesting, varied bar food: sandwiches, filled baked potatoes, ham on the bone, steak, and other pies, grills and daily specials. Youngs range of ales, including the seasonal "Winter Warmer". Seats at the front, side, and back of the pub.

OPEN: 11–3. 5.30–11.
Real Ale.
No children. Dogs on leads.

DUNSFOLD

Sun Inn   Tel: 01483 200242

The Common, Dunsfold, Surrey GU8 4LE
Friary Meux. Mrs J. Dunne, lease.

In the good old SMERSH and grab days of the Cold War, the chances are that some of the Sun Inn's customers would be in for refreshment between discreet spells of spying on neighbouring Dunsfield airfield, where the world's first successful Vertical Take-Off and Landing fighter – the Harrier Jump Jet – was developed and tested. The airfield is no longer as active, but the attractive 18th century pub near the cricket green certainly is. Inside there is a comfortable beamed interior, three open log fires, a cottage restaurant, and coffee and croissants served from 10.30 Monday to Saturday. Table d'hôte and à la carte menus are available in the restaurant. Everything is freshly cooked; the speciality of the house being local Dunsfold quail. Marstons Pedigree, King and Barnes Sussex and Friary Meux. Range of malt whiskies. Plenty of room in the garden which has a barbecue and a boules pitch for the more energetic. If you want to throw a party they have a 17th century hop barn for hire.

OPEN: 11–3. 6–11
Real Ale. Restaurant.
Children welcome. Dogs on leads.

EFFINGHAM

Sir Douglas Haig   Tel: 01372 456886

The Street, Effingham, Surrey KT24 5LU
Free House. Laurie Smart, licensee.

This is a slightly doubtful entry as they do switch the music on after 9pm, presumably to empty the pub: any earlier, do please let us know, and they'll get the chop. Virtually rebuilt several years ago, it remains a solidly reliable pub where you will be adequately fed and assured of a good pint. The bar menu includes home-made favourites with lots of fresh vegetables, and daily specials. They serve a roast lunch on Sunday. Boddingtons, Fullers London Pride, Gales HSB and Wadworths 6X. Seats on the lawn and the terrace.

OPEN: 11–3. 5.30–11 (11–11 Sat).
Real Ale. No food Sun evening.
Dogs on leads.
Bedrooms. N.B.
Music is put on after 9 pm.

ELSTEAD

Woolpack Tel: 01252 703106

Elstead, Surrey GU8 6HD
Friary Meux (Allied). Jill Macready & S. Askew, lease.

Originally built sometime in the 18th century to store bales of wool after shearing, the building was later licensed and has since evolved into the pleasant country pub you find today. Inside, the main bar is decorated with a number of artefacts which relate to its woolly past. Familiar pub stalwarts on the menu: home-made pies, ploughmans, casseroles, grills and ham on the bone, also daily specials and Sunday lunches. The puddings are another speciality – really home-made. Children's portions available. Greene King Abbot ale and one other from the cask. A selection of wines by the bottle and by the glass. Family room opening onto the garden, and a children's play area. Seats in the garden for the grown-ups.

OPEN: 11–2.30 (3 Sat). 6–11.
Real Ale. Restaurant.
Children in family room & restaurant. Dogs on leads.

ENGLEFIELD GREEN

Fox and Hounds Tel: 01784 433098

Bishopsgate, Englefield Green, Surrey TW20 0XU
Courage. John Mee and Robert King, licensees.

This pub is near the south-east corner of Windsor Great Park and ideally placed for a visit to the Savill Gardens. The same licensees run the Thatched Tavern at Cheapside. Both pubs are in the same Park – different counties. The Fox and Hounds is a comfortable old place with lots of charm serving reliable pub grub: home-made soup, sandwiches, filled baguettes, salads – specials on the blackboard. Actually most dishes are listed on blackboards – hand held ones in the candlelit restaurant. Courage Best and Directors with John Smiths and Greene King IPA as guest ales. Good wine list. Seats on the the terrace at the back of the pub and on the grass at the front, from where you can watch all the comings and goings.

OPEN: 11–3. 6–11
Real Ale. Restaurant.
Well behaved children. Dogs on leads in bar.

FARNHAM

Nelson Arms   Tel: 01252 716078

50–52 Castle Street, Farnham, Surrey GU9 7JQ
Scottish and Newcastle. Terry Parsons, manager.

The Georgian fronts on many of the buildings in Castle Street conceal their medieval origins. Farnham grew from a prehistoric settlement into a town which owed its importance to the agricultural development of the surrounding area in medieval times. The Norman Castle, which later became the Palace of the Bishops of Winchester, still has the remains of the 12th century stone walls, the keep and a Tudor tower. The nearby Nelson Arms, a listed building, is apparently linked to the Castle by an underground passage. It was visited by Emma Hamilton and Nelson, who, legend has it, left his glass eye behind, hidden in one of the beams! This is a "spot the beam with the eye game!" Our reporter, who came up with all these stories, says this is the best run pub in the Farnham area. Keeping to the Nelsonian theme, along with the traditional pub grub, they serve a Trafalgar pie and a half-Nelson chicken. Courage Best, Theakstons and Morlands Old Speckled Hen. Seats on the patio.

OPEN: 11–11
Real Ale.
Children welcome. Dogs outside at eating times.

LINGFIELD

Blacksmiths Head   Tel: 01342 833697

Newchapel Road, Newchapel, Lingfield, Surrey RH7 6LE
Free House. G.J. Galloway, licensee.

This is a nice old fashioned country pub two miles from the race course, 100 yards off the A22. Inside there is one L-shaped bar which naturally divides into two distinct areas. A busy family pub, serving interesting food, it has a landlord who has been running the place for over 30 years and is a qualified chef. They serve the usual bar snacks of home-made soups, sandwiches, filled rolls and ploughmans, also more substantial dishes from the daily changing menu: home-made fish pie, roast Surrey chicken, spaghetti Bolognese, crab salad, a risotto, and on Fridays either grilled cod, plaice or haddock. Beers are Friary Meux, King and Barnes Sussex and Ind Coope Burton Ale, though they change these from time to time.

OPEN: 11–3. 6–11 (12–3. 7–10.30 Sun)
Real Ale
Children welcome. Dogs on leads.
Wheelchair access.

OLD OXTED

Old Bell   Tel: 01883 712181

68 High Street, Old Oxted, Surrey RH8 9LP
Scottish & Newcastle. Michael Brown, manager.

Parts of this large roomy place are more than 400 years old. Enough old beams, inglenook fireplaces and creaking boards remain to remind one of its great age. One bar, a snug and a carvery that seats over 50. You'll find a large selection of bar food and snacks. Filled baguettes, sandwiches, ploughmans and salads. Specials on the blackboard could include peppered pork, chilli con carne, chicken Kiev or Cajun chicken. A printed, set menu offers battered haddock, vegetable tikka, crock-pots, ham hash and about four vegetarian dishes. Menus change frequently. Theakstons Best Bitter, XB and Courage Best. Good wine list. Plenty of seats in the garden.

OPEN 11–11. (12–10.30 Sun)
Real Ale
Children welcome. Dogs on leads, not in carvery.
Wheelchair access through back of pub.

OXTED

Haycutter   Tel: 01883 712550

Broadham Green, Oxted, Surrey RH8 9PE
Ind Coope. Barry Aldridge, tenant.

This charming old building, full of character, is set on the edge of Broadham Green. Inside there is a "U" shaped bar which encourages general chat, but if you want to get away from the friendly repartee there are lots of corners for more private conversations. The bar is decorated with Barry Aldridge's collection of hats and historical photographs. A wide choice of bar food is available ranging from soup, grilled sardines, prawns in garlic butter, omelettes, steaks, fish dishes, salads to the humble sandwich. Youngs, Friary Meux, Burton Bitter, Marstons Pedigree and Wadworths 6X ales. A short wine list. Seats in the garden to take advantage of the attractive Surrey countryside.

OPEN: 11–11.
Real Ale. No food Sundays.
Children in dining area. Dogs on leads.

PIRBRIGHT

Royal Oak   Tel: 01483 232466

Aldershot Road, Pirbright, Aldershot, Surrey GU24 OD4
Whitbreads. John Lay, manager.

The Royal Oak is 16th century, beamed and rambling. Lots of flowers inside and out during the summer; big log fires in winter. There is an interesting variety of bar food: steaks and grills, a vegetarian dish or two, chicken tango served in a fresh ginger and yoghurt sauce, fresh fish from the specials board, seasonal salads, not forgetting traditional bar snacks. Over eighteen ales are offered, occasionally some from the smaller, less well known breweries: Rev. James Crown Buckley, Hogs Back Traditional English Ale (TEA), Eldridge Pope Royal Oak, Boddingtons, Flowers Original, Marstons Pedigree, Youngs Special, and many, many more. Ask, and you'll probably be surprised. Seats among the flowers at the front, or in the quieter garden at the back. Good walking country.

OPEN: 11–11.
Real Ale. Restaurant.
Children in restaurant. No dogs.

SHAMLEY GREEN

Red Lion   Tel: 01483 892202

Shamley Green, Surrey GU5 0UB
Free House. Ben Heath, licensee.

Overlooking the village green and summer cricket matches, this listed 17th century pub has a comfortable, well furnished, polished interior. Really more of a restaurant than a pub, not a "drop-in-for-just-a-pint" place. You really have to book a table, or get there at an unbusy time of day. An interesting, reliable blackboard menu could offer home-made soup, ploughmans, stuffed mushrooms, peppered chicken breast, seafood tagliatelle, home-baked ham and eggs, salads and some vegetarian dishes, properly cooked vegetables and home-made puddings. A more substantial menu is available in the restaurant. Greene King Abbot Ale, Flowers Original and Friary Meux. Choice of wines. Tables in the garden.

OPEN: 11–11.
Real Ale. Restaurant.
Children welcome. No dogs.
Wheelchair access.

SHERE

White Horse Inn Tel: 01483 202161

Middle Street, Shere, Nr Guildford, Surrey GU5 9HS
Scottish & Newcastle. Mike Wicks, manager.

A pretty, flowery 14th century timbered village pub, high on the North Downs. Rambling beamed rooms with undulating floors and huge, handsome inglenook fireplaces. During the renovation of the building, some fascinating objects came to light; centuries ago these articles were buried in the walls in the hope that they would ward off the evil spirits. They are now on display in the pub. Old-style uncomplicated pub favourites and daily specials on the menu. Theakstons Best Bitter, Ruddles Best and Wadworths 6X. Seats outside in the attractive courtyard and garden. Lots of good walks nearby.

OPEN: 11.30–11.
Real Ale.
Children in eating area. Dogs on leads.

TANDRIDGE

Barley Mow Tel: 01883 713770

Tandridge Lane, Tandridge, Oxted.
Free House. Les & Sally Habgood.

At the foot of the North Downs between Godstone and Oxted – only a few minutes from the A25 – "this is a spacious, cheerful, friendly place with a wise-cracking host," said our informant. Walkers and hikers are welcome in the bar area, which loosly translated means you can come in with your boots on. The lounge is for those less likely to drop mud on the carpet. The restaurant – which leans towards the Italian – for those wanting the full menu, otherwise reliable bar food, and a specials board which could include baked aubergine, liver and bacon, chicken and spinach lasagne, beef curry, mushroom and broccoli quiche or warm Thai chicken salad with egg noodles. All dishes are home-made. The cask beers behind the bar are: Shepherd Neame Spitfire, Master Brew, Pilgrims Progress from Pilgrims Ales Reigate and Capels Old Cocky as a guest. Plenty of places to sit, either on the large terrace at the front of the pub, or in the garden at the back. Barbecue area.

OPEN: 11–3. 6–11. (7–10.30 Sun.)
Real Ale Restaurant
Children if eating, not in the bar. Dogs on leads.
Bedrooms.

THURSLEY

Three Horseshoes   Tel: 01252 703268

Dye House Road, Thursley, Godalming, Surrey GU8 6QD
Free House. Steve and Ann Denman, licensees.

Between the Devil's Punchbowl and Thursley Common, Thursley is an attractive village in the middle of this huge, wonderful nature reserve. In two acres of grounds, The Three Horseshoes, partly 16th century and Grade II listed, has a pleasant bar, log fires in winter and an ample supply of newspapers, guides and Parish magazines for you to read whilst enjoying your pint or two. Surrounded by a network of footpaths, it is a favourite meeting place for ramblers, – not more than six at once unless pre-warned, (just think of all those ruck-sacks and boots). Relaxed and friendly, the pub – with sparkling new kitchens and a new extension to the restaurant – serves good, home-made food using only fresh ingredients: soups, sandwiches and other snacks, beef and Beamish pie, Tuna pasta bake, chicken satay, daily specials and other dishes, the menu changes frequently. Gales HSB, BBB and Butser. Carlings Tennents Extra, Beamish and Scrumpy Jack also available, plus a wide range of country wines. Barbecues in the lovely large garden, which has a Gazebo with views over the spectacular surrounding countryside.

OPEN: 11–3. 6–11 (11–3.30, 6–11 Sat)(12–3.00, 7–10.30 Sun)
Real Ale. Restaurant.
Children over 5 in restaurant. Dogs in garden only

WALLINGTON

Dukes Head   Tel: 0181 6471595

6 Manor Road, The Green, Wallington SM6 OAA
Youngs. Bob Coomber, manager.

A 300 year old pub with a bar for every occasion. Four bars, and the snooker table in a room upstairs. If there's no room at the Inn, they also have a very big garden. The lounge bar doubles up as a restaurant at lunchtime – you can enjoy something from either the snack, à la carte menu, or the specials menu. Familiar bar snacks: sandwiches, ploughmans, filled jacket potatoes and daily specials from the blackboard such as steak and kidney pie, chicken and mushroom pie or liver and bacon. The à la carte menu is quite comprehensive, giving you a choice of home-made soup, several fish dishes, steaks and other grills. Youngs range of ales, including seasonal beers. Plenty of seats in the large garden for barbecue watching – weather permitting.

OPEN: 11–11. (12–10.30 Sun)
Real Ale. Restaurant.
No children. Dogs on leads.
Wheelchair access.

WALLISWOOD

Scarlett Arms   Tel: 01306 627243

Walliswood, Surrey RH5 5RD
King & Barnes. Mrs Pat Haslam, tenant.

Once a pair of 17th century cottages, the Scarlett Arms is a small, charming, unspoilt, popular, country pub. Inside there are beams, polished flagstones, solid, well-used furniture, and a timeless friendly atmosphere. Sometimes it is standing room only, but there are plenty of seats in the garden. Generous portions of good reliable bar food: sandwiches, ham, egg and chips, rabbit pie, curries, ham and mushrooms in a cheese sauce. Thursday is the day for a roast. King and Barnes Festive, Broadwood, Sussex and Mild, Old Ale in winter and a guest beer.

OPEN: 11–2.30. 5.30–11.
Real Ale.
No young children. Dogs on leads and very welcome.

WALTON ON THE HILL

Chequers   Tel: 01737 812364

Chequers Lane, Walton-on-the-Hill KT20 7SF
Youngs. Stephen Brough, manager.

Low beams, creaking floors and inglenook fireplaces are just what you would expect in an old village pub. Even the Victorians, who had a go at doing it up, didn't change that. At the end of the village, once on the edge of the country, the Chequers is now surrounded by houses. Sandwiches, ploughmans, filled jacket potatoes and salads make up the bar menu. From the restaurant you could choose home-made soup, paté, devilled kidneys, stuffed pancakes, fish stew, grilled Dover sole, fresh grilled tuna, fresh scampi, duck, steaks, a pasta dish or one of the daily specials. Weather permitting, the barbecue will be going full pelt from the end of April to the end of September. Youngs range of ales include the seasonal Wheat Beer (summer) Dirty Dicks (autumn) and Winter Warmer (winter). Plenty of room in the garden for you and the barbecue.

OPEN: 11–3. 5.30–11 (11–11 Thurs–Sat. 12–10.30 Sun)
Real Ale
Children in play area. Dogs on leads.

WRECCLESHAM

Sandrock   Tel: 01252 715865

Sandrock Hill, Wrecclesham, Farnham.
Free House. Andrew Bayliss, licensee.

On the edge of the village, this friendly local has one large and one small bar. The small bar serves as the games room and leads into the garden. A bar menu is served at lunchtime only: sandwiches, ploughmans, ham and eggs that sort of thing. Filled rolls only in the evening to go with the range of well kept ales. Eight pumps on all the time, and the beers change regularly. Banthams Best and Simpkiss Bitter from Enville are two of those on at the time of going to press. Lots of chairs and tables in the garden.

OPEN: 11–11 (12–10.30 Sun)
Real Ale
Children welcome. Dogs on leads.

S

SUSSEX

ASHURST

Fountain Inn   Tel: 01403 710219

Ashurst, Nr Steyning, W Sussex BN44 3AP (N of Steyning on B2135)
Free House. Maurice Caine, licensee.

The Fountain Inn, originally a farmhouse is in a largely unspoilt village with views towards the Sussex downs. The 16th century building was gentrified during Georgian times, when a new facade was added to make it appear grander than it really was. Turn right into the tap room with its flagstones, big fireplace, comfortable furnishings and well kept ales and into the larger carpeted room for the well-chosen bar food. Choice of soups, smoked salmon, vegetarian meals, steaks and a variety of fish dishes. Sunday roasts. Very popular, therefore very busy, so book for evening meals. Seats on the terrace and in the pretty garden. There are usually six ales available, among which could be Fullers London Pride, John Smiths, Youngs Special, Ruddles County, Courage Best and a changing guest ale.

OPEN: 11–2.30. 6–11.
Real Ale. Restaurant. No food Sun eves.
Children in restaurant till 8 pm. Dogs in garden only.

BERWICK

Cricketers Arms   Tel: 01323 870469

Berwick, Polegate, E Sussex BN26 6SD
Harveys. Mr P. Brown, manager.

A pleasing unspoilt country pub in a peaceful village at the foot of the South Downs, south of the A 27. Once two cottages, now a pub with an extension, which accounts for the mix of brick and stone. A friendly, busy place with a heavily beamed bar and good winter log fires. Home-made pub food – "nothing flash" to quote the landlord. Several daily specials, plus ploughmans and sandwiches. Harveys Bitter and seasonal ales from the cask. Seats in the attractive walled garden.

OPEN: 11–2.30. 6–11.
Real Ale. Food every lunchtime & Fri & Sat eves.
No dogs.

BILLINGSHURST

Blue Ship   Tel: 01403 822709

The Haven, Billingshurst, W Sussex RH14 9BS
King & Barnes. J R Davie, tenant.

Tucked away in the middle of the country, this little, unspoilt pub is originally 15th century, with Victorian additions. Very popular, particularly at weekends, it has a good choice of traditional bar food – ploughmans, sandwiches and home-made soups, a fish dish or two, cottage pie, steak & kidney pie and good puds. King & Barnes Sussex and Broadwood and Winter Old from the barrel. Tables in the garden and in front of the pub under the honeysuckle.

OPEN: 11–3. 6–11.
Real Ale. No food Sun or Mon eves.
Children in rooms without bar. Dogs on leads.

BLACKBOYS

Blackboys Inn   Tel: 01825 890283

Blackboys, Nr Uckfield, E Sussex TN22 5LG
Harveys. Patrick Russell, tenant.

Overlooking the attractive village pond, this pub had to be largely rebuilt after a serious fire a few years ago. Luckily the rambling beamed ground floor didn't suffer too much. Full of interesting bits and pieces, antique furniture and a big log fire in winter. There are window seats from where you have a view of the pond. Bar food is listed on the blackboard above the bar: sometimes home-made soups, usually ploughmans, fish, stuffed pancakes, steak & kidney pie and Cajun chicken. Seats outside and by the pond. Harveys ales, usually a choice of four.

OPEN: 11–3. 6–11 (12–3. 7–10.30 Sun)
Real Ale. Restaurant.
Children in restaurant. Dogs on leads.

BROADWATER

Cricketers   Tel: 01903 233369

66 Broadwater St West, Nr Worthing, W Sussex BN14 9DE
Bass Charrington. Mark Sinsbury, licensee.

Now within the boundaries of Worthing, Broadwater Parish dates back to
Saxon times and once governed the villages of Broadwater, Worthing and
Ottington. Formally the Brewers' Arms, the pub was renamed in 1878.
Always a popular meeting place, cricket has been played on the green since
early in the 18th century, and as you might expect, the pub is the home of
the local team. Home-cooked bar food, a table d'hote and an à la carte
menu. They specialise in seafood. Greene King IPA, Youngs Special, Bass,
Fullers London Pride, Harveys and Bass Worthington.

OPEN: 11–3. 6–11.
Real Ale. Restaurant every lunchtime + Wed–Sat eves.
Children in family room. Dogs on leads.

BURPHAM

George & Dragon   Tel: 01903 883131

Burpham, Nr Arundel, W Sussex BN18 9RR (off A27 E of Arundel).
Belchers Pubs. James Rose & Kate Holle, tenants.

In an attractive village, not far from Arundel Castle, the pretty George and
Dragon, built in 1742, is popular for its food and real ales. There is one
spacious bar and a smart, elegant dining room. Bar food, available both at
lunchtime and in the evening, varies from home-made soups, sandwiches,
mushrooms in garlic, ploughmans and jacket potatoes to the daily changes
on the blackboard: avocado and fresh Jersey crab, vegetarian chilli and Irish
stew for example. Home-made puddings too. Dinner is served in the
restaurant. Ales available include Arundel Best, Youngers, Cotleigh and
Ashvine. From the garden there are views towards the castle and River Arun.
The pub's resident ghost is a girl who was jilted on her wedding day. Lovely
walks nearby.

THE QUIET PINT

OPEN: 11–2.30. 6–11 (closed Sun eves winter).
Real Ale. Restaurant (no food Sun eves).
No dogs.
Occasional jazz evenings.

BYWORTH

Black Horse   Tel: 01798 342424

Byworth, Nr Petworth, W Sussex GU28 0HO
Free House. Neil Gittins & Michael Courage, licensees.

Byworth is a quiet hamlet near Petworth. The pub, built on the site of an old priory, has a Georgian façade which is hiding a much older building. Friendly busy bars with a good choice of changing bar food – all freshly made. Bar menu ranges from soups, filled potatoes, salads, ploughmans, steak & kidney pudding, chicken in tarragon sauce, pastas, spare ribs and steaks. The specialities of the house are the fish dishes and home-made puddings. Tables in the flowery courtyard or in the large garden which has views across the valley. Ales do change but could include Fullers London Pride, Gales HSB and guest ales which change in spring and summer. Also a good wine list.

OPEN: 11–3. 6–11.
Real Ale. Restaurant.
Children welcome. Dogs on leads.

CHIDDINGLY

Six Bells   Tel: 01825 872227

Chiddingly, Nr Lewes, E Sussex BN8 6HE (off A22 Uckfield-Hailsham).
Free House. Paul Newman, licensee.

Situated opposite the church, this 18th century pub is jolly, unassuming, friendly and not the quietest of places when the bands play. There is live music Tuesday, Friday, Saturday evenings and Sunday lunchtimes – in a separate building admittedly – but I think you could say the joint jumps. Pub grub only, all good, home-made and very reasonable. Soups, locally smoked mackerel, spicy meat loaf and salad, cheesy vegetable bake, spare ribs in barbecue sauce, lasagne, filled potatoes, etc. Puddings too. John Smiths and Courage Best Bitter on hand pump. Seats out in the large garden which has a fish pond. Good long walks nearby.

OPEN: 11–3; 6–11.
Real Ale.
Dogs on leads.
Live Jazz, Blues, etc. Fri, Sat & Sun eves. The Sunbeam M.C.C. meet the 1st Thurs. of every month.

CHIDHAM

Old House at Home   Tel: 01243 572477

Cot Lane, Chidham, Nr Chichester, W Sussex PO18 8SU
Free House. Mike Young, Terry Brewer, licensees.

Slightly off the beaten track and beautifully situated in the glorious West Sussex countryside. You should beat a path to the door if you want to enjoy the good home cooking and well-kept beers at this friendly, popular pub. They offer a good range of bar snacks – home-made soups with French bread. Chef's specials on the blackboard, lots of fresh fish, steaks and other dishes. Well stocked cellar. They have their own Old House beer Guest Session Bitter, Ringwood Best, Badger Best, Old Thumper and Premium Guest Bitter. Seats on the terrace and in the garden. The pub can get extremely busy, so to be sure of a table you should book, particularly in the evenings.

OPEN: 11.30–2.30 (12–3 Sat). 6–11.
Real Ale. Restaurant.
Children welcome. Dogs on leads.

CHRIST'S HOSPITAL

Bax Castle   Tel: 01403 730369

Two Mile Ash Road, Horsham, West Sussex RH13 7LA
Free House. John Wright, licensee.

Originally 15th century weavers' cottages, they were expanded into what you see today when the railway was built during the last century. The Bax Castle is ideally placed to stoke you up for a grand hike or cycle ride along the track that once carried the Guildford – Shoreham railway, and which links up with the South Downs Way. A small rural pub in a big garden, surrounded by trees and good walks. Inside, one bar leads into a dining area. An old cowshed, minus the cows, serves as a function room. As well as a bar snack menu, there will be a choice of 20 main dishes. A lot of fish on a special fish blackboard: trout, salmon, tuna and swordfish. Or you could have a mixed-grill, fillet steak or half a shoulder of lamb; perhaps a daily special or two such as minted lamb casserole. Draught Bass, Fullers London Pride, a Brakspears and a Robinsons beer.

OPEN: 11.30–2.30. 6–11. (11–2.30 Fri. 11–3 Sat. 12–3. 7–10.30 Sun)
Real Ale
Children welcome. Dogs in bar.
Car park. Childrens play area.

DANEHILL

Coach & Horses   Tel: 01825 740369

Danehill, Nr Haywards Heath, E. Sussex RH17 7JF
Free House. Peter Hayward, licensee

Just outside the village, in the heart of the Sussex countryside and set in large gardens which have spectacular views towards the South Downs. The old pub has a public and saloon bar, plus dining area, each with its own log fire. Bar snacks include toasted French bread with various toppings, grilled field mushrooms and bacon on wholemeal toast, home-made sweetcorn and mushroom quiche, ploughmans, sandwiches, seafood platter and children's portions. The evening menu could include smoked chicken and avocado salad, mushrooms en croute, grilled sea bass, grilled noisettes of English lamb and home-made puddings. Harveys Best and a weekly changing guest beer. Farm cider during the summer. Short wine list and wines by the glass. There is an enclosed children's play area.

OPEN: 11–2.30, 6–11 (12–2. 7–10.30 Sun)
Real Ale.
Children welcome Dogs on leads away from dining area.

DITCHLING

Bull   Tel: 01273 843147

2 High Street, Ditchling, E Sussex BN6 8SY
Whitbread. John & Jannette Blake, lease.

On the border of East and West Sussex, Ditchling has many fine old buildings, including the Bull Inn. The red-brick house in the High Street was where the sculptor Eric Gill lived and worked for many years. The Bull, a 14th century coaching inn, is a popular village local. Two bars in the pub, the main bar having some fine old furniture; the second is more simply furnished. There is also a no-smoking restaurant. Good wholesome bar food – garlic mushrooms with crispy croutons, tiger prawns in filo pastry with salad garnish, home-cooked gammon ham, home-made beef lasagne, a vegetarian dish, always fish, steaks and home-made puddings. Winter Sunday roasts. Morlands Old Speckled Hen, Flowers Original, King & Barnes Sussex, Brakspears and Boddingtons ales. Seats outside on the terrace and in the pretty garden, which has fine views towards Ditchling Beacon.

OPEN: 11–11.
Real Ale. Restaurant.
Children in restaurant. Dogs on leads.
Bedrooms en suite.
Wheelchair access.

DUNCTON

Cricketers   Tel: 01798 342473

Main Road, Duncton, Nr Petworth, West Sussex GU28 0LB
Free House. Philip & Toni Edgington, licensees.

A friendly, cheerful landlord runs this 15th century pub on the main road between Petworth and Chichester. Very popular with locals and travellers. There is a big log fire in the comfortable bar in winter, and two split-level eating areas decorated with cricket memorabilia, including framed cigarette cards. An interesting picture shows the village inhabitants and the local band outside The Cricketers celebrating King Edward VII's coronation. No fixed menu, but they offer a good range of bar food from ploughmans, filled jumbo rolls, jacket potatoes filled with crispy bacon to freshly prepared chicken or prawn salads. The restaurant menu offers such dishes as sliced duck breast with mango & lemon grass vinaigrette, grilled Duncton Mill trout, roast salmon fillet with a tomato and chive sauce or a prime sirloin steak. Good range of puds and ice-creams. Barbecue lunches on fine Sundays. Greene King IPA and Archers Golden Bitter, guest ales, a number of malt whiskies, and a good selection of wines. Seats in the attractive garden. The pub has its own skittle alley in an adjacent building.

OPEN: 11–2.30. 6–11. (12–3. 7–10.30. Sun.)
Real Ale. No food Sun & Mon eves.
Children over 14. Well behaved dogs.

EASEBOURNE STREET

Holly Tree   Tel: 01730 813380

Easebourne Street. Midhurst, West Sussex GU20 0BE
Free House. G D H Damerell, licensee.

At the far end of Easebourne (a village off the A272), the Holly Tree hides behind glorious window boxes. It's a friendly, welcoming pub, with a spacious beamed bar and an attractive restaurant. The lunchtime bar menu is supplemented with specials like fresh salmon mayonnaise, curried prawns and rice or whole grilled plaice. The dinner menu is more extensive and could include whitebait, smoked mackerel, smoked fish paté, snails in garlic butter, roast Aylesbury duckling, grilled Dover sole, gammon or fillet steak. Badger Best, Malthouse Bitter, Guinness, good wine list and a range of malt whiskies. On the edge of the South Downs, this is good walking country.

OPEN: Closed Mon. 11–2.30. (12–2.30 Sun) 6–11.
Real Ale. Restaurant.
Children welcome. Dogs on lead

EASTBOURNE

The Lamb   Tel: 01323 720545

36 High Street, Old Town, Eastbourne, East Sussex BN21 1HH
Harvey & Son. Steve Hume, tenant & licensee.

Less than a mile from the centre of Eastbourne, The Lamb is one of this seaside town's oldest buildings. The cellars date from the 12th century and it was licensed as an inn in 1603. An underground passage connecting the pub to the Old Parsonage is reputed to have been used by the local smugglers. An outstandingly friendly place, the low beamed main bar was once used as a ballroom and the carved chairs are believed to have been acquired from the German Embassy in London – very grand. Bar snacks: sandwiches or ploughmans. Light meals: Indian savouries, deep fried salmon and prawn delights, pasta dishes, fish, grills, steak and kidney pie, braised breast of duck and vegetarian dishes. Daily specials on the blackboard. Puddings too. Harveys Best Bitter, Pale and their seasonal ales. No garden, but tables on the adjoining terrace.

OPEN: 10.30–3. 5.30–11. (10.30–11 Fri & Sat. 12–4. 7–10.30 Sun.)
Real Ale
Children in lower bar. Dogs on leads.

EASTDEAN

Tiger Inn
Tel: 01323 423209

The Green, East Dean, Eastbourne, E Sussex BN20 0DA (village off A259
Eastbourne–Seaford)
Free House. Nicholas Denyer, licensee.

A good resting point if you are walking the South Downs Way. The white-
painted old pub amid the cottages that border the village green make for a
very attractive setting, especially in summer. Inside the Tiger Inn is a
comfortable low-beamed bar with good winter fires and a family room
upstairs. Interesting ever changing blackboard menu could include venison
casserole, garlic mushrooms, macaroni cheese with tomatoes, ploughmans
or fish and chips. Local fish, cheeses and fresh game will feature on the
menu. Seats outside, from where you can admire the scenery. Beers do
change but could include Flowers Original, Tanglefoot, Hard Tackle, Harveys
Best and Marstons Pedigree. There is also a good choice of bin-ends of
wine on the blackboard.

OPEN: 11–3. 6–11.
Real Ale.
Dogs on leads.
Occasional Morris dancers.

ELSTED

Three Horseshoes
Tel: 01730 825746

Elsted, Midhurst, W Sussex GU2N 0JX (W of Midhurst, off A272)
Free House. Andrew Beavis, licensee.

There are generous quantities of changing bar food here to help stoke up the
walkers and cyclists on the South Down Way. A very traditional 16th century
pub, originally serving the drovers travelling the South Downs. Cosy, low-
beamed rooms, full of old furniture with big fireplaces, blazing with logs in
the winter. A changing blackboard menu could offer: home-made soups,
ploughmans, casseroles, steak pies, steak in red wine sauce and fresh fish.
Filling puddings. Ales, which are kept behind the bar, could include Ballards
Best, Flowers Original, Fullers London Pride and Cheriton Potts Ale. They
often have some ales from smaller independent breweries. Farm cider. Seats
in the pretty garden which has a marvellous view of the South Downs.

OPEN: 11–3 (2.30 winter). 6–11.
Real Ale. Restaurant (no food winter Sun eves)
Well behaved children in eating areas. Dogs on leads.

ELSTED MARSH

Elsted Inn   Tel: 01730 813662

Elsted Marsh, Midhurst, W Sussex GU29 0JT
Free House. Tweazle Jones & Barry Horton, licensees.

Deep in the West Sussex countryside and well worth the journey for the very
good ales and imaginative food. White-painted, Victorian, built when there
was a railway station, now all alone, but certainly not forgotten. There are
two traditionally furnished bars and a separate dining room seating 30. All
the food is cooked on the premises using local seasonal produce: free range
eggs, locally baked bread, local fruit and vegetables. You could expect
soups, sandwiches, prawns in garlic, home-cooked gammon, salads,
venison stew, spinach roulade, chicken breast in a cream and caper sauce,
fresh fish and home-made ice creams. Ballards Ales, founded in 1980, used
to be brewed in this pub but have now moved to Myewood; however the
pub keeps a full range of Ballards Ales, Fullers London Pride and a couple
of the more unusual beers as guests. Tables outside in the large garden. Folk
music, a monthly band and barn dances during the summer.

OPEN: 11–3. 5.30–11 (6–11 Sat).
Real Ale. Restaurant.
Children in eating area & restaurant. Dogs on leads.
Folk Music and monthly band. Barn dances summer.
Bedrooms.

FINDON

Gun Inn   Tel: 01903 873206

High Street, Findon, W Sussex
Whitbread. Ian Cooper & Valerie Cleake, managers.

In a beautiful situation, surrounded by woods and rolling hills, Findon is a
charming, unspoilt, downland village. Dating from the 16th century, The Gun
is a homely and welcoming port of call. The low beamed lounge bar contains
beams that are reputed to be from old sailing ships. The sea is not far away,
nor is the great earthwork of Cissbury Ring, an Iron Age hill-fort which rises

600ft. above sea level. Generous helpings of home-cooked bar food. Up to seven real ales, among them: Morlands Old Speckled Hen, Flowers Original and IPA, Boddingtons and guest beers. You are in horsey country here – Josh Gifford's racing stables are nearby.

OPEN: 11–11.
Real Ale.
Children in family room. No dogs.

FIRLE

Ram Inn   Tel: 01273 858222

Firle, West Firle, Lewes, E Sussex BN8 6NS (off A27 Lewes–Polegate)
Free House. Michael & Keith Wooller, licensees.

Lots to see and do near here: Glyndebourne, a little more than an interval away; Firle Place, an imposing and apparently 18th century mansion disguising an old Elizabethan house to look at; and when you have had your pint and lunch, a quick dash up Firle Beacon, 713 ft high on the Downs, should put you right for the rest of the day. The Ram, a well run traditional pub, has a main bar and a cosy no-smoking snug. Fresh local produce is used in the daily changing menu written up on the blackboard. Good home-made soups, spicy chicken wings, salmon steaks, home cooked ham and interesting puddings. Harveys BB plus three other guest beers. A good choice of wines. There is a big walled garden to sit in.

OPEN: 11.30–3. 7–11.
Real Ale.
Children in non-serving bars. Dogs on leads.
Bedrooms.
Live Folk twice monthly.

FLETCHING

Griffin   Tel: 01825 722890

Fletching, E Sussex TN22 3SS (village off A272)
Free House. James & Nigel Pullan, licensees.

One of the most appealing villages in East Sussex, Fletching dates back to Saxon times and has a particularly fine church. Some of the knights killed in the Battle of Lewes in 1264 are said to lie buried in full armour below the

339

nave. The Griffin pub, a mere 400 years old, is all a village local should be. There is a heavily beamed main bar, a public bar with pool table and other games for those so inclined, and an attractively decorated restaurant. The very popular bar food changes daily and there is an à la carte menu in the restaurant. The bar menu could include home-made soups, local sausages with onion gravy, salmon fishcakes and grilled fish. Harveys and Fullers London Pride, also Groslsch Lager (for those that don't know, it is a full strength German lager), and a very good wine list. Splendid views of the Sussex countryside from the big garden.

OPEN: 12–3. 6–11.
Real Ale. Restaurant (not Sun eves).
Children welcome. Dogs on leads.
Piano Fri/Sat eves & Sun lunchtime.

FLETCHING

Rose & Crown   Tel: 0182572 2039

High Street, Fletching, East Sussex, TN22 3ST
Free House. Roger & Sheila Haywood, licensees

Nearly as old as the neighbouring Ashdown Forest, this pretty Sussex village is lucky to have two pubs, both blissfully quiet. The brick built 16th century Rose & Crown has one heavily beamed comfortable bar with a splendid inglenook fireplace and a restaurant offering a choice from either the – à la carte or the table d'hote menu. Bar snacks too: home-made soup, grilled jumbo prawns in garlic butter, gammon steak, fish omelettes, ploughmans, toasted sandwiches and several vegetarian dishes. Daily specials. Home-made puddings and ice-creams. Harveys Ales and Ind Coope Burton. Choice of wines, some by the glass and half bottle. Seats in the garden.

OPEN: 11–2.30. 6–11 (12–2. 7–10.30 Sun)
Real Ale. Restaurant.
Children in restaurant only. Dogs in bar only.
Wheelchair access.

FULKING

Shepherd & Dog   Tel: 01273 857382

Fulking, Nr Henfield, W Sussex BN5 9LU
Free House. Anthony & Jessica Bradley Hull, licensees.

Wonderfully situated at the foot of the South Downs, this 14th century pub has been continually popular. Originally sustaining the local shepherds and presumably their dogs – hence the name. A cosy bar with rustic artefacts and a changing bar menu: fresh fish, steaks, vegetarian dishes, sandwiches, ploughmans and home-made puddings. Flowers Best, Harveys Best, Boddingtons and guest beers from the smaller breweries. There are seats in the pretty garden. If you have had too good a lunch, there are some energetic walks on the South Downs nearby.

OPEN: 10–3. 6–11.
Real Ale.
Dogs on leads.

GRAFFHAM

Foresters Arms   Tel: 01798 867202

Graffham, Nr Petworth, West Sussex GU28 0QA
Free House. Lloyd F Pocock, licensee.

Decorated front and back in the summer with the most opulent hanging baskets, this picturesqe 17th pub is close to the South Downs Way and all those envigorating walks. Warm, friendly atmosphere in the heavily beamed bar and restaurant. Bar snacks like large baguettes filled with cheeses, bacon, lettuce, tomato and egg mayonnaise, or brown baguettes with smoked salmon. The attractive restaurant offers an à la carte menu of English country cooking, with game a speciality. Harveys Pale Ale, a varying number of interesting guest beers, plus a range of Belgian beers and a good wine list. The well stocked garden is particularly attractive.

OPEN: 11–2.30. 5.30–11. (12–3. 7–10.30 Sun.)
Real Ale. Restaurant.
Children at landlord's discretion. Dogs on leads.

GORING BY SEA

Bull Inn   Tel: 01903 248133

Goring Street, Goring by Sea, W Sussex BN12 5AR
Scottish & Newcastle. Bob Youll, manager.

Probably dating back to the 15th century, local smugglers were certainly making full use of the facilities by the 18th century. Still retaining much of its character, the pub, situated by the cricket green in the leafy Sussex countryside, now has the excitement of the local teams battling it out on a summers day. One large bar, divided into different areas, one of which is used for dining. During the summer food is also served in the large garden, where there are enough picnic tables to seat 80. Short reliable menu: soup, ploughmans, home-made curry, omelettes, fish, gammon, steaks and salads. Puddings from the blackboard. Theakstons Bitter, lagers and wines by the glass.

OPEN: 11–2.30. 5.30–11.
Real Ale. Restaurant.
Dogs on leads.

GUN HILL

Gun Inn   Tel: 01825 872361

Gun Hill (Nr Horam), Heathfield, E Sussex TN21 0JU
Free House. R J Brockway, licensee.

There were thriving iron foundries in this area during the 17th century; they used the trees of the Ashdown Forest to heat the iron ore and forge the guns. This explains why today the forest is mainly gorse, virtually treeless, and why the Gun is so named. The building which pre-dates the foundries, is now an attractive flower-bedecked country pub with rambling, beamed, rooms. It's very popular with the walkers from the Wealden Way – muddy boots and all. Lots of room to eat inside, big fires, a no-smoking area, good value food and well kept beers. Soups, French bread snacks, salads, ploughmans, seafood platter, moussaka, haddock pasta, beef Wellington and a cold buffet. The specials board usually has another fifteen dishes to choose from, including fresh fish, various pies and vegetarian dishes. If you've missed lunch, they do Sussex cream teas too. Flowers Original, Adnams, Larkins Chiddingstone and Harveys Sussex. Merrydown cider and wines by the glass. There is a big sheltered garden which has seats and a children's play area, also some tables at the front of the pub so you can admire the glorious, award winning, floral display.

OPEN: 11–11. (11–3. 6–11 winter)
Real Ale.
Children until 9 pm. Dogs on leads.
Wheelchair access via portable ramp to pub.

HERMITAGE Nr. Emsworth

Sussex Brewery   Tel: 01243 371533

36 Main Road, Hermitage, Nr. Emsworth, W. Sussex PO10 8AU
Free House. Malcolm & Pamela Roberts, licencees.

Another borderline case, only this time it is the county border that is confusing; Emsworth is over the border in Hampshire, Hermitage, in West Sussex – oh well, that's a problem for the post office – you know where you are. As the name suggests, The Sussex Brewery, a 17th century building, was, until fairly recently, brewing Hermitage bitter. Along the flagstone passage and up the staircase – where the hops were mashed – is now a cosy, heavily beamed small dining room. Downstairs, the bar floor is covered in fresh sawdust, not only to protect the floor from sloshed pints, but as the pub occasionally floods, to soak up the water. The printed menu offers a wide range of snacks. A more comprehensive list of specials such as mussels in wine and garlic, whole rack of lamb, Dover sole, or local plaice with home-made chips is also available. However the pièce de resistance are the special sausages made for the pub. Bill O'Hagan a free-lance writer and famous sausage maker provides a remarkable range of 41 pork, lamb, beef, speciality and vegetarian sausages. Guaranteed lean, with freshly blended seasoning, no preservatives or monosodium glutamate. No wonder this is called the sausage pub. Hermitage Best is still available, brewed by Burts, also their Newport Nobbler, Old Vectis Venom, Badger Best and Tanglefoot, Wadworths 6X and a monthly guest beer. Outside, there is a secluded walled courtyard filled with hanging baskets and tubs of flowers.

OPEN: 11–11. (12–10.30 Sun)
Real Ale. Restaurant.
Children welcome. Dogs, but not in restaurant.
Car park.

KINGSTON, Nr Lewes

Juggs   Tel: 01273 472523

Kingston, Nr Lewes, E Sussex (off A27, W of Lewes).
Free House. Andrew Browne, licensee.

The Juggs here aren't the sort of jugs you would put water in; these juggs were vessels the local women carried on their heads – full of fish brought from the nearby port to Kingston. Not far from Brighton, this small, pretty, tile-hung, rose-covered pub dates back to the 15th century. It has a rambling beamed main bar with a log fire, and a small no-smoking dining room in what used to be a hay store. The bar and restaurant share the same menu, and food includes a variety of sandwiches, locally made sausages, a vegetarian dish, pitta bread with a selection of fillings, steak & kidney pudding (speciality of the house), daily specials and a children's menu. King & Barnes, Harveys Sussex and guest beers on hand pump. Tables outside in the courtyard, on the sunny terrace and on the lawn.

OPEN: 11–2.30. 6–11.
Real Ale. Restaurant (not Sun lunchtime).
Children in two family rooms. Dogs on leads.
Wheelchairs have one step into pub.

LEWES

The Lewes Arms   Tel: 01273 473152

Mount Place, Lewes, E Sussex BN7 1YH
Beards of Sussex. Matthew Dargan, licensee.

Built at the beginning of the 18th century in the county town of East Sussex. Situated on a steep hill overlooking the River Ouse, Lewes is full of fine buildings from all periods. Off the busy main street, and just below the Castle Mound, the Lewes Arms is a pleasant, friendly, old-fashioned town pub. Two bars and a cosy snug. Food is all home-made – sandwiches and interesting hot snacks: pasta, De Ville Chicken – a speciality – vegetables au gratin, tagliatelle and hot Mexican food. The menu is contantly changing. Well kept ales: Beards Ales, Jennings Bitter and Buchanans Original, plus seasonal ales.

OPEN: 11–11.
Real Ale. Lunchtime food only.
Children in games room. Dogs on leads.
Limited access for wheelchairs.

LEWES

Shelley's Hotel Bar   Tel: 01273 472361

137 High Street, Lewes, E Sussex BN7 1XS
Free House. Graeme Coles, licensee.

Originally a private house owned by the poet's aunts, now an attractive hotel in the centre of the town – a splendid 16th century building. The hotel has a 'Victorian' bar serving a selection of interesting bar snacks: home-made soup, a seafood platter, grilled goats cheese salad, char-grilled salmon steak or chicken, filo parcels of spinach and brie, sandwiches, filled baguettes and toasted sandwiches. One real ale – the local Harveys. Other beers are bottled. Choice of wines. Seats in the garden.

OPEN: 11–3. 6–11.
Real Ale. Lunchtime snacks only.
Children not in bar. No dogs.

LICKFOLD

Lickfold Inn   Tel: 01798 861285

Lickfold, Nr Lodsworth, Petworth, W Sussex GU28 9EY
Free House. Ron & Kath Chambers, licensees.

Surrounded by lovely walks, this very attractive inn dates back to 1450 and has interesting, beamed, interiors, contemporary panelling and huge open fires. Lickfold, the village whose name means the garlic enclosure, was the home of Walter de Lykfold in 1332, and wild garlic still grows by the stream, not far from Lickfold Bridge. Talking of garlic naturally draws our attention to the bar menu, chalked on the blackboard and available only during lunchtime. There is a restaurant menu in the evening. Bar food includes a selection of sandwiches, ploughmans, tasty stews and pies and fish in season. There are Sunday lunchtime roasts. Here they rotate the ales but, there are usually about 8 on offer: Badgers Tanglefoot and Best, Ballards Best, Fullers London Pride, Harveys Best and Adnams, amongst others. There is also a resident ghost which the landlady has seen and says she is quite harmless. Psychic customers have felt her presence and one had a very strange experience in the gents' lavatory! Lots of seats in the large well planted garden.

OPEN: 11–2.30 (3 Sat). 6–11 (closed Mon eves).
Real Ale. No food Sun or Mon eves.
No children. Dogs on leads.
N.B. This pub is up for sale, so if you see the SOLD notice up – do let us know.

LODSWORTH

Halfway Bridge   Tel: 01798 861281

Lodsworth, Nr Petworth, W Sussex GU28 9BP
Free House. Sheila, Edric, Simon & James Hawkins, licensees.

Built as a coaching inn early in the 18th century, halfway between Petworth
and Midhurst, the Halfway Bridge is still serving the traveller with imaginative
food and good ales. Lots of room in the comfortable, spacious bars and
attractive dining room. An extensive blackboard menu lists food ranging
from mushrooms in cream and tarragon, garlic stuffed mussels, lambs liver
and bacon, steak kidney & ale pie to grilled fish and home-made puds.
Sunday roasts. Tables in the garden during the summer and on the sheltered
terrace at the back of the pub. Brakspears, Flowers Original, Cherton Brew
House Ale, Fullers London Pride and Gales HSB on hand pump. Also
changing guest beers. Farm cider and wine by the glass.

OPEN: 11–3. 6–11 (closed winter Sun eves).
Restaurant: not Sun evening.
Children over 10 in restaurant. Dogs on leads.

LURGASHALL

Noahs Ark   Tel: 01428 707346

Lurgashall, Nr Petworth, W Sussex GU28 9ET
Greene King. Kathleen & Ian Kennedy, tenants.

On the edge of the village green which is also used as the local cricket pitch
(a good six will land you on the cobbles in front of the pub), this very pretty
building, which was built as a pub in 1537, is extremely popular with locals,
cricketers and non-cricketers alike. Apparently Cromwell trained his New
Model Army nearby, worshipped in the village church and no doubt drank
in the pub. Two bars, both with lovely fires in the winter, also two menus. Bar
food includes toasties, ploughmans, chicken or ham salads, liver & bacon,
vegetarian tagliatelle. In the restaurant: langoustine, salmon, steaks, etc.
Tables in the front of the pub overlook the church and village green.
Rayments Special Bitter, Greene King IPA, Best Bitter and Abbot Ale. During
the summer they occasionally have concerts and a theatre group performing
in the garden.

OPEN: 11–2.30. 6–11.
Real Ale. Restaurant (no food Sun eves).

Children in family room & restaurant. Dogs on leads.
Occasional bands, concerts, theatre in garden during summer.

OVING

Gribble Inn   Tel: 01243 786893

Oving, Chichester, W Sussex PO20 6BP (E of Chichester).
Own Brew (Badger). Ron & Anne May, managers.

So named after a Mrs Gribble who, years ago, used to live in this 16th
century thatched cottage – now the local pub. Set in a very attractive
cottage garden and with its own brewery (tours can be arranged), the pub
has a heavily beamed bar with big log fires and a no-smoking family room.
Familiar home-cooked bar food – soups, ploughmans, sandwiches, salads,
ham and eggs, steak – also Sunday lunches. Specialities are Reg's pie –
steak and mushrooms cooked in Reg's ale, fishermans pie, Gribble braised
steak and Mexican chicken. Fish dishes and "fish of the day" from the
blackboard. "Old favourites" and vegetarian dishes. The specials board
changes at least once a day. Seats outside among the apple trees. The
pub's own skittle alley, along with the brewery, is on the other side of the car
park. Tanglefoot and Badgers Best and Own brew Pig's Ear Wobbler in the
winter, Gribble Ale, Reg's Tipple, Black Adder and the newest – Plucking
Pheasant.

OPEN: 11–2.30. 6–11.30. (12–3. 7–10.30 Sun).
Real Ale.
Children in family room. Dogs on leads.

PUNNETTS TOWN

Three Cups Inn   Tel: 01435 830252

Three Cups Corner, Punnetts Town, Nr Heathfield, E Sussex TN21 9LR
Free House. Leonard & Irenie Smith, licensees.

Yet another ghostly pub, although here the landlady hasn't seen the ghost,
but has just felt its presence. Thought to be 17th century, this is a very
friendly unspoilt local with a big, low-beamed bar and huge log fire in the
winter. Traditional bar food includes sandwiches, steak or chicken pie,
locally made sausages and filled baked potatoes. There is a no-smoking
eating area. Ales change every two to three weeks. At present they have
Beards Best, Theakstons, Adnams Broadside and Butcombe. There are

347

seats in the garden. This is also good walking country.

OPEN: 11–3. 6.30–11.
Real Ale.
Children in eating area & family room. No dogs.
Wheelchair access to all parts of pub.

RUDGWICK

Blue Ship   Tel: 01403 822709

The Haven, Rudgwick, Horsham, W Sussex
King & Barnes. John Davie, tenant.

A small unspoilt Sussex pub. On entering the public bar you could be forgiven for thinking you had slipped back a century or two. Flagstone floors, scrubbed deal tables, in winter a roaring fire in the big inglenook fireplace and farm dogs waiting patiently under the benches. No bar as such; drinks are served through the hatch. Food is all home-cooked; the blackboard menu changes constantly – ham, egg and chips is a speciality. Everything they serve is very wholesome. King and Barnes Broadwood and Sussex ales, Old is available during the winter. There are wonderful views from the garden over the surrounding countryside. It can get very crowded.

OPEN: 11–3; 6–11 (12–3; 7–10.30 Sun)
Real Ale
Children welcome. Dogs on leads.

RUDGWICK

Thurlow Arms   Tel: 01403 822459

Baynards, Rudgwick, Horsham, W Sussex
Free House. Julian Gibbs, licensee.

Tucked away down a side road, opposite the disused Baynards Park railway station, now a private house, this old pub has seen some changes in its lifetime. Not only was it moved in the late 18th century 500 yards to its present site, but since then it has been a private house, railway hotel, pub, private house again and now a pub once more. Traditional bar snacks are served , and there is a blackboard menu. Fresh fish is delivered daily and could include John Dory, lemon sole, mussels, skate wings or cod; there is frequently a choice of eight or more – other dishes too. King and Barnes

Sussex, Hall and Woodhouse Badger, Hardtackle, Tanglefoot and Wadworths 6X plus Over Draught, which is the pub's own brew. There are tables in the garden and the old railway track offers a lovely walk to Cranleigh.

OPEN: 11–3. 6–11 (12–3.7–10.30 Sun).
Real Ale. No food Sun eves.
Children welcome but not in bar. Dogs on leads.

RYE

Mermaid Inn   Tel: 01797 223065

Mermaid Street, Rye, E Sussex TN31 7EU
Free House. Robert Pinwill, licensee.

Thought to be one of the loveliest smugglers' inns in the county. Probably dating back to the 12th century. Certainly by 1300 the Mermaid was brewing its own ale and charging a penny a night for accommodation. Rebuilt in 1420, the pub looks much the same today as it did then, wonderfully beamed and panelled, with a really vast inglenook fireplace. Two very comfortable lounges, a bar and also a restaurant. Traditional bar food and a more elaborate restaurant menu. Marstons Pedigree and Morlands Old Speckled Hen on hand pump. House wines and sherries. Brass band concerts occasionally in the car park during summer.

OPEN: 11–11.
Real Ale. Restaurant.
Children welcome. Dogs on leads.
Bedrooms.
Classical music in one bar. Lounges and restaurant quiet.

SELHAM

The Three Moles   Tel: 01798 861303

Selham, Nr Petworth, West Sussex GU28 0PN
King & Barnes. John Gregorzek, tenant.

Once a station hotel, now just a solid, friendly, unpretentious country pub, south of the A272 between Petworth and Midhurst. You can't miss it, sitting as it does, high on the bank with a white porch and main gable, half-tile hung; the very positive inn sign on is on the edge of the road. No food, just a range of crisps and nuts, but they have won so many awards – including the 1995 National Runner-up Pub of the Year – that you can be sure of an excellent pint. King & Barnes Mild, Sussex, Old and Festive. Cider in summer. Picnic tables at the side of the pub.

OPEN: 11.30–2.30. 5.30–11. (11.30–11.Sat.12–10.30 Sun.)
Real Ale
No children. Dogs on leads

SCAYNES HILL Nr.

The Sloop   Tel: 01444 831219

Freshfield Lock, Scaynes Hill Haywards Heath W.Sussex RH17 7NP
Beards. David Mills, licensee.

Well off the beaten track, this popular old pub has been here since the 18th century, no doubt serving the bargees plying their trade on the now derelict nearby Ouse canal. Charles Dickens is said to have visited it while staying at Lindfield. Rebuilt a couple of times, the long carpeted saloon has a collections of pictures showing the pub over the years; there is also a public bar with a games room off it. A wide-ranging blackboard menu offers snacks such as 'Murphy's lunch' – potatoes with various fillings, 'Bakers Munch' – a cottage loaf filled with home-roast ham with salad, 'Neptunes lunch' – Iceland prawn cocktail, and more substantial main dish specials. There is a separate children's menu and range of puds. Harveys Best, Beards Best (brewed by Arundel) and a guest beer. Over 20 country wines. Outside you're spoilt for choice – there are three gardens. You are very near Freshfield Halt on the delightful Bluebell Line.

OPEN: 11–3. 6–11 (12–3. 6–11 Sun) Flexible!
Real Ale
Children if well behaved. Dogs in public bar only.

SIDLESHAM

Crab & Lobster   Tel: 01243 641233

Mill Lane, Sidlesham, Chichester, W Sussex PO20 7NB
Free House. Brian Cross, licensee.

Just outside Chichester, built as a pub in the 18th century, the Crab & Lobster backs onto the bird sanctuary in Pagham Harbour. There are two bars, both with fine log fires in winter, and no juke box or fruit machines anywhere. Total bliss. Bar food includes a variety of the usual bar snacks. During the summer the menu includes crab, lobster and prawns also a lasagne and two vegetarian dishes; in winter steak & kidney pie, beef in Guinness, and fish pie plus home-made puddings. Seats in the very pretty garden at the back of the pub. Gales Best and Butser, Arundel Stronghold and Fullers London Pride on hand pump.

OPEN: 11–2.30 (3 Fri & Sat). (12–3 Sun). 6–11 (7–10.30 Sun)
Real Ale.
Children in the garden. Dogs on leads.

SUTTON

White Horse Inn   Tel: 01798 869221

Sutton, Nr Pulborough, W Sussex RH20 1PS
Free House. Howard & Susie Macnamara, proprietors.

This 18th century building has served as the village ale house since 1746. Nestling at the foot of the South Downs in the lovely village of Sutton, the White Horse has a friendly, welcoming atmosphere. Lots of traditional scrubbed pine furniture in the bar, which extends through into the dining room. A good variety of country dishes, using fresh seasonal produce, are served in the restaurant and as a light meal in the village bar. The blackboard menu changes daily: cod and chips, liver and bacon being very popular, but there is quite a choice of exotic fare. Arundel, Courage Best and Directors, Youngs and Batemans ales. Tables in the attractive garden.

OPEN: 11–3. 6–11
Real Ale. Restaurant.
Children welcome. Dogs on leads in public bar only.
Bedrooms.

TICEHURST

Bell Hotel   Tel: 01580 200234

High Street, Ticehurst, Wadhurst, E Sussex.
Free House. Mrs Pamela Tate, licensee.

Situated in the village square, this pub has been run by the same family for over forty years. Parts of the Bell date back to 1296, but it is better known

351

as a 14th century coaching inn. The public bar has the pool table, juke box and fruit machine, but the lounge bar is unspoilt and free of any distraction – lots of ancient timbers and a hugh inglenook fireplace ablaze with logs in the winter, all you'll hear is friendly chatter and the clink of glasses. There is a fascinating display of between 300 and 400 bells in and around the lounge bar. Bar snacks and meals are freshly cooked to order from the menu. Harveys and Whitbread ales. Seats in the garden.

OPEN: 11–3. 6–11.
No food Sun eves.
Children welcome. Dogs on leads.
Bedrooms. Wheelchair access.

WEST ASHLING

Richmond Arms   Tel: 01243 575730

Mill Lane, West Ashling, Chichester, W Sussex PO18 8EA (out of village towards Hambrook).
Free House. Bob & Christine Garbutt, licensees.

For those of you interested in boxing history and wanting to sample a wide selection of beers, this simple friendly country pub is the place to be. The skittle alley – now used as a family room – is reputed to have been used for the last bare-knuckle fight in the country. As for the beers, four or five are available permanently: Timothy Taylors Landlord, Boddingtons, Wadworths 6X and Morlands Old Speckled Hen, another five or six are guest beers, many of them from the smaller, less well known breweries, offering a taste of the more unusual ales. Farm ciders and country wines too. There is a blackboard menu listing the usual bar snacks plus lasagne, chilli, baked potatoes and the daily specials.

OPEN: 11–3. 5.30–11 (all day summer Sats).
Real Ale.
Children welcome. Dogs on leads.
Tues Quiz nights.

WEST CHILTINGTON

Elephant & Castle   Tel/Fax: 01798 813307

Church Street, West Chiltington, W Sussex
King & Barnes. Charles Hollingworth, tenant.

Not immediately visible, but if you find the church, the Elephant & Castle is just behind it. Dating back to the 16th century, this popular friendly pub has its own golf society. Bar snacks include ploughmans, sandwiches, filled baked potatoes and quite a choice of main dishes: liver and bacon, steaks, grilled trout, gammon, salmon, steak and kidney pie plus daily specials. Among the normal English fare you will find a few South African dishes. King and Barnes Festive, Broadwood and Sussex. Good selection of malt whiskies. Wonderful views from the large garden, which has swings and slides for children.

OPEN: 11–4. 6–11 (Mon–Thurs). 11–11 (Fri & Sat). 12–10.30 (Sun)
Real Ale
Children welcome. Dogs on leads.

WINEHAM

Royal Oak   Tel: 01444 881252

Wineham Lane, Wineham, Nr Henfield, W Sussex BN5 9AY
Whitbread. Tim Peacock, tenant.

This attractive, unchanging, part-timbered, part tile-hung 14th century cottagey pub, with its low beams, huge inglenook fireplace and cosy back snug, is all you could wish for in a country pub. Ales straight from the cask. Food is limited to a good range of sandwiches, ploughmans and home-made soups in winter. Pompey Royal, Harveys BB and Flowers Original. Tables on the lawn at the front of the pub next to the old well.

OPEN: 11–2.30. 5.30–11 (6–11 Sat).
Real Ale.
Children in family room. Dogs on leads.

IN THE LICENSED TRADE BACKGROUND MUSIC POLICY CAN CHANGE OVERNIGHT

The entries in this Edition of the Quiet Pint were correct at the time of going to press. However, changes can occur very quickly in the licensed trade and a pub that has been free of background music can adopt a different policy overnight. The editors cannot therefore be held responsible for such changes and we rely on our readers to keep us informed.

WILTSHIRE

BOWDEN HILL

Rising Sun Tel: 01249 730363

Bowden Hill, Nr Laycock, Wilts SN15 2PP
Moles-owned free House. Dave & Denise Maxwell, licensees.

New licensees have taken over here, so things have changed a bit. The Rising Sun is a small, stone-built, 17th century pub, situated high on a hill above Laycock, with spectacular views on a clear day across the Avon Valley into five counties. It has flagstoned floors, open fires and a good following of friendly locals. Familiar bar food: filled baguettes and jacket potatoes, ploughmans, salads, fish and chips, steaks, a couple of vegetarian dishes and daily specials on the blackboard. Moles Ales from Melksham and a guest beer. Seats in the terraced gardens which are at a premium on a good clear day, so if you want to admire the view arrive early and bag a space.

OPEN: 11–3. 6–11 (12–3. 7–10.30 Sun)
Real Ale. No food Sun. eve. or Mon. lunchtime.
Live music Wed.
Children in eating area. Dogs? Don't even ask. Tolerated in garden only.

BRADFORD-ON-AVON

The Beehive Tel: 01225 863620

263 Trowbridge Road, Bradford-on-Avon Wilts
Free House. Mrs C. Crocker & Susan Ormsby, licensees

A detached pub on the A363 Trowbridge road next to Widbrook bridge on the Kennet & Avon canal. Ideal for those sailing the canal, towpath walkers and anyone else with a taste for a really quiet, warm and friendly pub, that has no musak, no T.V. and no gaming machines. A pleasing 'L' shaped room with one bar, scrubbed wooden tables, chairs to match and a settle; real log fires in the stone fireplace. Reasonably priced, tasty, home-cooked traditional bar food. Barbecues in the beer garden during summer. Eight or nine well kept real ales from an ever changing selection dispensed by handpump and gravity. Belgian and other foreign bottled beers also available. There is a dartboard and, when it is returned, a shove ha'penny board.

OPEN. 12–2.45pm 7–11
Real Ale. Lunchtime meals. Snacks (Not Sunday evening)
Children welcome. Dogs allowed, but watch out for the resident cats!

DEVIZES

Bear   Tel: 01380 722444

The Market Place, Devizes, Wilts SN10 1HS
Wadworths. W K Dickenson, tenant.

Before being converted into such an attractive, dependable looking old coaching inn, the Bear was the home of Sir Thomas Lawrence, the 18th century portrait painter. It's at its glorious best in summer, when wonderful flowery eyebrows bloom extravagantly over the bay windows and the handsome pillared doorway. Inside is what you would expect – beamed, panelled and polished. Traditional bar food plus hot steak sandwiches, all day breakfasts and New York style bagels with a choice of fillings. Daily specials too. A more extensive menu is served in the Lawrence Room Restaurant. There is also the elegant Master Lambton Restaurant, if you are really pushing the boat out. Wadworths ales, which are brewed locally. Morning coffee. Tables in the courtyard.

OPEN: 10–11. (10–3. 6–11 winter)
Real Ale. Restaurant (closed Sun eve).
Children in eating area. Dogs on leads.
Bedrooms.

EASTON ROYAL

Bruce Arms   Tel: 01672 810 216

Easton Royal, Nr Pewsey, Wiltshire,SN9 5LR
Free House. Jackie & John Butler, licensees.

Charming and unspoilt – an old fashioned country pub. Built in the 1840's it still has the old wooden benches and long tables – visually unchanged, except for the central heating. Rose, the previous landlady, having come to the pub as a child in 1919, took over from her parents when they retired. If she and her dog liked the look of you, you got served, a bottle of whisky under the counter if you were a good friend. The present licensees, who were Roses' friends, looked after the pub while she was ill, taking over when she died. None of the good things about the pub have changed, only now you are sure to be served! Well filled cheese and onion rolls and home-pickled eggs to go with the Strong Country Bitter, Wadworths 6X and Thatchers local organic cider from the cask. Seats in the garden.

OPEN: 11–2.30. 6–11 (12–3, 7–10.30 Sun)
Real Ale.
Children welcome, not in the bar. Dogs on leads.

EBBESBOURNE WAKE

Horseshoe Inn   Tel: 01722 780474

Ebbesbourne Wake, Nr Salisbury, Wilts SP5 5JF
Free House. Andrew & Patricia Bath, licensees.

It's tucked away in a fold of the Wiltshire Downs, well away from the rush of the modern world, and covered in rambling honeysuckle and roses. The bars are traditionally furnished with open fires and walls decorated with country artefacts. Good value bar food, all "cooked that day," is listed on the blackboard: pies, quiches, patés, fresh fish, plus the stalwarts – sandwiches, ploughmans and a hot dish or two. Sunday: roast lunches. Adnams Broadside, Ringwood Best and Wadworths 6X from casks behind the bar, plus farm ciders and a choice of malt whiskies. Seats in the pretty, flowery garden overlook the Ebble Valley.

OPEN: 11.30–3. 6.30–11.
Real Ale. Restaurant. No meals/snacks Mon eve.
Children in eating area of bar. No dogs.
Bedrooms.

HINDON

Lamb Inn   Tel: 01747 820605

Hindon, Salisbury, Wilts SP3 6DP
Free House. John & Paul Croft, licensees.

This interesting old stone coaching inn, on the most important corner site in the village, is considerably older than its Georgian frontage. It pre-dates the coaches, and in the 15th century served as a court house for the local assizes. The big, old, beamed bar with its a huge inglenook fireplace has plenty of room for you to enjoy a drink and sample the short, well chosen bar menu from the blackboard. There is a no-smoking restaurant with an evening table d'hote menu: fresh asparagus, steamed cushion of salmon with prawn and brandy sauce, or fillet of beef with peppercorn sauce. A similar à la carte menu is available at lunchtime. Wadworths 6X, Boddingtons, Oakhill, Ringwood Best, Batemans Dark Mild, Ash Vine and Hook Norton on hand pump. Picnic tables outside.

OPEN: 11–11
Real Ale. Restaurant.
Children welcome. Dogs on leads.
Bedrooms.

KILMINGTON

Red Lion   Tel: 01985 844263

Kilmington, Warminster, Wilts.
Free House. Chris Gibbs, licensee.

The Red Lion is on the B3092, three miles North of Mere (A303) half a mile from Stourhead Gardens. Like the marvellous nearby gardens at Stourhead, the Red Lion is owned by the National Trust and is an ideal base for the many good, country walks that radiate from it – so there will be lots of serious walking boots around. Comfortable, appealing bars, with winter log fires and simple but satisfying bar food which could include home-made soups, home-cooked ham, ploughmans, filled baked potatoes, popular toasted sandwiches, game, steak and kidney, lamb and apricot or a creamy fish pie and a vegetarian dish. Butcombe Bitter and Wadworths 6X with a changing guest beer. Farm ciders. Seats in the large garden.

OPEN: 11.30–2.30. 6.30–11.(12–3. 7–10.30. Sun)
Real Ale.
Children in eating area 'til 9pm. Dogs on leads.
Bedrooms.

LACOCK

Red Lion   Tel: 01249 430456

High Street, Lacock, Nr Chippenham, Wiltshire
Wadworths. Peter Oldacre, manager.

An imposing, red brick building built in the 1700's. Probably re-built – the back looks so much older. An attractive place with an equally attractive, comfortable, beamy bar and huge inglenook fireplace – very atmospheric. This is another one of our film stars – the Red Lion had a part in the recent production of Pride and Prejudice. Here they serve good pub food and keep prices down by not having a restaurant. Quite a lot of fish dishes, baked pies, steaks, chicken Kiev and vegetarian pasta. You also have a changing specials board. Wadworths 6X IPA and seasonal ales. Wines by the glass, and a range of malt whiskies. Picnic tables at the back, among the raised flower beds.

OPEN: 11–11 (11–3. 6–10.30. winter)
Real Ale.
Children welcome. Dogs on leads.

LITTLE BEDWYN

Harrow   Tel: 01672 870871

Little Bedwyn, Nr. Marlborough, Wiltshire SN8 3JL
Free House. Claude Munro, licensee.

The village had to buy the Harrow and run it, or lose it altogether. So a couple of dozen locals got together, bought it, and installed Angela and Luis Lopez to run it. Angela is English; Luis hails from Granada, so, although the food on offer is predominently English, a number of Spanish specialities appear on the bar and no-smoking restaurant menus. Garlic soup in winter, gazpacho in summer, tapitas in the bar and paella on Sundays. Hook Norton Best Bitter, and a couple of monthly changing guest ales. Good selection of wines from Spain and from the New World . Seats in the pretty enclosed rear garden. Not far from the Kennet and Avon canal.

OPEN: 11–2.30. 5.30–11 (6–11. Sat)
Real Ale. Restaurant.
Children welcome. No dogs.

LOWER CHICKSGROVE

Compasses Inn   Tel: 01722 714318

Tisbury, Lower Chicksgrove, Nr Salisbury, Wilts SP3 6NB
Free House. Sarah Dunham & Tony Lethbridge, licensees.

Near Tisbury, a village on a steep slope above the River Nadder with a fine
12th century church, you'll find Lower Chicksgrove and The Compasses Inn.
Look for the thatched roof and you'll find a popular 14th century pub,
offering a well chosen, changing menu of home-cooked bar food, a good
selection of beers and a barbecue on summer Sundays. Plenty of room in
the beamed main bar which has lots of country and farming bits and pieces
hanging from the beams and walls. Bass, Adnams, Wadworths 6X plus a
guest beer. Seats in the garden and courtyard. There is a children's play
area.

OPEN: 11–3. 6–11. N.B. Closed Mon.
Real Ale. Restaurant.
Children in eating area. Dogs on leads.
Bedrooms.

LOWER WOODFORD

Wheatsheaf   Tel: 01722 782203

Lower Woodford, Nr Salisbury, Wilts SP4 6NQ
Badger. Peter & Jennifer Charlton, tenants.

If you happen to go to the Wheatsheaf on an evening when there's a meeting
of the local rugby club, you may think we have mistakenly classified this pub
as quiet. Don't be misled, that is only the rugby club's record player – it is
not permanent wallpaper music. A wide selection of bar food is available
ranging from soups, open sandwiches, chicken curry, basket meals, salmon,
trout and steaks, to a full vegetarian menu. Badger ales, Tanglefoot and Hard
Tackle. Hofbrau Lager. Seats in the big garden and on the terrace.

OPEN: 11–2.30. 6.30–11 (10.30 Mon–Thurs Winter)
Real Ale. Restaurant.
Children in eating areas. Dogs on leads.

MARSHFIELD

Catherine Wheel   Tel: 01225 892220

High Street, Marshfield, Wilts, SN14 8LC
Free House. Royston & Carole Elms, licensees.

This pub has a Georgian frontage behind which lies a much older Elizabethan building. The attractive interiors, particularly the dining room, reflect more of the Georgian than the Elizabethan. The beamed main bar with big fireplace, pine tables and country chairs is friendly and welcoming. Traditional bar food, plus imaginative additions and daily specials. Wadworths IPA and 6X, Courage Bitter, farm cider and a good wine list.

OPEN: 11–3. 6–11. Closed Mon lunch except Bank Holidays.
Real Ale. Restaurant. No meals Sunday evening.
Children in eating area until 8.30 Dogs on leads.
Thurs. eve Sing-alongs.

RAMSBURY

Bell   Tel: 01672 520230

The Market Square, Ramsbury, Wilts SN8 2PE
Free House. Graham Dawes, licensee.

On the River Kennet, with its large population of well-fed ducks, Ramsbury is an attractive, quiet village with some very handsome buildings. It is also the home of The Arab Horse Society. (This is a very horsey county). The 350 year old Bell is a popular pub with a reputation for serving imaginative, carefully prepared food. The same concise menu, featuring in both the restaurant and the bar, offers home-made soups, paté, single course snacks, fish dishes, steaks, lots of fresh vegetables, school puds and proper ice creams. Sunday roast. There is also a daily changing blackboard menu. Wadworths 6X, IPA, Hook Norton Best plus a guest beer. About 20 malt whiskies. Seats in the garden and good walks not far away.

OPEN: 12–3 (11–3 Sat). 6–11.
Real Ale. Restaurant.
Children in eating area & restaurant. Dogs on leads.

ROWDE Nr. Devizes

George and Dragon Tel: 01380 723053

High Street, Rowde, Nr Devizes, Wiltshire SN10 2PN.
Wadworths. Tim Withers, licensee.

This area – about three miles from Devizes – is full of history and Cromwellian stories. Did the Lord Protector pay a visit, or didn't he? – that sort of question could easily start a discussion in the 17th century George and Dragon. It's small, beamed, unmodernised and atmospheric, with a reputation for being big on fish. The bar and restaurant menus are one and the same. Fresh fish, from Newlyn, could be roast hake and aioli, or monkfish with bacon served with a mustard and cream sauce. Our reporter says it is pricey, but good. Wadworths 6X and IPA, a glass of wine or two. Small garden and small car park.

OPEN: 7.30–11 Mon. otherwise 12–3. 7–11.
Real Ale. Restaurant.
Children welcome. Dogs on lead in bar.

SALISBURY

Haunch of Venison Tel: 01722 322024

1 Minster Street, Salisbury, Wilts SP1 1TB
Courage. Antony & Victoria Leroy, lease.

There is a salutory lesson in this pub for anyone contemplating cheating at cards. Next to the 600 year old fireplace, thought to date back to the pub's early days, is a mummified hand, discovered earlier this century, holding some 18th century playing cards. Was this some awful 18th century gamblers' retribution? Inside, the pub is heavily beamed, with timbered and panelled walls and open fires. Good traditional bar food: sandwiches, ploughmans and a variety of pies, and salads. Over 140 malt whiskies. Courage Best and Directors ales served from a pewter bar counter. A charming pub, not to be missed.

OPEN: 11–11.
Real Ale. Restaurant. No meals/snacks Sun eves. Jan–March.
Children away from bar. Dogs on leads.

SHERSTON

Rattlebone Inn   Tel: 01666 840871

Church Street, Sherston, Wiltshire SN16 0LR
Free House. David & Ian Rees, licensees.

We can do no better than quote our researcher. "Wonderful country pub atmosphere. Comfortable seating, a log fire on cold days. Five of us ate there recently and everybody approved of everything they ate. Inspired menu, home-cooking, good portions, hot plates, lovely vegetables, young, pleasant staff, unpretentious attitudes. I can't remember when I last enjoyed such a pleasant supper in a pub where everything seemed perfect. Good value for money." Well. You can't improve on that. Here are just a few things from the menu: smoked salmon and yoghurt mousse, mixed bean salad, grilled goats cheese with nut dressing, Italian salad with mozarella cheese, tomato, basil and olive oil; for a main course: medallions of pork with a stilton and cream sauce topped with cashew nuts, escalope of lamb with raspberry and mint coulis, mushroom and chestnut stroganoff served on a bed of rice. Delicious puds too. Smiles, Bass, Wadworths 6X and a guest beer. Fruit wines, cider, lots of malt whiskies and decent wines. Small, pretty, flowery garden.

OPEN: 11.30–3. 5.30–11. (11.30–11. Sat.)
Real Ale. Restaurant.
N.B. Juke box in the public bar. Otherwise no music.
Children in eating areas. No Dogs.

SIXPENNY HANDLEY

The Roebuck   Tel: 01725 552002

22 High Street, Sixpenny Handley, Salisbury, Wilts SP5 5NR
Free House. Roger & Marielle Greenhalgh, owners, licensees.

Little remains of the original 18th century Roebuck. Some describe the main bar's decorative style as continental; others think it's like someone's front room. Whatever; nicely decorated, it has comfortable chairs, lots of flowers and a good fire. Ploughmans and freshly made sandwiches are available but the blackboard menu features more sophisticated fare. At lunchtime in summer emphasis is on varied and well-dressed salads – smoked duck breast, spinach tart, chicken livers in garlic butter. Evenings it could be sea-bass baked with ginger and spring onions, pot roasted guinea fowl, rack of lamb in cream sauce with green peppercorns, a fillet steak or a chicken dish.

Marielle, who is French, does all the cooking herself –so be patient – it is worth waiting for. Ringwood Forty-niner, Best Bitter and guest ales, mainly from the local breweries. Hop Back Summer Lightening is a favourite. Wide range of wines from all parts of the world, some by the glass. Seats in the garden among the flowers.

OPEN: 11.30–2.30. 6.30–11.(12–3. 7–10.30. Sun)
Real Ale.
Children welcome. No Dogs.
Car park.

WINGFIELD

Poplars Inn   Tel: 01225 752426

Wingfield, Nr Trowbridge, Wilts BA14 9LN
Wadsworth. Mike & Sue Marshall, licensees.

Originally a shop; before that two cottages. Now it's the village pub. Licensed at the beginning of the Second World War, it is a traditional early Georgian building, situated in the centre of the village, with the unusual addition of its own cricket field. Just a paddock for many years, it was then decided to convert it into a cricket pitch. Locals sit and drink and watch the local teams play. The usual range of bar food, from cheese rolls to steaks. Wadworths range of ales.

OPEN: 11–3. 5.30–11 (12–3. 7–10.30 Sun).
Real Ale.
No children under 14. Dogs on leads.

WOOTTON RIVERS

Royal Oak   Tel: 01672 810322

Wootton Rivers, Nr Marlborough SN8 4NQ
Free House. John and Rosa Jones, licensees.

It's half timbered, thatched, and in an attractive village deep in the Wiltshire countryside. You dive down winding country lanes off the A346 or the B3087 to find this pretty place. You can even float down the Kennet and Avon canal which passes through a lock at the lower end of the village. Inside the Royal Oak you'll find a wealth of beams holding up walls and ceilings, polished tables, flowers and a general feeling of well-being. Four different eating areas, so you can be sure you'll find somewhere to rest your plate. Freshly made sandwiches and several different ploughmans available at lunchtime only. Otherwise you could order home-made soup, avocado pear with prawns, own house paté, a seafood starter, deep fried whitebait or crispy plaice dippers with a sweet and sour sauce, a basket meal, salad, local pink trout, mixed fried seafood or fresh grilled escalope of salmon, steaks, grilled chicken or Wiltshire ham and eggs. Good puds too. Whitbread Best, Wadworths 6X and Ushers Four Seasons. Comprehensive wine list. Small sitting out area near the car park.

OPEN: 11–3.30. 6.30–11 (12–10.30 Sun)
Real Ale. Restaurant.
Children welcome. Dogs on leads.
Car Park. Bed and Breakfast accomodation.

WYLYE

Bell Inn Tel: 01985 248338

High Street, Wylye, Warminster, Wilts BA12 0QP
Free House. Steve & Ann Locke, licensees.

Next to the church, not far from Stonehenge and situated in a picturesque valley between Salisbury and Warminster, The Bell has been catering for the traveller since 1373. A traditional stone building with an interior reflecting its great age. The home-cooked bar food from a continually changing menu includes daily specials, children's dishes and a selection of vegetarian meals, plus a Sunday roast. Wadworths 6X, Badger Best plus a guest beer. 21 different varieties of fruit and country wines. Seats in the garden and on the terrace.

OPEN: 11.30–11. (11.30–2.30. 6–11 winter).
Real Ale. Restaurant.
Children in eating areas. Dogs on leads.

Y
YORKSHIRE

APPLETREEWICK

Craven Arms   Tel: 01756 720270

Appletreewick, Nr Skipton, N Yorks BD23 6DA
Free House. Jim & Linda Nicholson, licensees.

This is a pretty hillside village with some exceptionally fine buildings: 17th century Mockbeggar Hall and, not far away, the terraced gardens of Parcevall Hall. Overlooking the Wharfdale Valley is the stone-built Craven Arms, a popular stopping place for walkers enjoying the wonderful North Yorkshire countryside. Traditionally furnished, beamed, cosy rooms with winter fires. Ample portions of pub food: soups, sandwiches, ploughmans, Cumberland sausages and onion gravy, vegetarian dishes, steak & kidney pie and daily specials. Theakstons Best, XB and Old Peculiar. Tetleys, Black Sheep Bitter and Riggwelter as guest beers. Choice of wines and a selection of malt whiskies. Seats at the front of the pub to admire the view.

OPEN: 11.30–3. 6.30–11.
Real Ale.
Children welcome. No dogs.
Wheelchair access to pub only.

AUSTWICK

Game Cock   Tel: 015242 51226

Austwick, Nr Settle, N Yorks LA2 8BB
Thwaites. Fanny Traddock, tenant.

Not far from the A65, in the wildness of the Yorkshire dales – a favourite stopping place for walkers and villagers alike. The pub overlooks the main street; inside you have a beamed, simply furnished friendly bar, separate dining room and a glassed in terrace sheltering you from the prevailing wind. All the bar food is made "in pub". The changing menu always has a few culinary surprises. The restaurant is no-smoking. Thwaites range of ales. There is a play area for children in the garden.

OPEN: 11–3. 6.30–11.
Real Ale. Restaurant.
Children in restaurant. No dogs.
Bedrooms.

BECK HOLE

Birch Hall Inn
Tel: 01947 896245

Beck Hole, Goathland, Whitby, N.Yorks YO22 5LE
Free House. Colin Jackson, licensee.

This area is closely associated with the dawn of railway travel. Beck Hole Incline was part of the Whitby-Pickering Railway built by railway pioneer George Stephenson, and where he located his hydraulic engine to haul horse-drawn vehicles up to the old Bank Top Station – which can still be seen. In Beck Hole itself, they built a small ironworks in 1860 to exploit the rich, local ironstone veins, but it closed after four years, so the natural beauty of the valley has not been impaired. It's down here that you'll find the Birch Hall Inn, which also doubles as a village shop and boasts a priceless and unique inn-sign painted by Algernon Newton R.A. in the 1940's. Algernon Newton was a very well known artist and this is not the usual medium for a conventional painter. The pub itself dates back to the 17th century; it has a small bar with a serving hatch and an open fire, an even smaller bar opening onto the garden, and a shop selling sweets, ices and soft drinks between the two bars. Just what a village pub should be – all things to all people. Local pork, turkey and ham pies, Beck Hole butties with generous fillings of ham, cheese, paté or corned beef. Theakstons Best XB (Mild in summer), Black Sheep, local beers and guests – all from the cask. Family room, seats in the garden. A lovely part of Yorkshire, good walking country.

OPEN: 11–11 (summer). 11–3. 7.30–11 (winter).
Real Ale.
Children welcome. Dogs on leads.

TIMOTHY TAYLOR'S

LANDLORD

CHAMPIONSHIP WINNER
JUDGE IT FOR YOURSELF

Brewed by Timothy Taylor at Knowle Spring Brewery, Keighley, West Yorkshire
Telephone: 01535 603139 Fax: 01535 691167

BEVERLEY

White Horse Inn   Tel: 01482 861973

22, Hengate, Beverley, N. Yorks
Sam Smiths. John Southern, lease.

Originally a walled town with five mediaeval gates, only one – the North gate – remains at North Bar. Not far away, on the corner of North Bar Within and Hengate, you'll find the church of St. Mary's and having found that landmark, you'll find the White Horse Inn nearby. Known as "Nellies" – after a redoubtable landlady – the pub has a timeless quality which is much appreciated in these days ot "themed" and "restored" pubs (the gas lighting here is original). Reasonably priced traditional bar food plus a roast on Sundays. There is a no-smoking room behind the bar. Sam Smiths Ales, no guest beer.

OPEN: 11–11
Real Ale. Lunchtime meals and snacks. (Not Mon)
Children welcome (not in main bar). Dogs on leads.

BREARTON

Malt Shovel   Tel: 01423 862929

Brearton, Harrogate, N. Yorks HG3 3BX
Free House. Les & Charlotte Mitchell, licensees.

An unspoilt 16th century, family-run pub in a small North Yorkshire village. Cosy, heavily beamed with panelled rooms and good winter fires. A popular meeting place which has a reputation for well-chosen, well-cooked food, with the attention to detail that lifts it above the ordinary. Concise, daily changing blackboard menus could include char-grilled tuna steak, lamb braised in white wine with garlic and mint, a seafood gratin, poached Scottish salmon with a dill and cucumber sauce, mushroom and spinach lasagne or a potato and tomato curry. All the puddings are home-made. Five real ales at all times, usually: Theakstons Bitter, Daleside Nightjar and Old Mill Bitter and two others which could be either: Durham Magus, Moorhouse Pendle Witches Brew, Croptons Two Pints or Blacksheep Riggwelter. They have served well over 100 different ales in the last 18 months. Farm ciders. Seats on the terrace at the back of the pub.

OPEN: 12–3. 6.45–11. Closed Monday.
Real Ale. No food Sun evening or Mon.
Children welcome. Dogs on leads.

BURNSALL

Red Lion   Tel: 01756 720204

Burnsall, Skipton, N. Yorks BD23 6BU
Free House. Elizabeth Grayshon, licensee.

Lots to see in Burnsall. There is the impressive, five-arched bridge over the river, St Wilfred's Church which has a 16th century tower, Norman font, Jacobean pulpit and 10th century gravestones, the 15th century school, now the primary school, and finally – the whole point of being here – the 16th century Red Lion, originally a ferryman's inn on the bank of the River Wharfe. Lucky them, they have fishing rights over seven miles of the river. Inside, the pub has a panelled main bar and a no-smoking lounge bar with good no-nonsense bar food. Soups and lunchtime sandwiches, locally smoked chicken, local cheese for the ploughmans, gammon with free range eggs, lots of fish, game in season and good puddings. Favourites from the menu include fresh fish, steak and kidney braised in ale and topped with a suet crust, organically raised beef or medallions of venison, panfried, served on a garlic croute. All the food is freshly prepared. Tetleys Bitter, Theakstons Best, Black Sheep and a guest beer. Choice of malt whiskies. Seats at the front and at the back of the pub.

OPEN: 11.30–11 (12–10.30 Sun).
Real Ale. Restaurant.
Children welcome. Dogs on leads. (not in hotel rooms).
Bedrooms.

CRAY

White Lion   Tel: 01756 760262

Cray, Buckden, Upper Wharfdale, N. Yorks. BD23 5JB?
Free House, Frank and Barbara Hardy, licensees.

On the B 6160 Fell walkers route in the Yorkshire Dales National Park,(at the foot of Buckden Pike), between Wharfdale and Bishopdale. The White Lion, a welcoming, traditional Dales pub is an excellent place to stop and refresh the parts your walking boots have tired out. Flagstoned floors, beams, an open fire and home-cooked meals, Moorhouses Pendle Witches Brew, Premier, Tetley Bitter and a guest beer. Seats on the sunny terrace at the front of the pub, overlooking the beck on the other side of the road.

OPEN: 11–11 (11–2.30. 6.30–11 winter weekdays)
Real Ale
Children in specific areas. Dogs on leads.
Bedrooms.

EAST WITTON

Blue Lion   Tel: 01969 24273

East Witton, Nr Leyburn, N. Yorks DL8 4SN
Free House. Paul Klein, lease.

A good, reliable-looking, old stone coaching inn. Built in the 19th century, evidence of its past can still be seen in the stone archway – designed to accommodate the coaches – at the entrance to the stable courtyard. Only one bar. This has high backed settles and a big log-filled fireplace. Popular, interesting home-made bar food from a blackboard menu. There is also a candlelit restaurant for residents. Theakstons Best, Timothy Taylors Landlord and Boddingtons on hand pump. Selection of wines and old English liqueurs. Seats outside the front of the pub and in the big, attractive garden at the rear.

OPEN: 11–11.
Real Ale. Restaurant (closed Sun evening).
Children welcome. Dogs on leads.
Bedrooms.

FARNDALE

Feversham Arms   Tel: 01751 433206

Church Houses, Farndale, N. Yorks (Nr Kirkby Moorside).
Free House. Fran & Ray Debenham, licensees.

Situated in the lovely, remote Farndale Valley, which is carpeted with miniature daffodils in springtime and thought locally to be the inspiration behind Wordsworth's poem. A delightful, beautifully kept old pub. One wall of the small bar has a fine example of an old Yorkshire range. There is an à la carte menu in the restaurant, which is in a handsome converted old barn. Very generous portions, both in the restaurant and the bar – a hearty appetite is a necessity. All the food is home-cooked: gammon and egg pie, steak & kidney pie, soups and salads. One of the specialities in the restaurant is a fillet of pork en croute stuffed with garlic and shallots; also tournedos Rossini. Sunday lunches (must book). Full Yorkshire breakfast if you stay. Tetleys ales; also stouts and lagers. Seats in the garden.

OPEN: 11–3. 5.30–11 (summer). 12–2.30. 7–11 (winter). Closed Mondays in Jan, Feb and March.
Real Ale.
Children welcome. Dogs on leads.
Bedrooms. Wheelchair access to pub.

GOATHLAND

Mallyan Spout Hotel   Tel: 01947 896206

Goathland, Whitby, N. Yorks YO22 5AN
Free House. Judith Heslop, licensee.

From the hotel it is a short walk down a steep track to the Mallyan Spout, a 70 foot waterfall over a mossy cliff into the Esk Valley below. Situated on a pretty village green, with the local sheep as very efficient lawnmowers, the Mallyan Spout Hotel is an ivy-covered stone building. With years of experience at serving the discerning traveller, it has a reputation for solid dependability. Three lounges with big winter fires overlook the garden; a comfortable bar serves well kept ales and there is a very attractive restaurant. Bar food includes home-made soups, patés, home-made chutneys with the ploughmans, their own handraised pork and chicken pie, local salmon trout (in season), fresh fish from Whitby which could include: Monkfish, Seabream, Turbot, Brill, prawns and mussels too. Also daily specials. They host special gourmet weekends. Theakstons Best and the local Malton Double Chance Bitter. Extensive wine list and choice of malt whiskies. They even have a Coachhouse shop selling Mallyan Spout chutneys, pickles, jams, home-cured ham and beef, other goodies, also Christmas puddings.

OPEN: 11–11. Daily bar snacks 12–2. 6.30–9. Daily evening restaurant.
Lunch in restaurant only on Sunday. Afternoon teas.
Real Ale. Restaurant.
Children welcome until 8.30. Dogs on leads.
Bedrooms.

HANDSWORTH

The Cross Keys   Tel: 0114 2694413

400 Handsworth Road, Handsworth, Sheffield
13 Wards. Jean Colman, tenant.

Reputed to be 11th century and the oldest occupied building in Sheffield, this small traditional pub, with only three rooms, was built on a graveyard

371

belonging to the adjoining St. Mary's church. A tunnel used to connect the pub with the church, allegedly an escape route for priests at the time of the Reformation. Food is mainly restricted to lunchtime sandwiches to accompany Wards range of beers.

OPEN: 11–11
Real Ale
No Children. Dogs on leads.

HEATH

Kings Arms   Tel: 01924 377527

Heathcommon, Nr Wakefield, W. Yorks WF1 5SL
Clarks. John & Karen Battle, managers.

Overlooking acres of common land, this 18th century pub in a very attractive setting is totally unspoilt. Small and flagstoned, its panelled bars are still lit by gas, and one of them has an old range to help keep away the winter chill. Last year a conservatory was built to provide more elbow room. It opens onto the garden. Dependable bar food with daily specials and home-made puddings. Clarks Bitter and Festival Ale, Tetleys and Timothy Taylors. Lots of seats at the front and the side of the pub.

OPEN: 11.30–3. 5.30–11.
Real Ale. Restaurant.
Children welcome. Dogs on leads.

HETTON

Angel Inn   Tel: 01756 730263

Hetton, Nr Skipton, N. Yorks BD23 6LT
Free House. Dennis Watkins, licensee.

Whilst you can definitely still get a pint and sandwich (open – smoked salmon with cream cheese, smoked bacon and home-made chutney), you will understand when I say this isn't exactly one of your pint and a wad places. You can eat in the informal Bar Brasserie, or in the elegant restaurant which has a greater choice of dishes on its fixed price menu. Food here is not just sustaining – it's an experience. Seafood filo parcels, char-grilled lamb, salmon en croute, confit of duck and good puddings too. Special gourmet evenings are organised throughout the year. Marstons, Black

Sheep and Boddingtons. Quite a wine list and choice of malt whiskies. There is a no-smoking snug and seats outside on the terrace.

OPEN: 12–2.30. 6–10.30 (6–11 Sat).
Real Ale. Restaurant (closed Sun evening)
Well behaved children welcome. Dogs outside only.

HUBBERHOLME

George Inn   Tel: 01756 760223

Hubberholme, Nr Skipton, N. Yorks BD23 5JE
Free House. Jerry Lanchbury & Fiona Shelton, licensees.

Another of the many solid stone-built Dales pubs which can withstand all the weather this part of the world can throw at them. Luckily, they always seem to be in just the right place to sustain the traveller in this rugged terrain. On the banks of the River Wharfe, and virtually on the Dales Way, it is understandably a favourite with the big boot and hairy stocking brigade. Traditional, beamed and stone-walled bars serving substantial steak in ale pies, pheasant Normandy, vegetable and cheese parcels, cod and salmon mornay, steaks and daily specials. More specials are available during the evening and the number of vegetarian dishes on the menu has increased considerably. The dining room is no-smoking. Theakstons Blackbull, Youngers Scotch and Ruddles County. A selection of Scotch whiskies and a choice of wines. Seats outside for the view and for gazing at the river.

OPEN: 11.30–3. 6–11 (11.30–11 Sat).
Real Ale. Restaurant.
Children in eating area. Dogs on leads.
Bedrooms. Wheelchair access to bars only.

HUDSWELL

The George & Dragon   Tel: 01748 823082

Hudswell, Richmond, N. Yorks
Free House. Derek and Anita Bastow, licensees.

A small village in lovely countryside. "It's a was town" says the landlord of the George & Dragon. "You drive through it in a few seconds and say 'that was Hudswell!'" The pub is about 300 years old and is a cosy old fashioned. Three small rooms inside, two at the front and a newly-built one at the back.

THE QUIET PINT

You have a choice of over 16 dishes on the bar menu along the lines of steak and kidney pie, fish and chips, steaks or gammon – the usual reliable pub fare. Theakstons BB, XB, Old Peculiar and John Smiths Magnet on handpump. Another pump is kept for a guest beer. The pub has a beer garden, a garden and a field (somewhere to park the horse). Plenty of space for wheelchairs. The pub often has disabled people in from the nearby St John Centre at Catterick Camp.

OPEN: 12–3. 6.30–11 (N.B.CLOSED Mon lunchtimes. Sun. 12–3. 7–10.30)
Real Ale.
Children welcome. Dogs in garden.

HULL

Ye Olde White Harte   Tel: 01482 326363

25, Silver Street, Hull HU1 1JG, N. Yorks.
Scottish Courage. Brian & Jenny Cottingham, managers.

The property of kings and the home of governors, this was an important private residence and not until the 18th century did the building became licensed. Aptly named, and not to be confused with the modern White Hart which is not far away. This one really is old, with the beams, panelling, two huge sit-in fireplaces and all the architectural features you would expect of a building dating back to the 16th century. Here in 'Ye Plotting Parlour', now part of the restaurant, the decision was made by the then Governor of Hull to lock the gates of the City against Charles 1. Not that it did him much good, as he was beheaded by the Parliamentarians soon after. Almost destroyed by fire in the 19th century, this exceptional old building has outlived the owner of the mysterious skull it houses and which has been passed down through the generations. Very busy during weekday lunchtimes. The bar food includes: sandwiches, paté, pies, salads, changing specials and Ye Olde White Harte's special mixed grill. An excellent Sunday lunch – all the normal roasts, an à la carte menu and jam roly poly or bread and butter pudding for afters. The dining area is up the fine old staircase. Youngers IPA, No 3, Theakstons XB, Old Peculiar and Courage Directors plus a weekly changing guest beer. Selection of malt whiskies. (An interesting note: Women weren't admitted to the pub until 1969).

OPEN: 11–11.
Real Ale. Lunchtime restaurant.
Children in room upstairs to eat (not in bar). No dogs.

LANGTHWAITE

Red Lion   Tel: 01748 884218

Langthwaite, Arkengarthdale, Richmond, N. Yorks. DL11 6RE
Free House. Mrs Rowena Hutchinson, licensee.

A delightful pub with a cosy beamed bar, a tiny snug and a very glamorous
life. The bar has been the location for many TV and film parts. Signed photos
of the good and famous adorn the walls. Spot the pub in All Creatures Great
and Small, A Woman of Substance and Escape from the Dark – to name but
a few – but fame thank goodness, has not gone to anyone's head – it is still
as it should be – entirely unspoilt. Good sustaining food to go with the beer.
Youngers Scotch, Theakstons XB and the local Black Sheep Bitter. Still very
much a local. An oasis in the desert.

OPEN: 10.30–3. 6.30–11.(Fri.11–3. Sun. 10.30 for coffee, otherwise 12–3.
7–10.30)
Real Ale.
Children at lunchtime. No Dogs.
Wheelchair access.

LEDSHAM

The Chequers Inn   Tel: 01977 683135

Claypit Lane, Ledsham, Nr South Milford, W. Yorks. LS25 5LP
Free House. Chris Wraith, licensee. Turn left where the A63 joins the A1.

The only one we know, probably the last in the country to be closed on
Sundays. All due to some quirky local licensing laws. Not to worry, they
make up for it the rest of the week. A creeper-covered, well kept village local.
Beams, a bit of panelling, log fires and a nice old-fashioned air. Familiar,
reliable bar food: home-made soup, sandwiches, ploughmans, home-baked
hams – that sort of thing and several daily specials. There is also a more
formal restaurant. Youngers Scotch & No. 3, Theakstons Best and John
Smiths. Outside is a flowery, two level beer garden.

OPEN: 11–3. 5.30–11. (11–11 Sat) closed Sunday.
Real Ale. Restaurant.
Children in own room. No Dogs.

LEEDS

Whitelocks   Tel: 01132 453950

Turks Head Yard, Brigate, Leeds LS1 6HB
Youngers. Julie Cliff, manager.

If you want to see Victorian pub architecture at its best, this is the place. Stained glass windows, fine mirrors, red banquettes, and marble tiles on the bars. There is a panelled dining room at the back of the pub. Good choice of bar food: sandwiches, pies, sausages, filled Yorkshire puddings and Scotch eggs. Wallow in nostalgia by reading the pre-War prices which are still etched on the mirrors. Theakstons Bitter and Youngers ales. A selection of wines. Seats outside.

OPEN: 11–11.
Real Ale. Restaurant (not Sun evening).
Children in restaurant. Guide dogs only.

LINTHWAITE

Sair Inn   Tel: 01484 842370

139 Lane Top, Hoyle Ing, Huddersfield, W. Yorks HD7 5SG
Free house. Ron Crabtree, licensee.

Two very important things to bear in mind here – this pub only opens in the evenings and you won't get fed. I am not saying there isn't a bag of crisps or nuts behind the counter, but that is all. You would only be here for the beer. This is what a Yorkshire pub used to be all about – serious beer. Traditionally furnished, big fires, flagstone floors and views across the Colne Valley. Own brew ales are: Linfit Mild Bitter and Special, Janet Street Porter, Old Eli, Leadboiler, Autumn Gold, Enoch's Hammer and English Guineas (a stout) plus a guest beer. Farm ciders and some malt whiskies. The Huddersfield Canal – with its 25 locks and the longest canal tunnel in Britain – is not far away.

OPEN: 7–11 Weekdays. 12–3. 7–11 Sat, Sun & Bank hols.
Real Ale
Children away from bar. Dogs on leads.

LITTON

Queens Arms Tel: 01756 770208

Litton, Nr Skipton, N. Yorks BD23 5QJ
Free House. Tanya & Neil Thompson, licensees.

When there are very few roads – perhaps one or two – in a vast expanse of countryside, you know you are in serious walking country. Here you are surrounded by fells, crags, peaks and all those places that have to be either walked up or over. Even more reason for wanting to know about the Queens Arms. A charming old stone pub giving shelter, warmth and sustenance in spectacular surroundings. Bar food includes the stalwarts: soup, sandwiches, ploughmans, filled baked potatoes and steak or rabbit pie – Danish sandwiches too. Youngers and Theakstons ales on hand pump. Wonderful views from the two-level garden.

OPEN: 12–3 (11.30–3 Sat). 6.30–11 (7–11 winter).
Real Ale
Children in eating areas & own room. Dogs on leads.
Bedrooms.

MALTON

Crown Hotel (Suddaby's) Tel: 01653 692038

Wheelgate, Malton, N. Yorks YO17 0HP
Free House. Neil Suddaby, licensee.

The Crown is a focal point in this old market town which grew up around a Norman church. The original old coaching inn was burnt down; the building you see today is the Georgian replacement. In the same family for 120 years, Neil Suddaby is the 5th generation. His two-year old son is the 6th. Food is served in either the bar or the conservatory – only a bar menu giving you a choice of home-made soups, which could be carrot and coriander or fish chowder, home-made lasagne, veggie burgers, hamburgers and lots of daily specials. The family are brewers too. They make Malton Pale Ale, Double Chance, Pickwicks Porter, Owd Bob and Crown Bitter. When the spirit takes them, they will produce some special brews. They also have John Smiths and some guest beers. Sounds as though you're spoilt for choice!

OPEN: 11–3. 5.30–11.(11–11 Fri. 10.30–4 7–11 Sat)
Real Ale
Children welcome. Dogs on leads.
Wheelchair access into bar only. Nine bedrooms.

MOULTON

Black Bull Inn   Tel: 01325 377289

Moulton, Nr Richmond, N. Yorks DL10 6QJ
Free House. Audrey and Sarah Pagendam, licensees.

If and when you get to Moulton, remember the route is so complex that you cannot get onto the Northbound A1 without a map, probably a compass and detailed instructions – but why bother – after a decent lunch go the scenic way – the slower country route. Well worth the effort to get to the Black Bull. You'll find a lovely log fire in the bar where they serve hot and cold snacks; there is a seafood restaurant open in the evenings – no booking necessary; dining a deux? – a Pullman carriage from the Brighton Belle has just eight tables and an à la carte menu; for small parties there is a flowery conservatory complete with grape vine. Very impressive. In the bar there are oysters, home-made soups, smoked salmon sandwiches, paté, seafood pancakes, herby fishcakes, hot tomato tart with black olives, barbecued spare ribs, bangers and mash with onion gravy and much more. Theakstons and Tetleys ales. Good choice of wines and sherries. Seats outside in the courtyard.

OPEN: 12–2.30. 6–10.30 (11 Sat). Closed Sun evening.
Real Ale. Restaurant (not Sun evening). No bar meals Sun lunchtime.
Children (aged over seven only) in restaurant. No dogs.

MUKER

Farmers Arms   Tel: 01748 886297

Muker, Nr Richmond, N. Yorks DL11 6QG
Free House. Chris & Marjorie Bellwood, licensees.

An unspoilt popular old village pub, handy for walkers on the Pennine Way, or just exploring the Yorkshire Dales. Inside it has flagstone floors so walking boots are acceptable. Traditionally furnished with a good warming fire. Excellent value bar food, lunchtime and evenings: soups, filled baps, baked potatoes, home-made steak pie, gammon and egg, other home-made dishes and a childrens' menu. Butterknowle Bitter, John Smiths and Theakstons ales on hand pump.

OPEN: 11–3; 6.30–11 (11–11 Sat) (7–11 winter evening).
Real Ale.
Children in eating area. Dogs on leads.
Self-catering flat for two available all year.

OAKWORTH

Grouse Inn   Tel: 01535 643073

Oakworth, Nr Keighley, Yorkshire
Taylors. Joseph Procter, tenant.

If you want a comfortable, interesting, old-fashioned pub with a friendly
landlord in the middle of Brontë country, then this is it. Popular with walkers
and tourists – Howarth is only two miles away. Mrs Proctor's bar food is
good and freshly made, usually soups, sandwiches, salads and daily
specials. The pub also has a charming restaurant. Ales include Timothy
Taylors Golden Best, Dark & Mild, Best Bitter, Landlord, Ram Tam XXXX and
Porter. Good walking country. The Keithley and Worth Valley Railway runs
through five miles of the glorious Pennine countryside nearby and was the
line that starred the film "The Railway Children".

OPEN: 11–3. 6.30–11. Closed Mon except bank holiday.
Real Ale. No food Mon.
Well behaved children. Dogs on leads.
Wheelchair access.

PICKERING

White Swan Hotel   Tel: 01751 472288

Market Place, Pickering, North Yorkshire YO18 7AA
Free House. Victor Buchanan, licensee.

The White Swan is both pub and small hotel in this ancient Celtic town that
dates from the 3rd century. Its panelled bar is the popular meeting place.
Well thought out traditional menu: home-made soup, salads, sandwiches,
steak pie, hot-pots and daily specials. A more elaborate menu is offered in
the restaurant. Theakstons Best Bitter and Camerons Bitter. The wine list is
considerable, mostly from the St. Emilion region of France.

OPEN: Tues–Fri 11–3. 6–11. (Mon & Sat. 11–11. Sun. 12–3. 7–11)
Real Ale. Restaurant.
Children's room. Dogs on leads.
Car park. Wheelchairs: one step from the street.

THE QUIET PINT

REDMIRE

Kings Arms Hotel   Tel: 01969 622316

Redmire, N. Yorks DL8 4ED
Free House. Roger Stevens, licensee.

This is an attractive small village with old stone houses surrounding the green and views of Penn Hill (1792 ft.) and the River Ure. Superbly located within the village, the Kings Arms offers a wide choice of home-made bar food: soups, paté, omelettes, steak & kidney pies and daily specials. Fruit pies and crumbles to follow. A Sunday roast and freshly ground coffee. The restaurant is no-smoking. John Smiths, Theakstons Best, Black Sheep Bitter and guest beers. Could be Shepherd Neame, Websters Yorkshire or Tetleys. Panoramic views from the terrace and seats in the attractive garden. NB : Radio turned on at about 10.30 each evening for the locals' benefit.

OPEN: 11–3. 5.30–11.
Real Ale. Restaurant.
Children in eating area. No dogs.
Live music last Friday of month.
Bedrooms.

RICHMOND

Black Lion   Tel: 01748 823121

Finkle street, Richmond, N. Yorks DL10 4QB
Pubmaster. Stephen J. Foster, tenant.

There are walks along the River Swale from this old market town, where the ruins of the Norman Castle dominate the skyline above the cobbled market place. The Black Lion Hotel is tucked in a side street, just opposite the market square. It's an old coaching inn with comfortable, heavily beamed bars, big fires, good familiar bar food and well kept ales. Food available includes soups, paté, ploughmans, salads, leek bake, steaks, quiche and roast of the day. As the restaurant has music, stay in the bars. Camerons Strong Arm, Flowers Original, Tetleys Imperial, Yorkshire wines and a choice of malt whiskies.

OPEN: 10.30–11.
Real Ale. Restaurant.
Children welcome. Dogs on leads in bar only.
N.B. Music in restaurant.

SAXTON

Greyhound Inn   Tel: 01937 557202

Main Street, Saxton, N. Yorks LS24 9PY
Sam Smiths. Mr & Mrs McCarthy, managers.

Not only the local inn, but also the post office (before opening times). A really old-fashioned tiny village pub, thought to be one of the smallest in England, and time has not changed it. Beer is still in casks and sandwiches have to be ordered during the week – although they are always readily available at weekends – crisps and nuts too. The ale is Samuel Smiths Old Brewery Bitter. Pretty in the summer when the roses are out. Seats in the courtyard next to the church. Nearby is the Edwardian mansion at Lotherton Hall which consists of a museum and a bird park created to re-introduce birds to the wild. It is well worth a visit.

OPEN: 12–3. 5.30–11 (11–11 Sat).
Real Ale.
Children in games room. Dogs in tap room only.

SETTLE

Royal Oak   Tel: 01729 822561

The Market Place, Settle, N. Yorks BD24 9ED
Whitbread. Brian & Sheila Longrigg, tenants.

An excellent centre for country walks. Limestone cliffs overhang this old market town, which has a handsome square, 18th and 19th century houses and lots of small courts and alleys. The Royal Oak is a big, low, stone building dating back to 1684. The bars are roomy with snacks on offer including soups, open and closed sandwiches, home-made breaded mushrooms served with a garlic dip, steak & kidney pie, cottage pie, Cumberland sausages, filled Yorkshire puddings, fish, vegetarian dishes and other traditional fare. Chef's specials on the blackboard. Children's menu available. Boddingtons, Flowers IPA, Castle Eden, Timothy Taylors Landlord and one guest ale. Range of malt whiskies. NB: Music is occasionally played in the restaurant.

OPEN: 11–11.
Real Ale. Restaurant.
Children welcome. Dogs on leads
Bedrooms.
Wheelchair access.

THE QUIET PINT

SHEFFIELD

Fat Cat Tel: 0114 2494801

23 Alma street, Sheffield, S3 8SA
Own Brew. Steven Fearn, licensee.

Opening in 1981, this was Sheffield's first real ale house, and in 1990 started brewing its own Kelham Island beer next door to the pub. Filling home-made soups, stews, pies and daily specials, plus a number of imaginative vegetarian dishes and usually, one fish dish. Good English puddings – crumbles and pies with cream or custard. Ten draught ales always available: Marstons Pedigree, Timothy Taylors Landlord, two from Kelham Island and six guest beers. Draught Belgian beers are available together with Belgian fruit jenevers. Draught cider. Country fruit wines and small barrels of Kelham Island Beer can be ordered in advance to take away. Seats in the courtyard at the back of the pub.

OPEN: 12–3. 5.30–11.
Real Ale. Lunch time meals, snacks only.
Children in beer garden and upstairs room. Dogs on leads.

SUTTON-UPON-DERWENT

St Vincent Arms Tel: 01904 6604349

Main Street, Sutton-upon-Derwent, N. Yorks YO4 5BN
Free House. Philip Hopwood, licensee.

I suppose the pub should be called 'The Admiral St. Vincent' as it is meant to be named after one of Lord Nelson's naval chums who was ennobled. Inside there is a comfortable panelled bar with an open fire, a main restaurant and a smaller no-smoking dining room. This really is a family run business: Philip Hopwood and his wife Enid run the pub. Enid is the pie and pudding specialist; son Adrian is the chef and son Simon the bar manager. Simon's wife, Christine, is the restaurant manager. One menu for the pub bar and restaurant. Always a number of specials on the board, among them, perhaps, peppered steak, fillet steak with wild mushrooms, steak and kidney pie, half a chicken or scampi. Freshly made sandwiches too. Always nine or ten beers on the go. Among them: John Smiths, Timothy Taylors landlord, Fullers London Pride, Chiswick and ESB, Boddingtons and Exmoor Gold. Well chosen wine list. Seats in the pleasant garden.

OPEN: 11.30–3. 6–11. (12–3. 7–10.30 Sun)
Real Ale. Restaurant.
Children welcome. Dogs in garden only. Car park.

TAN HILL

Tan Hill Inn   Tel: 01833 628246

Tan Hill, Keld Nr. Richmond, N. Yorks BL11 6ED
Theakstons. Margaret Baines, licensee. Maureen Keating, manager.

The highest Inn in England. Grouse, sheep and The Tan Hill Inn, 1,732 ft
above sea level – in the clouds. I think you could call it permanently bracing,
it must be one of the few pubs to keep a fire burning all year. Isolated you
could call it – four miles to the nearest neighbour, and eleven to the corner
shop. Their own water and electricity supply, freezers full of food and parking
for the snow plough helps them through the year. Hearty food from
sandwiches to filled Yorkshire puddings. Theakstons XB, Best and Old
Peculiar. The barrels have been known to freeze! Ice is really de trop here!
Hugely popular place in summer; in the depths of winter, the odd lonely
traveller finds a very welcome refuge in this rarified air. Hundreds of acres
of moorland to get lost in.

OPEN: 11–11 (12–10.30 Sun)
Real Ale
Children welcome. Dogs – yes-ish: you have to keep an eye on the
resident Jack Russell. Seven bedrooms.

TOTLEY

Crown Inn   Tel: 01142 360789

Hillfoot Road, Totley, Sheffield S17 3AX.
Bass Taverns. R. Crownshaw, manager.

On the Baslow Road, next to Penny Lane. Stone built, 16th century. "Very
old, very warm and very welcoming. Not what you would expect on the edge
of Sheffield", says the landlady. Low doors, the 6ft 2in son of the house has
to duck. All very quaint and tiny too. A one room pub with a central bar.
There are a lot of fish dishes and some steaks – all written up on the
blackboard. Bass range of ales.

THE QUIET PINT

OPEN: 11–11 (12–10.30 Sun) N.B. Slightly borderline. Maybe tapes at opening times – otherwise quiet.
Real Ale
Children welcome. No dogs.
Wheelchair access.

WASS

Wombwell Arms   Tel: 01347 868280

Wass, N. Yorks YO6 4BE
Free House. Alan & Lynda Evans, licensees.

In a delightful situation, at the foot of the Hambleton Hills and near the ruined 12th century Byland Abbey where you can still see the remains of an entire monastic site. Charming 17th century inn serving an interesting selection of pub food. Each day's selection is written on the blackboard and is based on fresh local produce only: sandwiches, ploughmans with local cheeses and home-made pickle, rabbit cooked with cider, cream and apples, pan fried beef fillet, pot roasted lamb, Whitby cod fillet with a crumb and cheese topping, other local game, vegetarian dishes and good puddings. Timothy Taylors and Black Sheep plus a guest beer. Choice of wines.

OPEN: 12–2.30. 7–11 (closed Sun eve & Mon. Oct–April & one week Jan)
Real Ale.
Children in eating area (not under 5 in evening). No dogs.
Wheelchair access to pub.

WATH-IN-NIDDERDALE

Sportsmans Arms   Tel: 01423 711306

Wath-in-Nidderdale, Pateley Bridge, Harrogate, N. Yorks HG3 5PP
Free House. Ray Carter, licensee.

High above Nidderdale are Brimham Rocks, fantastic sandstone outcrops shaped by centuries of wind and rain. They are a feature of the Nidderdale countryside from and provide magnificent views from this comfortable 17th century old stone inn, which is set in its own grounds amidst picturesque woods through which flows the river Nidd. More of an hotel than a pub; however, it does have a central bar which is popular with the locals and where you will find an interesting selection of bar food. Home-made soups, ploughmans with local cheese (you have a choice of nearly twenty, some local), lots of fresh fish, chicken in garlic butter – nothing fried – no chips here! Good puddings too. They do some real ales – John Foster, Courage Best, Youngers Scotch Bitter and Theakstons, but the concentration is on the wine list. A choice of malt whiskies and several Russian vodkas. Seats outside so you can take full advantage of the wonderful countryside.

OPEN: 12–3. 6.30–11.
Real Ale. Evening restaurant (not Sun eve).
Children welcome until 9 pm. Dogs on leads & well behaved.
Bedrooms.

WIDDOP

Pack Horse Inn   Tel: 01422 842803

The Ridge, Widdop, Hebden Bridge, W. Yorks HX7 7AT
Free House. Andrew Hollinrake, licensee.

The Pack Horse is on a moorland road between Hebden Bridge and Colne, near Slack Top, Widdop reservoir and the Pennine Way. A haven for walkers during the summer, it can be difficult in winter, although you'll find a warm welcome (if they're open) in this sturdily built 17th century converted farmhouse. Lots of freshly made sandwiches, beefburgers, individual pot meals, steak and kidney pie, gammon and two eggs, steaks, salads and specials from the blackboard – good sustaining food. Draught Thwaites Traditional Bitter and Craftsman ale, Theakstons XB and Youngers IPA. Good range of wines, with New World additions. One hundred single malts for you to try.

OPEN: 12–2. 7–10. (closed weekday lunchtimes, and all day Mon. Oct–Easter)
Real Ale
Children until 8pm. Dogs on leads.
Wheelchair access. Car park.

WE'RE NOT AGAINST ALL MUSIC

We are not against all music in pubs. Live music is totally acceptable and the pub piano is part of that tradition. Moreover, publicans nearly always announce an event giving those who want to avoid it a chance to drink elsewhere. What most QUIET PINT readers object to is having to compete against a constant barrage of background music to hear or be heard.

LONDON

The area within the periphery of the M25

Pubs are listed alphabetically by name and also in
postal districts at the end of this section.

LONDON SW18

Alma   Tel: 0181 870 2537

499 York Road, Wandsworth
Youngs. Charles Gotto, tenant.

First it was an hotel, built on the Old York Road a few years after the battle
of Alma; now a popular pub. Green shiny tiles outside, opulent Victorian
decor inside. Virtually opposite Wandsworth Town Railway station, it is a
favourite stopping place with rugby followers after a match at Twickenham
before wending their way to the mainline station at Waterloo to face the
hazards of a British Rail journey. Here you get friendly service in attractive
surroundings. The pub has a central bar with a dining room at the back filled
with interesting antique kitchen and restaurant artefacts. The bar menu
offers sandwiches and soup, baguette du Café Alma (with char-grilled steak,
salad and grainy mustard), assiette de charcuterie (French version of
ploughmans) filled filo parcels, rack of spring lamb, steaks, fresh fish, salads
and daily specials. Youngs ales and a good choice of wines by the bottle or
glass. Both Espresso and ordinary coffee. Youngs Brewery and their
magnificent Shire horses are just around the corner.

OPEN: 11–11.
Real Ale. Restaurant. No food Sun eve.
Children in eating areas. Dogs on leads.
Wheelchair access to pub.

LONDON SW7

Angelsea Arms   Tel: 0171 373 7960

15 Selwood Terrace SW7 3QG
Free House. Patrick Timmons, licensee.

An early Victorian pub which isn't that small; but can get very crowded, and
when it does, the party continues outside as it does with so many other

popular London pubs – but here they don't need the pavement, they have their own spacious forecourt. A comfortable, friendly atmosphere inside the pub and efficient service, even with all those al fresco drinkers. Food is good pub grub – basically sandwiches (doorsteps – you have been warned), ploughmans, pies, a choice of three hot dishes and a roast on Sundays. A good range of ales: Fullers London Pride, Marstons Pedigree, Harveys, Adnams, Boddingtons, Brakspear SB and Youngs Special – all on handpump. A selection of malt and Irish whiskies.

OPEN: 11–3. 5–11 (7–11 Sat)
Real Ale. No food Sun eve.
Children lunchtime only. Dogs on leads.

LONDON EC4

Black Friar   Tel: 0171 236 5650

174 Queen Victoria Street EC4 4DB
Nicholsons (Allied). Mr Karl Becker, manager.

Originally built in the 1870's, it was not until it was redecorated at the turn of the century in a flamboyant art-nouveau style, that it merited a second glance. Now it is full of the most wonderfully florid Edwardian decorations, mosaics, marble walls, pillared fireplaces, mirrors and a bronze bas relief of monks – to remind you that you are on the site of the old Blackfriars monastery. Busy, busy, busy – and that's not just the customers. They have a simple lunchtime bar menu of filled rolls, baked potatoes with various fillings, and a few hot dishes. A favourite watering hole in early evening for the thirsty hordes refreshing themselves before the journey home. Tetleys, Brakspears, Adnams, Marstons Pedigree and Nicholsons which is brewed by Allied – all on handpump. No garden, but there is a good pavement for standing on.

OPEN: 11.30–10.00 weekdays. Closed weekends & Bank Holidays
Real Ale. Lunchtime meals.
No children. No dogs.

LONDON SE3

British Oak   Tel: 0181 858 1082

109 Old Dover Road, Blackheath SE3 8SU
Scottish & Newcastle. Bob Wale, manager.

The nearest pub to Blackheath Rugby Club. I'm not sure what advantage that is, but that is what I've been told. Perhaps it's a warning that things can get boisterous on Saturday evenings. But back to basics: this is a popular local pub known for its bitters. They also serve good value food during the day – an all-day breakfast of double sausage, egg, bacon, tomato and chips, or steak and chips, served until 7 o'clock, Monday to Saturday. Courage Best and Directors, Theakstons Best Bitter, Old Peculiar, XB and Greene King IPA are the beers. You can sit in the sheltered, paved walled garden at the back of the pub.

OPEN: 11–11 (12–10.30 Sun)
Real Ale
Children in garden. Dogs on leads.

LONDON SW13

Bulls Head   Tel: 0181 876 5241

373 Lonsdale Road, Barnes SW13 9PY
Youngs. Dan Fleming, tenant.

The reason they don't have piped music in the Bulls Head is that no-one would hear it anyway – certainly not during the evenings or Sunday lunchtimes when modern Jazz groupies congregate there. Mid-day is blissfully quiet as they gird themselves for another session. The top jazz groups, who come here to play, do have their own room, but playing jazz is not the quietest of occupations; they can certainly be heard throughout the pub, and frequently half-way down the road as well! Food in the bar is all home-made, including the bread, sausages and ice-cream. At lunchtime there is a popular carvery and a selection of hot dishes. Youngs Bitter, Special, and nearly a hundred malt whiskies.

OPEN: 11–11.
Real Ale. Restaurant evenings only. No food Sun eve.
Children welcome. Dogs on leads.
Live jazz every evening in own room with bar.

LONDON WC1

Calthorpe Arms   Tel: 0171 278 1207

252, Gray's Inn Road, London WC1X 8JR
Youngs. J. Read & A. Larner, tenant.

Pleasant, comfortable local on the eastern fringe of Bloomsbury. A popular neighbourhood pub serving lunchtime food, in the bar and in the upstairs restaurant. A favourite with staff from ITN catching up with the local gossip. Low volume TV on most of the time. That no doubt is also for ITN to check nothing is going on behind their backs. Youngs Bitter, Special and Winter Warmer. Seats on the pavement – for people watching.

OPEN: 11–3. 5.30–11. (11–11 Thurs–Sat)
Real Ale
No children. No dogs.

LONDON E2

Camdens Head   Tel: 0171 613 4263

456 Bethnal Green Road, Bethnal Green.
Wetherspoons. Iain Middlebrough & Lisa Bell, managers.

This pub, as with all others in the Wetherspoon chain, is blissfully quiet but the Camdens Head has another thing going for it too – the real beer – there seems to be a dearth of it locally. All the surrounding pubs seem to be serving the fizzy stuff. So the locals crowd into the Camdens Head. Here they provide a large no-smoking area, and a reliable full menu, including vegetarian dishes, to go with the cask conditioned beers: Theakstons Best, Theakstons XB, Greene King IPA, Courage Directors plus a guest beer – all on hand pump.

OPEN: 11–11
Real Ale
Children in garden only. No dogs.
Wheelchair facilities.

LONDON NW8

Clifton   Tel: 0171 6242 5233

96 Clifton Hill, St John's Wood.
Nicholsons. John Hale, manager.

When our correspondent went into the Clifton some years ago, he noticed the calm of the place and inquired of the young Irish barman whether there was any piped music. Shocked at the suggestion, he replied: "gracious no, Sir – this is a talking pub!" And so it has remained to this day. The building, originally an old merchant's house was converted into a public house 130 years ago. The U-shaped bar serves three small, attractively decorated rooms. The restaurant – which seats about 25 – is in the conservatory. One menu serves both the bar and restaurant: soup of the day, filled jacket potatoes, filled baguettes, deep fried mushrooms with dips, lasagne, a selection of pies, steaks and haddock or scampi with chips. Ales are Tetleys, Nicholsons, Adnams and one changing guest beer. There are seats on the leafy terrace at the front of the pub.

OPEN: 11–11. (11–10.30)
Real Ale. Restaurant.
Children welcome. Dogs on leads.

LONDON W1

Coach and Horses   Tel: 0171 437 5920

29 Greek Street
Taylor Walker. Norman Balon, tenant.

Open all day; this is a serious drinking pub. The Coach and Horses has become synonomous with its tenant and is called 'Normans' by the regulars. Immortalised as 'The Regulars' in the Private Eye column, it is the pub where Jeffrey Barnard did most of his drinking, where Private Eye meet every other Wednesday for their fortnightly editorial lunches, and the rest of the locals come to drink the Burton Ale, Tetleys and Eldridge Pope's Dorchester Bitter.

OPEN: 11–11. (12–10.30 Sun.)
Real Ale.
No children. No dogs.

LONDON NW10

The Coliseum   Tel: 0181 961 6570

Manor Park Road, Harlesden.
Wetherspoons. Kevin McDonnel & Susan McDonnel, managers.

Stars of the silver screen take pride of place in what used to be one of the local cinemas before Wetherspoons snapped it up. A 20ft mural recreating a scene from the film, "The Cowboy and the Lady" starring Gary Cooper and Merle Oberon is the main feature; other bits and pieces of film memorabilia are used to decorate the interior. Food all day, and always six different beers and one guest.

OPEN: 11–11
Real Ale.
No children. No dogs.
Wheelchair facilities.

LONDON N7

The Coronet   Tel: 0171 609 5014

338–346 Holloway Road, N7 6NJ
Wetherspoons. Tony Purcell & Olive Rooney, managers.

With 6,000 square feet of customer space as' them what know' put it, we
have here a big, big drinking area: a sort of transported 'Bier Keller.' This
place was yet another redundant cinema. Originally the Savoy, then the
ABC, finally the Coronet before being converted into this huge, popular
Wetherspoon outlet. Keeping an eye on things is a life size statue of Fred
Astaire. Between five or six real ales, one guest and food served all day.

OPEN: 11–11
Real Ale.
No children. No dogs.
Wheelchair facilities.

LONDON SW3

Coopers Arms   Tel: 0171 376 3120

Flood Street, Chelsea
Youngs. Lisa Pendlebury, licensee.

A stucco faced pub, built in 1874. Inside, framed drawings by the cartoonist
Jak and a selection of daily newspapers so you can catch up on world
events whilst enjoying your drink. Quite a young crowd in the evenings;
lunchtime is the local professionals' turn. The interesting, imaginative menu
changes daily, but there could be country paté, Creole fish stew, panfried
breast of chicken with mushrooms and fresh tarragon, roasted
Mediterranean vegetables on tagliatelle, garnished with Feta cheese and
fresh basil, char-grilled or roast chicken, navarine of lamb, poached salmon
fillet and grilled swordfish. Desirable desserts. Youngs range of ales. Also an
interesting selection of New World, French, Italian, Spanish and other wines
listed on the blackboard.

THE QUIET PINT

OPEN: 11–11 (12–10.30 Sun).
Real Ale.
Children welcome. Dogs on leads.
Wheelchair access.

LONDON N19

The Dog   Tel: 0171 263 0429

17–19 Archway Road
Wetherspoons. Paul Rush & Mandy Andrews, managers.

Only a few minutes from Archway underground station, this is one of the
Chains smaller pubs. It started life as the head office until they outgrew it,
and put it to the most obvious use – one more pub. Lots of pictures and
references to dogs all around, but not a real one to be seen. A more personal
kind of place attracting a loyal band of local regulars. The usual reliable
beers, guest beer and menu.

OPEN: 11–11
Real Ale
No children. No dogs.
Wheelchair facilities.

LONDON W1

Dog & Duck   Tel: 0171 437 4447

Frith Street
Nicholsons (Allied). Mrs Gene Bell, manageress.

A very small corner pub in the heart of Soho. At busy periods there is
virtually standing room only, although an upstairs bar has recently been
opened to cope with the overflow. As with a lot of well frequented Central
London pubs, you will find the pavement serves as an extra room in good
weather. Only sandwiches are served, but there is a good range of ales:
Tetleys, Timothy Taylors Landlord, Nicholsons – brewed by Allied especially
for the pub – and two guest beers.

OPEN: 12–11. Closed Sat & Sun lunchtimes (6–11 Sat eve)
Real Ale. No food weekends.
No children. No dogs.

LONDON W6

Dove   Tel: 0181 748 5405

19 Upper Mall, Hammersmith
Fullers. Brian Lovrey, tenant.

The Dove has an enviable riverside terrace on which to sit and watch the comings and goings on the river. Lunchtime is quiet-ish, but come evening, space is at a premium. You get to it via a quiet alley by Hammersmith Bridge. It is 17th century and claims to have the smallest bar in England – on the right as you go in – where five people are a crowd. The main bar is bigger, beamed and panelled, retaining much of its old charm and character. Well cooked lunchtime bar food: filled baked potatoes, various pies, salads, ploughmans and changing daily specials on the blackboard. Very well regarded Thai food is served during the evening. Fullers London Pride and ESB ales. Those patriotically minded among you might like to know that a copy of the score of Rule Britannia is on a wall of the bar. James Thompson, who wrote it, had a room here.

OPEN: 11–11
Real Ale.
Children welcome. Dogs on leads.

DENHAM VILLAGE

Falcon Inn   Tel: 01895 832125

Denham Village, Nr Uxbridge, Middx.
Whitbread. Don & Sue Petty, tenants.

Small and cosy. There has been an inn on this site since 1670. Brick built, under a tiled roof and situated opposite a green which serves as an extra room in the summer. In winter there will be two big log fires at either end of the traditionally furnished bar. Only lunchtime food is available, the exception being Friday evenings when they serve a fish and chip supper. Familiar bar snacks: ploughmans, sandwiches and always a daily special. Brakspears ales, Morlands Old Speckled Hen and Pedigree, Flowers IPA, also the usual range of lagers.

OPEN: 11–3. 5.30–11 (12–3; 7–10.30 Sun)
Real Ale.
No Children. Dogs on leads.

LONDON EC2

Flying Horse　　　　　　　　　　　　　　　Tel: 0171 247 5338

52 Wilson Street
Dalkeith Inns. Michael Freeman, licensee/manager.

In this area there is only one like it left – an old fashioned pub nestling between tall, modern office blocks, reminding all of us what the City of London used to look like. Long established, it is a busy, friendly, chatty drinking place. Only two bars, with a real coal fire. Lunchtime bar snacks are simple and straightforward – just what the clients want: sandwiches, filled French bread and rolls filled with cuts off the hot roast. Ales include Youngs Bitter, Courage Best, Marstons Pedigree and Websters.

OPEN: 11–10 (closed Sat & Sun)
Real Ale.
No parking, no garden, no children, no dogs.

LONDON SE1

Founders Arms　　　　　　　　　　　　　　Tel: 0171 928 1899

52 Hopton Street
Youngs. Lyn Foreman, tenant.

In the shadow of Blackfriar's Bridge, next to the site of the new Tate Gallery, opposite St Paul's Cathedral and near the new Globe Theatre; culturally you are going to be spoilt for choice. Built only 16 years ago on the edge of the Thames, the Founders Arms is virtually all glass, with a terrace cut into the banks of the river from where you have a wonderful view of the City of London. Quieter after the weekday "happy hour" when, to quote our informant, "the city types have hit the road". Quite a choice of bar food: twelve different salads, cornish pasties, hand-raised pies, smoked trout and hot dishes of the day. The restaurant is à la carte, but specialises in fresh fish and steaks. All Youngs ales: Bitter, Special, Ramrod and in winter, Winter Warmer. Every year, the pub sponsors a five-mile run along the river to raise money for the Guide Dogs for the Blind Association, and they welcome blind people into the restaurant.

OPEN: 11–11
Real Ale. Restaurant.
Children and dogs on leads.

LONDON SW1

Fox and Hounds   Tel: 0171 730 6367

29, Passmore Street, (corner of Graham Terrace), SW1
Bass Charrington at moment. Diane Harvey, tenant.

You are only here for the beer. Well, that, the ambience, charm of the two small panelled rooms, and according to our researcher the charm of the landlady and her ability to pour, and I quote, "a beautiful White Shield Worthington". This pub is his favourite place for a beer in the capital. As our Nick has quite a palate, be assured this pub is serving a good pint. I don't think I'll repeat what he says about the house wine though – it's probably actionable. Just stick to the beer or cider: the Fox and Hounds only has a Beer, Cider and Wine license. It's a tiny corner pub, at the end of an early 19th century terrace on the edge of the Grosvenor Estate. A toasted sandwich is all that is offered by way of food. Draught Bass, Adnams, Greene King IPA, something from Harveys Sussex Brewery, cider and bottled White Shield Worthington, correctly poured, are the liquid refreshments.

OPEN: 11–3. 5.30–11. (11–3. 6–11. Sat. 12–2. 7–10.30 Sun)
Real Ale.
No children. No dogs.

LONDON SW10

Fox and Pheasant   Tel: 0171 352 2943

1 Billing Road
Greene King. Mrs Sian Angelo, licensee/manager.

Not much has changed in this pub since it was built in 1848, except for the obvious concessions to the 20th century and the occasional coat of paint. So with its well polished traditional furnishings, it has a nicely mellowed atmosphere appreciated by the customers of both public and saloon bars. There really isn't a great difference between them, except that the saloon has a square of carpet and the public bar a darts board. As the Fox and Pheasant is situated on a private side road off the Fulham Road, there is no parking outside the pub. But it does have a small garden with five picnic tables which are very popular on a balmy summer evening. The bar menu is short and hearty: basket meals – chicken nuggets, plaice goujons, scampi, vegetable nuggets and sausage and chips. Ales include Greene King IPA, Abbots and one of their seasonal beers: Sorcerer, Black Baron or

Royal Raven. Water for the dog.

OPEN: 12–3. 5.30–11. (12–3. 6–10.30 Sun)
Real Ale
Children in garden. Dogs on leads.

LONDON SW3

Front Page   Tel: 0171 352 0648

35 Old Church Street
Courage. Christopher Phillips & Rupert Fowler, lease.

Turn off the busy Kings Road, look for the white painted pub with the hanging baskets and you've found the Front Page. Those of you familiar with the pub years ago will remember it as the Black Lion. Wonderfully airy inside, there are big ceiling fans to keep you cool when the temperature rises, and an open fire in winter to keep you warm. Never so full that you have to fight your way to the bar, just gently busy. Still very much a local and well frequented. Friendly staff and good dependable bar food. Dishes are listed on blackboards at either end of the bar: home-made soup, chicken paté, smoked salmon and scrambled eggs, salmon fish cakes, sausage and mash, various salads and puddings. John Smiths, Theakstons, Boddingtons and Websters Yorkshire ales on handpump. Also a choice of wines.

OPEN: 11–3. 5.30–11 (6–11 Sat)
Real Ale.
Children welcome lunchtimes. Dogs on leads.

LONDON E11

The George   Tel: 0181 989 2921

High Street, Wanstead.
Wetherspoons. Cathy Reynolds & Trevor Cohen, managers.

This Group really believes in packing them in. Before conversion, this was a furniture showroom. Now it's a large, friendly, comfortable pub. All the usual Wetherspoon attributes with the addition of between one and two thousand books on display – whether to look at or read, I don't know. Full menu and Theakstons XB, Best, Courage Directors, Youngers Scotch Bitter and a guest.

OPEN: 11–11
Real Ale.
No children. No dogs.
Wheelchair facilities.

LONDON SE1

George Tel: 0171 407 2056

77 Borough High Street, Southwark
Whitbreads. John Hall, manager.

What can you say about the 17th century George that hasn't been said before. We should all be grateful to the National Trust for saving it from almost certain destruction when, in 1937, it accepted this magnificent old coaching inn as a gift from London & North Eastern Railway. The original pub was destroyed in a fire that swept through Southwark in 1676 – ten years after the great fire of London – and what you see today is the replacement built in that year. It was one of the many inns in the area playing an important part in the long distance waggon trains plying to and fro, from Kent, Sussex and Surrey to Southwark. Stage Coaches started using the George in 1732 and by the early 19th century it had become one of the most important inns in Southwark, with huge stables and yards. It was these that attracted the LNER's predecessor, the Great Northern Railway, to buy the George in 1874 to use as a depot. By 1937, they had pulled down or sold off many of the old buildings, leaving the Inn, a couple of houses within the structure, and only one of the magnificent galleries to posterity in the care of the National Trust. Today the George caters for a totally different traveller. The remaining galleries of the South range look over the courtyard where you can sit and enjoy your food and drink, occasionally entertained by visiting Morris men or players from the nearby Globe Theatre – quite medieval. There is a simple bar menu of sandwiches, home-made pies and salads. Boddingtons, Greene King Abbot, Whitbread Castle Eden, Flowers Original, a guest beer and Farm Cider. If you don't know the pub, search it out, as it is not clearly visible behind the huge gates on Borough High Street.

OPEN: 11–11.
Real Ale. Restaurant (not Sun); lunchtime meals & snacks.
Children in eating area. No dogs inside – in courtyard only.

LONDON E15

The Goldengrove   Tel: 0181 519 0750

146–148, The Grove, Stratford.
Wetherspoons. Edward & Susan Guyatt, managers.

Built on the site of the poet Gerard Manley Hopkins' grandfather's house.
Gerard Manley Hopkins was born in Stratford Grove in 1844, and lived there
for the first eight years of his life. The name 'Goldengrove' is taken from one
of his poems. Less poetically, before being converted into the place you see
today, the site housed London's largest discount jeans store. Big, open plan,
with a bar at the front and ample seating. A full menu is served all day.
Youngers Scotch Bitter, Courage Directors, Theakston XB and Best plus a
guest beer. A large beer garden overlooks the nearby Theatre Royal.

OPEN: 11–11
Real Ale.
No children. No dogs.
Wheelchair facilities.

LONDON SW15

Green Man   Tel: 0181 788 8096

Wildcroft Road, Putney
Youngs. Mr F. Egan, manager.

On the edge of Putney Heath, which was notorious in the 18th century as
the haunt of highwaymen and vagabonds, nothing ever changes: by another
name shall ye know them. The charming Green Man dates back to the 16th
century and has its own shady past, Dick Turpin being part of it. It is now
busy looking after the needs of the law abiding modern man. Inside are two
airy bars with views over the Heath. There is quite an extensive menu with
the addition of daily specials. All summer they have a daily barbecue
(weather permitting); lots of different casseroles in winter. Youngs Bitter,
Special, Dirty Dicks and Premium. London Lager and guest beers. Seats in
the flowery courtyards and in the garden at the back where there is also a
children's play area.

OPEN: 11–11
Real Ale. No food winter eves.
Children in garden. Dogs on leads.

LONDON SW1

Grenadier Tel: 0171 235 3074

Wilton Row
Watneys (Courage). Paul Gibb, licensee.

Years ago you could drive through the mews and park outside the pub, no doubt much to the annoyance of the residents of the houses opposite. In the evenings it was one of "the places" and was heaving, the overspill continuing the party in the mews, leaning against the cars. Perhaps not so frightfully crowded now – you certainly can't drive up to the front door – but it is still very popular, so search it out; it has lost none of its charm or character. As the name suggests, it leans towards the military; the Duke of Wellington's officers used it as their mess in the 18th century. Painted patriotically in the colours of the Union Flag, a sentry box stands next to the front door, and a Guard's bearskin guards the bar. There is a small candlelit dining room where, naturally enough, you can order Beef Wellington. Good hearty bar food: soup, ploughmans, fish and chips, sausage and mash, scampi and chips and a vegetarian dish or two. The bitters change frequently; there is always a guest beer and they stock quite a range of lagers, cider, bottled beer and Guinness. The Grenadier has its own very special 'Bloody Mary', the recipe for which is passed on from landlord to landlord.

OPEN: 12–3. 5–11
Real Ale. Restaurant.
Children in restaurant. Dogs on leads.

LONDON EC2

Hamilton Hall Tel: 0171 247 3579

Liverpool Street Station
Wetherspoons. Dave Chapman & Bernice Hartnett, managers.

Built at the turn of the century as the grand ballroom of the Great Eastern Hotel, it is now, still with its splendid, soaring Baroque decor, one of the expanding Wetherspoon Chain of pubs which are proving so popular. Closed for over 50 years, Wetherspoons converted the ballroom a few years ago, creating a comfortably furnished mezzanine floor, a great part of which is no-smoking. Reliable bar food with a choice of daily specials and puddings is served from 11am to 10pm every day. Beers in this Chain are frequently cheaper than elsewhere. Greene King Abbot and IPA, Courage Directors, Theakstons Best and XB, Youngers Scotch and a guest beer, all on hand-pump.

OPEN: 11–11.
Real Ale.
No children. No dogs.

LONDON SW19 (Wimbledon)

Hand in Hand   Tel: 0181 946 5720

6 Crooked Billet, SW19
Youngs. Christopher Marley, licensee.

It looks over a small green, much used for lolling on during balmy summer
evenings. A cottagey sort of pub, hung about with flowering baskets and
window boxes, it enjoys the added bonus of a sunny courtyard at the front.
Originally just an ale house, it is now a popular family pub with a no-smoking
family room. Burgers, scampi and a pasta dish to satisfy the inner man and
accompany the range of Youngs beers. Wide selection of wines from many
countries of the world.

OPEN: 11–11
Real Ale.
Children in family room. Dogs on leads.

LONDON NW11

JJ Moons   Tel: 0181 423 5056

3 Shaftesbury Parade, Shaftesbury Circle, Nr. South Harrow.
Wetherspoon. Joanne Salter, manager.

Another good thing about this Chain – if you are so minded – is that a lot of
them hold beer festivals. JJ Moons has one twice a year. Apart from that
nugget of information, you may like to know that this is one of the older
outlets and smaller than most; even so, it still has a sizable no-smoking area
and offers a full menu. Beers are Greene King Abbot, Theakstons XB,
Theakstons Best, Courage Directors, Youngers Scotch Bitter and a guest
ale.

OPEN: 11–11 (12–10.30 Sun)
Real Ale
No children. No dogs.
Wheelchair facilities.

LONDON WC1

Kings Arms Tel: 0171 405 9107

11A Northington Street, London WC1
Bass. Clive & Linda Gilbert, tenant.

This 200 year old pub is in a Georgian area of London, off Theobalds Road and John Street, not far from Gray's Inn, one of the four Inns of Court. Within the gardens of Gray's Inn is a Catalpa tree, reputed to have been planted by Francis Bacon from a cutting brought into the country by Sir Walter Raleigh. The Kings Arms is a friendly, cosy pub – one of the few in London with a real coal fire in winter. Snacks and straightforward pub food are served in the downstairs bar: sausage and mash, liver and bacon, ploughmans, toasties and sandwiches. During the evening, the upstairs function room, which also has a bar, becomes a Thai restaurant. Bass, Fullers London Pride, Greene King IPA and Everards Tiger Best Bitter, (a Leicester brew) are the ales.

OPEN: 11–11 Mon–Fri. (Closed Sat & Sun).
Real Ale.
No Children, Dogs on leads.

LONDON WC1

Lamb Tel: 0171 405 0713

95 Lamb's Conduit Street
Youngs. Richard Whyte, manager.

Just off Theobalds Road, this is an old Victorian pub, full of atmosphere, with a friendly efficient staff. Inside, the pub still retains some of the original Victorian fittings. The U shaped bar and glass snob screens are worth noting, also the old photographs of the Holborn Empire, a famous musical hall bombed in the last war. Usual bar snacks, (no sandwiches Sunday) plus some worthwhile home-cooked daily specials, beef in red wine being a favourite. Choice of salads, and on Sundays there is a carvery in the restaurant. For the health conscious, there is a small no-smoking room where you can enjoy your pint without a fug. Youngs Bitter, Special, Dirty Dicks, in winter, Winter Warmer and a guest beer. Some seats in the small courtyard.

OPEN: 11–11
Real Ale.
Children in eating area. No dogs.

LONDON EC3

Lamb Tavern   Tel: 0171 626 2454

Leadenhall Market, London EC3.
Youngs. David & Linda Morris, managers.

In the heart of the City of London, the wonderfully Victorian Leadenhall market, (poultry, fish and game) has hidden depths. Underneath, are the remains of our past – a huge basilica and forum, an important market and meeting place in Roman London. Built on a piece of history, The Lamb has height rather than depth: four floors of it. So busy is it, that another floor was squeezed in to accompany the other three. Full of city types drinking gallons of beer – Draught Bitter mostly – and enjoying slices cut off the roast rib of beef and slapped between two pieces of French bread. Four large joints of beef are consumed each day. Youngs range of beers and some lagers to accompany the hearty food.

OPEN: 11–9.30, Mon–Fri only.
Real Ale.
No children. Dogs on leads.

LONDON WC2

Lamb & Flag   Tel: 0171 497 9504

33 Rose Street
Courage. Terry Archer & Adrian Zimmerman, lease.

A busy, popular pub in an alley between Floral and Garrick Streets, the Lamb and Flag dates back to the 17th century and retains much of the character and atmosphere of that time. Low ceilings, panelled walls – still with the original built-in benches. Dickens knew this pub when he was working in nearby Catherine Street and would still recognise it. It has two small bars downstairs, and an upstairs dining room. Frequently crowded in the early evening, you'll find the customers spilling out onto the pavement enjoying a pre-prandial drink. Bar food includes roast beef filled baps, paté, ploughmans with farmhouse cheeses and a variety of hot dishes. John Smiths, Morlands Old Speckled Hen, Courage Best and Directors, Wadworths 6X and a guest beer. They have a selection of malt whiskies.

OPEN: 11–11.
Real Ale. Lunchtime meals (snacks 12–5 only). Not Sun.
No dogs.
Live Jazz Sun eves.

LONDON NW1

Man in the Moon Tel: 0171 482 2054

40–42 Chalk Farm Road, Camden
Wetherspoons. Carol Ross & Richard Leith, managers.

"New customers wanted, apply within, no experience necessary." We like pub managers with a sense of humour but we know they can't be serious. This place heaves with customers, particularly at the weekend – they do, after all, serve the cheapest pint in the area. Opposite Camden Market, they are also on the tourist route. Full menu with at least four daily specials. They also feature a beer, food and wine of the month. Five or six real ales and one guest.

OPEN: 11–11
Real Ale
No children. No dogs.
Wheelchair facilities.

LONDON WC2

Marquess of Granby Tel: 0171 836 7657

51 Chandos Place, WC2
Allied Domecq. Matthew Ward, licensee.

This is a quiet pub for a reason. The musicians who frequent it simply don't want any musak. Music is after all their profession and they want a rest – a bit of 'ush, so they can concentrate on a relaxing drink. This pub looks quite a reasonable size from the front but shrinks towards the back: as it is built on one of those odd shaped – "we can just jam another one in here" – sites. Bar food is served all day to go with the beers. Adnams, Tetleys, Marquess Bitter, Burtons and guests such as Marstons Pedigree and Youngs Special.

OPEN: 11–11. (12–10.30 Sun.)
Real Ale
Children in room upstairs. No dogs.

CHRISTMAS

Pub opening times at Christmas can vary. Some don't open at all. A few open all day, while others open at mid-day only. If you plan to visit one at Christmas, check by calling them on the telephone.

THE QUIET PINT

ENFIELD

Moon under the Water   Tel: 0181 366 9355

115–117 Chase Side, Enfield EN2 6NN
Wetherspoons. Barry McParland, manager.

Another large outlet converted from a restaurant and shop in 1988 though
it has had a lick of paint since then. Reasonably priced beer, full menu and
daily specials served throughout the day. Not only does this Chain eschew
music but you won't find a TV or pool table either – just people enjoying
themselves.

OPEN: 11–11
Real Ale
No children. No dogs.
Wheelchair facilities.

LONDON WC1, Bloomsbury.

Museum Tavern   Tel: 0171 242 8987

Gt. Russell St.(corner of Museum Street).
Scottish & Newcastle. L. Mackay & A. Hughes, managers.

On an important corner site opposite the British Museum, this pub was not
always thus. Known as the Dog and Duck until the Museum was built in
1761, it chose to emulate the atmosphere of learning that the newly built
Museum gave the area, and renamed itself the British Museum Tavern.
However, not satisfied with just a change of name, the pub was rebuilt
several times, the last being in the mid 19th century. Largely unaltered since
then, this is the building you see today. Students, scholars and tourists all
come here. Karl Marx used it while he was studying at the British Museum.
Very popular at lunchtime, or indeed anytime between 11am and 10pm –
food is served all day. Traditionally furnished, it has a carvery at the end of
the bar serving a variety of cold meats, salads, ploughmans, pies, pasties
and a choice of hot daily specials which will include one vegetarian dish.
Sunday roasts. Courage Best and Directors, Theakstons Best and Old
Peculiar, Brakspears, Wadworths 6X and a guest ale.

OPEN: 11–11.
Real Ale.
Children welcome but not in bar. No dogs – pub cat in residence!
Wheelchair access to pub.

LONDON EC4

Ye Olde Cheshire Cheese   Tel: 0171 353 6170

Wine Office Court, (off Fleet Street)
Sam Smiths. Gordon Garrity, licensee.

Like so much of London, the original Cheshire Cheese was burnt to the ground in the great fire of 1666; only the cellars remained. The present building, rebuilt on the original foundations two years later, is much as you see it today. After 300 years it was feeling a little shaky and in need of support, so it was recently made more secure and extended to cope with the demands of the 20th century. On four floors – not counting the cellars – there is a formidable number of dining rooms, four ground floor bars and the original panelled chop room which has famous literary connections. Anybody who was anybody in the literary world crossed the threshold of this charming, timeless old pub. Only sandwiches are available in the cellar bar (which has piped music): elsewhere in the pub there is quite a choice of places to sit and eat: ask and ye shall be directed. Good hearty English fare on offer: soups, smoked salmon or black pudding as a starter; lots of different fish dishes, salads, grills, steak, kidney and mushroom pie, vegetarian dishes, and bubble and squeak for a main course. Various puddings. Sam Smiths beers on handpump.

OPEN: 11–11. Closed Sun eve.
Real Ale. Restaurant (closed Sun Eve)
Children welcome. No dogs.

LONDON EC1

Olde Mitre   Tel: 0171 405 4751

Ely Place
Taylor Walker (Allied). Don O'Sullivan, manager.

This Olde Mitre takes its name from an earlier inn, built in the 16th century to provide for the Bishop of Ely's staff. Rebuilt during the mid 18th century, it remains much as it was, a picturesque, delightful pub just off Hatton Garden, next to the 13th century St Ethelreda's Church. The small, panelled rooms are crowded during weekday lunchtimes when they serve a variety of sandwiches, scotch eggs, filled rolls and sausages – simple but good. Ind Coope Burton, Friary Meux and Tetleys on handpump. There are seats among the plants in a delightful small yard between the pub and the Church.

OPEN: 11–11. Closed Sat & Sun & Bank Hols.}
Real Ale.
No children. No dogs.

LONDON EC2

The Old Monk   Tel: 0171 377 9555

128 Bishopsgate
Free House. Charles & Michelle Smythe, managers.

This was originally a wine bar until it was taken over by Gerry Martin, adding to his embryonic empire. Traditionally laid out and furnished, it has two biggish bars, accomodating about 300 people. Popular with City businessmen, the bar food includes soups, filled jacket potatoes, omelettes, chicken Kiev, filled enchilladas and a weekly special. Theakstons Best, XB and Old Peculiar, Wadworths 6X, Greene King IPA, Courage Directors and Marstons Pedigree ales.

OPEN: 11–11 (closed Sat & Sun)
Real Ale.
No children. Guide dogs only.

LONDON WC1

The Old Monk   Tel: 0171 831 0714

39–41 Grays Inn Road Free House. Andrew Posner, manager.

Once two shops, a wine bar five years ago, now celebrating its third birthday as a pub. One large open space with a U shaped bar, comfortably furnished and with plenty of room to sit and eat. Bar snacks include soup of the day, garlic bread, jumbo sausages, selection of burgers, Mexican chilli and scampi. Scottish and Newcastle and Courage are the main suppliers of beer. Guest ales come from several British micro-breweries.

OPEN: 11–11 (12–3. 7–10.30 Sun)
Real Ale
No Children, Dogs when not too busy – weekends

LONDON BARNET

The Old Monk & Holt   Tel: 0181 499 4280

193 Barnet High Street, Herts
Courage. Darren & Lisa Anderson, licensees.

Between Hadley Common (to the left) and Barnet High Street (to the right).
Once The Bell, this pub is another Gerald Martin has added to his budding
chain of Monkish pubs. Comfortable, small and well-established, they serve
a traditional pub menu consisting of soup, club sandwiches, filled jacket
potatoes, various pies and fish and chips. Ales are Theakstons Best,
Wadworths 6X, Courage Directors and Marstons Pedigree. Seats in the beer
garden.

OPEN: 11–11 (12–3 7–10.30 Sun)
Real Ale.
Children in Beer Garden before 9pm No Dogs.

LONDON SW3

Phene Arms   Tel: 0171 352 3294

9 Phene Street, London SW3
Courage. Lesley Davis, tenant.

On the corner of Phene Street and Margaretta Terrace. Named after Dr. John
Phene, who, in the middle of the last century, developed this area and built
the pub; he also planted the trees, making this one of the most attractive
places in Chelsea. Outside the Phene Arms is a pleasant front garden; just
the place to be on a warm summer evening. Inside are a bar and small dining
room. French, bistro-like food, steak in Ciabatta bread to fill a medium size
gap, and a 'good selection of proper wines' according to our researcher.
Roast lunch on Sundays. Websters beers, Courage Best and Directors,
Morlands Old Speckled Hen and something from Adnams.

OPEN: 11–11
Real Ale.
Children welcome. Dogs on leads.

LONDON TWICKENHAM

Popes Grotto   Tel: 0181 892 3050

Cross Deep, Twickenham
Youngs. Stephen Brough, manager.

Surrounded as you are here by Popes in various guises – mainly temporal – Alexander Avenue, Popes Grove and Grotto Road – what else could you possibly call a pub but Popes Grotto. Having said that, Walpole Road and Tennyson Avenue aren't a million yards away, so the literary choice was in fact wide open, but Alexander Pope did in fact live nearby. Popes Grotto is a comfortable, spacious pub with three bars and an attractive terraced garden at the back. Good, well chosen bar food ranges from soup, filled baked potatoes, king prawns in herbs and garlic, steaks, salads and daily specials. On Sundays they do a roast lunch. Ales are Youngs Bitter and Special, and Winter Warmer when appropriate.

OPEN: 11–3; 53.0–11; (11–11 Sat)
Real Ale.
Dogs on leads.

LONDON WC1

Princess Louise   Tel: 0171 405 8816

208 High Holborn
Free House. Joseph Sheridan, licensee.

Named after the fourth daughter of Queen Victoria, the pub was built in 1872, but didn't become licensed until 1891, when it was bought and decorated by Arthur Chitty. Listed Grade II* makes it a building of considerable note. The interior is a monument to the very best in late Victorian decoration. Polished granite pillars, gilt mirrors, ornate plasterwork, elaborate tiling and a huge mahogany U-shaped bar. The gents lavatory has a separate listing! Downstairs, a variety of well-filled, freshly made sandwiches are available from 11–10.30 every day except Sunday. Upstairs at lunchtimes Monday to Friday they serve a selection of Thai food in the lounge bar. Beers change regularly but they usually have eight or nine on offer, and wines by the glass.

OPEN: 11–11 (12–3. 6–11 Sat)
Real Ale. No food Sundays.
No children. Dogs on leads.

LONDON NW6

Queens Arms   Tel: 0171 624 5735

1 Kilburn High Road
Youngs. John Conroy, manager.

Poor old pub: it has suffered quite a few upheavals in its life-time. Quite literally during the last war, when it was bombed out of existence. Rebuilt after the war, it then burnt down in the 50's. Rebuilt yet again, this time in the style of a town house, it is now up and flourishing. A favourite with local office staff and musicians from the London Orchestras who use the nearby St. Augustine's Church for recording sessions. Two bars, a lounge and saloon combined, and public bar. Simple, first rate food served by courteous staff: ploughmans, sandwiches, steak and kidney pie, cottage pie and a daily special. Youngs Special, Ramrod and Bitter. The Queens Arms boasts a roof garden, which they have difficulty maintaining as some thieving lot keep pinching the plants. (High trellis – that's what they need – thieves can't stand it because as it is too unstable to climb over). There are a few seats on the terrace at the front of the pub, surrounded by lots of flowers.

OPEN: 11–11, (Sat & Sun lounge bar closes from 4–7)
Real Ale
Children at lunchtime only. Dogs in public bar only.

LONDON SW1

Red Lion   Tel: 0171 930 2030

Duke of York Street. SW1
Free House. Michael Brown, licensee.

Drink all day if you want to, but it is more of a lunchtime pub. If you're also looking for something to eat, note that bar snacks – not much more than a sandwich – are only served from 12–2.30 – handy if you're doing a little shopping in either Piccadilly or Jermyn Street. The exception is Saturday when they serve fish and chips: its a favourite with the tourists. On the small side for a gin palace, but a Victorian gem, virtually unspoilt, the cut glass twinkling away in the sunlight. Ales are constantly changing . Most of them are guests from the smaller breweries; ales are specially brought in for the regulars. When we spoke to the landlord he had Burton Ale and Wells Eagle IPA. This is another pub that has a loo worthy of note. "Going to the loo is an adventure in itself", says Michael Brown, "we tend to count the customers going down to make sure we don't lose them!"

THE QUIET PINT

OPEN: 11.30–11 (closed Sun)
Real Ale
No Children. No dogs.

LONDON W1

Red Lion

Tel: 0171 499 1307

Waverton Street
Scottish & Newcastle. Raymond Dodgson, manager.

Much has changed in the area since the Red Lion was built three hundred years ago. Then it was on a muddy lane alongside the grand Chesterfield House. Only an 'umble ale house, it was frequented by the "rougher" local traders from Shepherds Market, servants, and later the builders and masons who were slowly transforming the area in the 18th and 19th centuries into the London you see today. Its humble past forgotten, the Red Lion is now a very smart pub in a smart part of London. The small panelled bar serves food all day: home-made sausages and mash, char-grilled burgers and cajun chicken sandwiches are very popular, salads and hot daily specials. The food in the restaurant goes up a notch: three different set menus to choose from or you could have Dover sole, grilled wild Scotch salmon, half a roast duck, best end of lamb or fillet of beef Wellington. Greene King Abbot and IPA, Courage Directors, Fullers London Pride, Theakstons Best and XB, John Smiths, Wadworths 6X and Gillespies Stout, Guinness too, and a weekly guest beer. Or you could have the 'house special' the Red Lions' very own Bloody Mary.

OPEN: 11–11 (12–3; 6–11 Sat)
Real Ale. Restaurant
Children in eating area. Only Guide Dogs.
Wheelchair access.

LONDON SE10

Richard 1st

Tel: 0181 692 2996

52–54 Royal Hill, Greenwich SE10 8RT
Youngs. Keith Ellis, manager.

Ancient, unspoilt, with a panelled interior, and books to read if you're kept waiting. Not far from the glories of Greenwich Park and The Maritime Museum – they're just a brisk walk away. This pub is a very family friendly place at the weekend, when, if the weather is fine, you can enjoy a barbecue in the garden. In addition there is good, hearty pub fare to go with the Youngs beers: Bitter, Special and Ramrod plus the seasonal Wheat Beer. Seats in the beautiful walled garden.

OPEN: 11–11. (12–10.30 Sun)
Real Ale.
Children in garden. Dogs on leads.

LONDON W8

Scarsdale   Tel: 0171 937 1811

23a Edwardes Square, W8
Scottish & Newcastle. Fred Hill, licensee.

A London pub with an outside seating area. Edwardes Square is one of the more attractive of the London Squares, and the Scarsdale pub is the icing on the cake. The outside is exhuberant with flowers; inside, full of well polished mahogany, brass and shining glass. The big attraction for the customers are the seats in the shady flowery area at the front of the pub. If you want something to eat they offer lots of steaks, chops and anything else you can grill. Bar food is served at lunchtime and evening. John Smiths, Courage Directors, Ruddles Best and Theakstons. Lots of lagers and, I quote, "all the fashionable drinks like Sub-Zero, Ginsing and Miller Light".

OPEN: 12–11 (12–10.30 Sun)
Real Ale. Food served: 12–2.30. 6.30–9.45.
Children in restaurant and garden only. Dogs on leads – any barking and they're out!

LONDON WC2

Seven Stars   Tel: 0171 242 8521

53 Carey Street, WC2
Courage. Geoff Turner, lease.

One of the smallest, and probably one of the oldest – early 17th century – pubs in London. Near the bankcruptcy courts, so ideally placed for "dutch courage" beforehand, and drowning sorrows afterwards. Many a tear must have been shed into the beer here. Food is served all day until 7o'clock. Bar snacks vary from sausages in French bread, freshly filled sandwiches (can be doorsteps), Cornish pasties and pork pies. Main dishes range from Oriental beef to chicken Creole and lamb casserole. Courage Best and Directors, Guinness, Simmonds Scrumpy Jack and Blackthorn Dry Cider. Lots of lagers. The gents loos are a talking point here – if you're a gent – they are up an extremely narrow flight of stairs.

OPEN: 11–9.30 Mon–Fri.
Real Ale
No children. No dogs.

LONDON SW18

Ship Tel: 0181 870 9667 41

Jews Row, Wandsworth
Youngs. Charles Gotto, Desmond Madden, Lenore Macnamara, licensees.

The riverside terraces at the Ship are on two levels, and there is nothing nicer than to come here for lunch on a summery Sunday, enjoy a barbecued lunch and a pint, and watch the Thames slip by –along with hundreds of others. Incredibly popular, even though it is tucked away and not easy to find, consulting your A–Z should enable you to find your way. Walk if you can, as parking is a bit tight. It has a wonderfully airy conservatory opening onto the garden and a public bar – the locals' favourite. Weather permitting, anything that can be barbecued will be, including ostrich, emu and kangaroo burgers; if not, it's back inside for the bar menu, which features soups, baguettes, steak sandwiches, char-grilled chicken, Caesar's salad, fish cakes with pecan sauce, ploughmans with a choice of British cheeses and daily specials from the blackboard. All the pork is free-range and along with the lamb, comes from the Gotto farm. Good puds too. Youngs range of well kept ales, a guest beer and a good selection of wines, many by the glass. Fantastic evening celebrations for the last night of the Proms; a huge television screen gives an opportunity to all budding Simon Rattles to practice their conducting, and the firework display on Guy Fawkes night is enough to satisfy all pyrotechnically-minded people.

OPEN: 11–11
Real Ale. Newly renovated Restaurant.
Children in eating area. Dogs on leads.

LONDON SW10

Sporting Page Tel: 0171 376 3694

6 Camera Place, Chelsea
Courage. Rupert Fowler, lease.

It's off Park Walk and between the Fulham and Kings Road, so take a bus as parking can be difficult. Once called the Red Lion, it has been transformed from a pub into more of a wine bar. Quite smart, decorated as you would expect, with panels, prints and pictures depicting sporting " greats". The television will be on for all big sporting events. Well chosen bar food includes: soup, pasta, hot chicken salad, smoked salmon and scrambled eggs, home-made salmon fishcakes and hollandaise sauce – also steak sandwiches. Theakstons, Websters Yorkshire Bitter, Boddingtons and John Smiths. There is a choice of house wines.

OPEN: 11–3. 5.30–11. (6–11 Sat).
Real Ale.
Children outside. Dogs on leads.

LONDON SW1

Star Tel: 0171 235 3019

Belgrave Mews West
Fullers. Bruce & Kathleen Taylor, managers.

Situated in an attractive flowery mews off Belgrave Square, this has always been a haven from the noisy frenetic life of London just a few yards away. Three comfortably furnished rooms downstairs – and an upstairs room if it gets too crowded. Bar food includes lunchtime sandwiches, salads and favourite hot dishes such as fish and chips and steak pie. There is a greater selection during the evening. Fullers Chiswick, London Pride and ESB.

OPEN: 11.30–3. 5–11 (6.30–11 Sat). 11.30–11 Fridays & daily for 2 weeks before Christmas
Real Ale.
Children if eating. Dogs on leads.

LONDON SW3

The Surprise   Tel: 0171 352 4699

6 Christchurch Terrace
Youngs. Grayburn Owen, tenant.

The landlord thinks his pub was named after the ship "Surprise", which brought Charles II back to England after the civil war and, as if to emphasise the point, the walls of the bars are hung with reproductions of nautical paintings. In complete contrast, the pub, well favoured by the racing fraternity, celebrates the "Sport of Kings" by festooning the rail over the bar with assorted members' badges from Newbury and other racecourses. Two bars: the saloon bar with the carpet, the public bar without. Those unfamiliar with the pub from their early days as impoverished young things struggling up life's ladder, use the carpeted side. The late impoverished young, now succesful City high flyers, still use the public bar, although they themselves are not necessarily local any more. Such loyalty! Food is served lunchtimes only, Monday to Saturday: gammon and eggs, pies cooked in the pub and a selection of pasta dishes. When winter sets in, steaks are added to the menu. If the kitchens are closed, you can get toasted sandwiches from the bar. Ales are Hancocks, Timothy Taylors Landlord as a guest, Bass and occasionally another guest beer in the winter.

OPEN: 11–11
Real Ale.
Children, not encouraged. Dogs on leads.

LONDON W9

Warrington Hotel   Tel: 0171 286 2929

93 Warrington Crescent
Free House. John Brandon, licensee.

Listed Grade II, it is a wonderful relic of the Victorian Naughty Nineties, with ceramic pillars at the entrance, mosaic steps, semi-circular marble bar, sweeping staircase, high ceilings, cherubs and art nouveau – what they used to call a gin palace. What is extraordinary is that despite its music-hall associations – it was a favourite with Marie Lloyd – and its present-day popularity, it has no piped music. It was recommended for listing in THE QUIET PINT by a local who told us "it has been free of music pollution since the infernal machine broke down. There are no plans to replace it." Bar meals at lunchtime only. During the evenings the food is Thai – and they say it's good. You have to book. Ales are London Pride, ESB, Brakspears Special, Marstons Pedigree, Youngs Special Bitter and guests. The Warrington is lucky to have a garden with 20 tables. Arrive early if you want one on a summer's day.

OPEN: 11–11. (12–10.30 Sun)
Real Ale.
No children. Dogs on leads.

LONDON W 14

Warwick Arms   Tel: 0171 603 3560

160 Warwick Road London
Fullers. Peter Biggs, manager.

At lunchtime, rumour has it that this charming late Georgian pub is full of revenue men, a far better description – and probably more polite that the usual definition – of the modern tax inspector; also office workers from the DHSS. Comparing notes? Inside the Warwick Arms the bar fittings are at least 100 years old, if not older, and the pump handles are Wedgewood – very smart! The bar is decorated with two large detailed prints of the battles of Trafalgar and Waterloo. Bar food includes the traditional ploughmans, toasties and salads with the addition of hot dishes such as chicken Kiev and Chilli. Fullers ales: Hock, ESB, London Pride and IPA.

OPEN: 11–11
Real Ale
Children not encouraged. Dogs on leads.

LONDON RICHMOND

White Cross Hotel   Tel: 0181 940 6844

Water Lane, Richmond
Youngs. Quentin & Denise Thwaites, licensee/managers.

It really was an hotel until 17 years ago. Now it is just a pub in a super setting with a garden overlooking the Thames. The building dates back to 1835 and has one large bar with two fireplaces, one of which is directly under the picture window overlooking Richmond Bridge, and the question always is, "where's the chimney?" No free beer for the right answer! There is also a family room on the mezzanine floor which has a balcony overlooking the

THE QUIET PINT

river. Sometimes during the summer there is live music in the garden. On one occasion they had a harpist on the balcony; dressed in a flowing white dress, she gave some of the clients a nasty shock – they thought they had suddenly joined the heavenly hordes. (Good strong beer here!). Food is all self-service from a buffet in the bar; cream of garlic soup, squid in lemon and garlic, venison and pork burgers, various pies, vegetarian dishes, salads, lamb's liver in sherry sauce, chicken in a mushroom sauce and venison casserole with juniper berries are among the dishes on offer. Youngs Bitter, Special, Ramrod, Wheat beer and Best Mild. 30 wines by the glass or bottle.

OPEN: 11–11 (12–10.30 Sun)
Real Ale
Children in garden or family room. Dogs very welcome. Bonzo, the pub dog keeps them in order.
Instead of the harpist on the balcony there is every possibility you will be transported by a recorder duo playing classical music.

LONDON SW6

White Horse   Tel: 0171 736 2115

1–3 Parsons Green, Fulham
Bass. Rupert Reeves, Mark Dorber, managers.

A spacious Victorian building on the edge of Parsons Green. It has a wonderfully sunny terrace at the front of the pub which is the place to be for lunch, and to relax in the early evening. Big comfortable bar, hugely popular, so arrive in good time if you want a meal and somewhere to eat it. There is a blackboard menu with perhaps paté, salads, beef and ale casserole with dumplings, sausages, steak and kidney pie and other dishes using different ales as the marinade. An à la carte menu features during the evening. Sunday lunch is served upstairs. Quite a selection of well kept ales: Adnams Extra, Bass, Harveys Sussex, Highgate Mild and a guest beer; 55 Belgian, Dutch and German beers and 80 different wines.

OPEN: 11–11 (11–10.30 Sun)
Real Ale.
Children in eating area (not evening). Dogs on leads.
Occasional jazz nights.

LONDON SW13 (Barnes)

Ye White Hart   Tel: 0181 876 5177

The Terrace, Barnes.
Youngs. John and Patricia Lockwood, licensees. Stewart Sell, manager.

This is a well run and wonderfully situated pub on the banks of the Thames between Barnes Bridge and Mortlake Brewery. An ale house has stood on the site since 1662; the present building dates from 1780, and was extended in 1898. A more recent addition is an outside terrace and gazebo overlooking the river. The balcony at the back of the White Hart is the place to be on boat race day. In the one spacious bar there is a collection of old photographs and prints of the race. Good traditional hot and cold bar food served at lunchtime only: sandwiches, salads, jumbo sausages, fish and chips – that sort of thing. Excellent, imaginative changing wine list (that's our Nick again – he's into wine, and White Shield Worthington in the bottle which they don't have any more!). This pub has the full range of Youngs beers, including their Wheat Beer.

OPEN: 11–3. 5.30–11. (11–11 Sat. 12–10.30 Sun)
Real Ale. Food lunchtime only.
No children. Dogs on leads.

LONDON. Richmond.

White Swan   Tel: 0181 940 0959

Old Palace Lane, Richmond, Surrey.
Courage. A.V.H. Savage, licensee. Bruce Holland, manager.

Described by regulars as "the village pub" on the edge of Richmond. There has been an ale house here since the late 17th century; then next to the Palace of Richmond, since demolished. (The swans on the inn sign, remembering their regal past, still wear a crown around their necks). In an almost rural setting this is a charming, friendly small pub with a panelled bar and conservatory extension – more like a restaurant, where you can have a `proper' lunch or dinner. A constantly changing menu could include for lunch: sandwiches, ploughmans, ocean pie, chilli, a curry and a vegetarian dish or two. The evening menus offer a wider choice. Courage Best and Directors, John Smith Extra Smooth and the occasional guest. Two tables on the terrace at the front of the pub, and a garden beyond the conservatory.

OPEN: 11–3. 5.30–11. (11–11 Sat. 12–10.30 Sun.)
Real Ale.
Children in conservatory. Dogs in garden.

LONDON SW4

Windmill   Tel: 0181 673 4578

Clapham Common, Southside, SW4 9DE
Youngs. James & Rachel Watt, managers.

There really was a windmill here in the mid 17th century, but the fine building
you see today wasn't mentioned in local records until 1729. The inn was
later to be immortalised by J P Herring, who used it as the background in
his painting "Return from the Derby", which now hangs in the Tate Gallery.
Here you have a traditional pub within a smart hotel. Comfortable main bars
which are understandably popular – sometimes it seems as though half
London has moved in on the first Monday of the month when it is "treat"
night. Opera à la Carte in the conservatory and monthly jazz nights in the
back bar; last but not least, good familiar bar food and well kept ales.
Sandwiches, filled baguettes, ploughmans, salads, vegetarian dishes and
daily specials. Youngs range of ales, a large choice of wines, all by the glass.
Outside there is a barbecue going full pelt during the summer; seats here
and among the tubs of flowers in a non-barbecue courtyard.

OPEN: 11–11
Real Ale. Restaurant.
Children in no-smoking conservatory. No dogs.
Bedrooms.
Live Opera 1st Monday of the month. Jazz 2nd Thursday of the month.
Wheelchair access.

LONDON W8

Windsor Castle   Tel: 0171 727 8491

114 Campden Hill Road, Holland Park
Bass. Matthew O'Keeffe, manager

The summit of Campden Hill is as high as the top of St. Paul's Cathedral,
and when the Windsor Castle pub was built on Campden Hill Road in 1828,
it had uninterrupted views across country to Windsor Castle, nearly 20 miles
away to the West. The views may have changed over the years, but not this
charming old pub, which has three panelled bars – each with its own
entrance and customers – and a small dining room. The pub fills up rapidly
on summer evenings when its attractive, shady walled garden comes into
its own. Interesting pub grub is served all day: seafood chowder, gazpacho,
spinach, walnut and stilton salad, mushroom and bacon salad, chicken

Basque style, Windsor game pie, old English rabbit pie, Cook's specials on the blackboard, treacle tart or apple pie for afters and a tremendously popular roast beef and Yorkshire pudding for lunch on Sunday. Ales are Bass, Adnams Extra and Hancocks HB. Guest beers change monthly. There are also house wines, a very reasonable Champagne and various malt whiskies.

OPEN: 12–11
Real Ale.
Children welcome. Dogs on leads (not in garden!).
Wheelchair access to garden.

LONDON PUBS BY POSTAL DISTRICT

E2 Camdens Head	SE3 British Oak	SW20 Sporting Page
E11 The George	SE10 Richard 1st	W1 Coach & Horses
E15 The Goldengrove	SW1 Fox & Hounds	W1 Dog & Duck
EC1 Olde Mitre	SW1 Grenadier	W1 Red Lion
EC2 Flying Horse	SW1 Red Lion	W6 Dove
EC2 Hamilton Hall	SW1 Star	W8 Windsor Castle
EC2 Old Monk	SW3 Coopers Arms	W8 Scarsdale
EC3 Lamb Tavern	SW3 Front Page	W9 Warrington Hotel
EC4 Ye Olde Cheshire Cheese	SW3 Phene Arms	W14 Warwick Arms
EC4 Blackfriar	SW3 Surprise	WC1 Princess Louise
N7 Coronet	SW4 Windmill	WC1 Calthorpe Arms
N19 The Dog	SW6 White Horse	WC1 Kings Arms
NW1 Man in the Moon	SW7 Anglesea Arms	WC1 Lamb
NW6 Queens Arms	SW10 Fox & Pheasant	WC1 Museum Tavern
NW8 Clifton	SW13 Bulls Head	WC1 Old Monk
NW10 Coliseum	SW13 Ye White Hart	WC2 Lamb & Flag
NW11 JJ Moons	SW15 Green Man	WC2 Marquess of Granby
SE1 Founders Arms	SW18 Alma	WC2 Seven Stars
SE1 The George	SW18 Ship	
	SW19 Hand in Hand	

Denham The Falcon Inn	Barnet Old Monk & Holt
Enfield Moon under the Water	Richmond White Swan
Twickenham Popes Grotto	Richmond White Cross Hotel

S
SCOTLAND

ABERDEEN

Prince of Wales   Tel: 01224 640597

7–11 St Nicholas Lane, Aberdeen, AB10 1HE
Free House. Peter Birnie, licensee.

Built on granite, out of granite quarried from Rubislaw Pit near Hazelhead
Park, Aberdeen is known as the 'Granite City'. Its handsome buildings
overlook the fishing harbour and docks. In a cobbled lane, just off the busy
shopping centre, the old Prince of Wales, with its comfortable, popular, long
main bar and side lounge, is just the place for a pint of well kept ale and a
generous lunchtime snack. The menu listing the home-cooked food changes
daily. No distractions from juke boxes or TVs, just blissfully quiet, so you can
chat to your neighbour and enjoy either the Draught Bass, Caledonian 80/
-, Orkney Dark Island, Courage Directors, Theakstons Old Peculiar or
Youngers No. 3. guest beers too. Fresh coffee is a new addition.

OPEN: 11–midnight.
Real Ale.
Children in eating area. No dogs.
Live music Sunday afternoons.
Wheelchair access to pub.

ABERDEEN

St Machar Bar   Tel: 01224 483079

High Street, Old Aberdeen, Aberdeen AB24 3EH
Free House. James Alexander owner/licensee.

Our tip-off came from one of the Editors of The Stirling Observer, and I can
do no better than to quote him. "The bar was once christened the best
licensed corridor in the world. The St. Machar Bar is situated deep in
Aberdeen University territory and can on occasion be overrun by student
types, but catch a pew when the University is not in session, and you can

420

spend an idyllic few hours with just a book or crossword and a pint of McEwan's 70/- in hand. Famous for the enormous sandwiches that cross the bar for extrememly reasonable prices." McEwans Export 70/-, 80/-, Theakstons Best Bitter, Murphys and Beamish.

OPEN: 11-11 (12.30–10.30 Sun)
Real Ale
No Children. No Dogs.
No garden. No car park.

AUCHENCROW

Craw Inn   Tel: 01890 761253

Auchencrow, Berwickshire, Borders TD14 5LS
Free House. Nigel Matheson & Kirsty Lowe, owners/licensees.

The Craw Inn has the dubious distinction of being where the last witch in Scotland was hanged, early in the 16th century. Why from a tree in this particular back garden the locals have not been able to say, except that there was a lot of witchcraft in the area at that time. The tree is still there; a living reminder of that dreadful deed. First licensed in the 18th century, the Craw is "in the middle of no-where, but hellishly busy", according to the landlord. Just as it should be. It's an attractive old place: one bar with low, beamed ceilings and big log fire, a dining room and a snug for private parties. In spite of its gruesome past it's a jolly sort of place. Murphy (the owners' horse) is frequently found at the bar, and when collecting for Lifeboats, or Riding for the Disabled, anything can happen. It has been known for Nigel Matheson to ride his motorcycle into the cellar, through the bar – then accidentally end up in the hedge – all for a good cause. In between these exciting events someone is doing interesting things with food. Lots to choose from: sauteed scallops in fresh ginger, spring onions and crême fraiche, moules marinieres, fresh sardines, terrine of smoked salmon, fillet of halibut with creamy lobster sauce, whole local trout, Dover sole, or spiced pork casserole with apricots. From "one of the best smokers in the world" they get smoked alligator, ostrich, quail and oysters. Steaks and all the puddings are cooked or made by the landlord. Belhaven Best Bitter, Border Breweries Best and Old Kiln, something from Greenmantle and Stonehouse Cider. Beers change quite frequently. Seats on a small terrace. There is also an eighteen hole putting green.

OPEN: 12–3. 7–11. (7–12 Fri & Sat. 7–10.30 Sun)
Real Ale. Dining Room.
Children if well behaved. Dogs on leads.

THE QUIET PINT

BALERNO

Johnsburn House   Tel: 0314 493847

Johnsburn Road, Balerno, Lothian EH14 7BB
Free House. Martin and Linda Mitchell, licensees.

A 17th century gentleman's baronial mansion to the west of Edinburgh at the foot of the Pentland Hills – now a country pub with over 60 awards to its credit. Martin Mitchell is a Master Chef, Master Cellarman and Master Restaurateur. Gosh! Linda looks after the front of house while Martin conjures up delectable dishes – some of Scotland's best food – in the kitchen. From the menu you could have an oyster souffle with black pudding and stilton, confit of duck with cranberries or smoked venison. Our reporter says "quality abounds in the whole operation and this pub is indeed a yardstick by which others will be measured". They also have a bar menu to go with the five ever changing cask ales. Adding to the list of awards: two silver medals for wine pub of the year, 1994 and 1995.

OPEN: Tues–Fri. 12–3. 6.30–11 (12–12 Sat. 12.11 Sun.) CLOSED MON.
Real Ale. Restaurant.
Children and dogs welcome.

BANFF

Ship Inn   Tel: 01261 812620

8 Deveronside, Banff, Grampian AB45 1HP
Free House. Moire MacLellan, owner/licensee.

Banff, which boasts some fine Georgian buildings, is a seaport and resort at the mouth of the river Deveron. The Ship Inn overlooks the harbour; this largely silted up in the 19th century and is now used mainly as a sailing centre. The Ship is another of our film stars, but quite a long time ago. "In 1982 it was done up for the film 'Local Hero'", says the landlady; still comfortable in its fading finery, you would come for the view and the beer. No food, only a crisp and a nut. If you are really desperate, they could probably rustle up a sandwich, but nothing fancy. Courage Directors, McEwans 80/-, Murphys and various guest ales.

OPEN: 11–11 (Closed Sun morning, otherwise 7–10.30)
Real Ale
Children in the lounge bar. Dogs – bit dubious as landlady has three of her own and the latest is not too friendly towards other dogs. Go carefully. Wheelchair access.

BROUGHTY FERRY

Fishermans Tavern Hotel   Tel: 01382 775941

10–14 Fort Street, Broughty Ferry, Dundee DD5 2AD
Free House. Jonathan Stewart, licensee.

Once an old fishing village, Broughty Ferry has now become a suburb of
Dundee. However, there are still fishing boats in the harbour which is
overlooked by the 15th century Broughty Castle, now a museum. The small,
rambling old pub is known for its well kept ales and good traditional bar food
which could include a home-made soup of the day, beefsteak roll with
onions, toasted sandwiches, steak or chicken and mushroom pie, filled
jacket potatoes and daily specials. Belhavens 60/-, 80/- and St Andrew's,
Maclays 80/- and a daily changing guest beer. If you look up river from the
harbour you see the bridge over "the glorious River Tay".

OPEN: 11–midnight. (12.30–12 Sun)
Real Ale. Limited bar food Sun.
Children in eating area. Dogs on leads.
Bedrooms. Wheelchair access.
(Folk music Thurs eves.)

CERES

Brands Inn   Tel: 01334 828325

High Street, Ceres, Fife, KY15 5NF
Free House. Ms. Lesley Bate, licensee.

The attractive village of Ceres is situated in the rolling Fife countryside, the
Inn used to be a staging post between Edinburgh and St. Andrews. Among
old weavers cottages, it adjoins the Fife Folk museum, with exhibits
illustrating Fife's agricultural and domestic past. In June every year, the
village stages Highland Games, celebrating the villagers' return from Robert
the Bruce's victory over Edward II at Bannockburn in 1314. To help build up
your strength they serve some tasty bar food in the pub: soups, sandwiches
and filled rolls of course, also spicy sausage cassoulet or chicken in a
mushroom and tarragon sauce. Two real ales always available plus
Guinness, Caffreys, Tennents Lager and 70/-. Good selection of malt
whiskies. A garden to sit in.

OPEN: 12–3. 5.30–12 Mon–Thurs.(12–12 Fri & Sat. 12.30–11.30 Sun)
Real Ale.
Children and dogs welcome. Car park.

CLEISH

Nivingstone House Hotel   Tel: 01577 850216

Cleish, Nr Kinross, Tayside KY13 7L5
Free House. Allan Deeson, licensee.

An attractive, solid, faintly baronial, small country hotel, set in 12 acres at the foot of the Cleish hills. A very comfortable (carpets and upholstered furniture) bar and friendly staff. Well presented bar food – served both at lunchtime and in the evenings – ranges from soup and home-made paté to a dish of smoked salmon and prawns plus daily specials. There is a very elegant restaurant with a reputation for serving imaginative, creative food. Yorkshire Bitter, over 50 malt whiskies and naturally, a good wine list. The seats at the front of the hotel overlook the sweeping lawns to the hills beyond.

OPEN: 12–2.30. 6–11 (6–11.45 Sat)
Real Ale. Restaurant.
Children welcome. Dogs on leads.
Bedrooms

CRINAN

Crinan Hotel   Tel: 01546 830261

Crinan, Argyll, PA31 8SR
Free House. Nicholas Ryan, licensee.

The Crinan Hotel is in a most spectacular position at the north end of the Crinan Canal, below wooded slopes and looking out over Argyll's rugged coastline. It's a great white building which, in this tiny hamlet, you can hardly miss. If it's a light lunch you are after, you have a choice of either eating in the public bar or a having a sandwich in the coffee shop/bakery by the fishing-boat dock. Lots of fish included in the bar menu: local mussels, trout, princess clams, seafood stew, also honey roast ham, chicken stuffed with leeks and mushrooms. Lots of salads and daily specials. Tennents 70/-, 80/-, and Theakstons Best Bitter. A choice of malt whiskies and a good wine list. During the evenings, when there is a shift of emphasis towards the restaurant, the atmosphere does become more formal. Seats outside on the terrace from where you can enjoy the view.

OPEN: 11–11 (11–2.30. 5–11 winter).
Real Ale. Restaurant. Bar meals lunchtimes.
Children in eating area of cocktail bar. Dogs on leads.
Bedrooms.

EARLSFERRY

The Golf Tavern   Tel: 01333 330610

5, Links Road, Earlsferry, Fife, KY9 1AW
Free House. Douglas Duncanson, licensee.

Aptly named. You would be right in thinking that with a name and address like this you are near a golf course. The 19th hole to be precise. The Golf Tavern is an old Victorian style pub alongside the course at Earlsferry. Years ago there actually was a ferry across the Forth to Dunbar. Now the pub sustains just golfers, locals and land-bound travellers. Home-made soups in the bar, also steak sandwiches with a side salad, toasties – that sort of thing. Maclays of Alloa 80/-, Caledonian Brewery IPA, Guinness, Tennents Lager and a guest beer. No garden. Just gaze at the golf course.

OPEN: 11–12 Mon–Thurs. 11–12 Fri. 11–1am Sat. 12.30 –1am Sun. (11–2.30. 5.30–12 Oct–Easter)
Real Ale.
Children and dogs welcome.

EDINBURGH

Abbotsford   Tel: 0131 225 5276

3–5 Rose Street, Edinburgh EH6 2PQR
Free House. Colin Grant, licensee.

A favourite place for the "lunchtime" crowd. Ideally placed, as it is parallel to Prince's Street, Scotland's greatest thoroughfare. Only one centrally situated bar in this efficient, well-run, Victorian pub. There is nevertheless, plenty of room for you to enjoy the well-kept ales and reasonably priced, varied choice of bar food. Soups, ploughmans, pork and cider casserole, roast beef, liver and onions, steaks, grills and puddings. McEwans 80/-, 70/- and two weekly guests. Choice of about 50 malt whiskies.

OPEN: 11–11 (Fri.Sat.Sun 12–12).
Real Ale. Restaurant.
Children in eating areas. Dogs on leads.

EDINBURGH

Bannermans Bar   Tel: 0131 556 3254

212 Cowgate, Edinburgh, EH1 1NQ
Free House. Douglas Smith, licensee.

Busy, popular, and in the heart of the city, it is a favoured by locals and students – always full of a friendly, cheerful crowd. A well-liked, functional, traditionally furnished bar, offering a short reliable lunchtime menu and simple snacks in the evening. Filled rolls, soup, ploughmans, filled baked potatoes, vegetarian dishes and daily specials. Among the eight ales could be Theakstons Best, McEwans 80/-, Caledonian 80/- and IPA and Youngers No.3. Good selection of malt whiskies and bottled Belgian beers.

OPEN: 11–midnight (11–1 am Sat)
Real Ale. Lunchtime meals & snacks. Evening snacks only.
Children in eating area, daytime only. Dogs if well behaved.
Frequent eve. folk bands. N.B. Tapes played after 9pm on Friday and Saturday evenings.

EDINBURGH

Bow Bar   Tel: 0131 226 7667

80 West Bow, Edinburgh
Free House. Grant Cairncroff, licensee

You could be forgiven for thinking you were in a time warp – transported into the late 19th century, the heyday of a traditional Edinburgh drinkers' bar – all glass mirrors, mahogany panelling, gas fires, and barmen in long white aprons; even the beer pumps are over 90 years old. Over 12 well-kept ales at any one time, chosen from the 80 which are tried during the year. Well over 100 malt whiskies and a choice of gins, rums and vodkas. Cheap and cheerful bar snacks of the filled rolls, pies and bowl of soup variety.

OPEN: 11–11.15pm
Real Ale. Lunchtime snacks.
No children. No dogs.

EDINBURGH

Cafe Royal Circle Bar   Tel:0131 556 1884

17 West Register Street, Edinburgh
Scottish & Newcastle. Maureen DiPonio, manager.

If you want to catch up with the daily news in congenial surroundings – enjoy a drink and perhaps a quick snack – the circle bar is just the place. Refurbished in the Victorian style, but far more comfortable than the original, it has marble floors, handsome light fittings and a big central bar counter with interesting Doulton tile portraits of famous Scotsmen – whose inventions changed the world. Filled rolls: cheese & tomato and slices off the hot roast are available at lunchtime only. McEwans 80/-, Morlands Old Speckled Hen and Theakstons Best. Nearly 50 malt whiskies.

OPEN: 11–11 (midnight Thurs, 1 am Fri & Sat, closed Sun)
Real Ale. Restaurant. Snacks lunchtime only.
No children. No dogs.

EDINBURGH

Kay's Bar   Tel: 0131 225 1858

39 Jamaica Street West, Edinburgh EH3 1HF
Scottish & Newcastle. David Mackenzie, manager

Choice of nine different ales at any one time, 70 malt whiskies and nearly a dozen blended ones. One malt a night and you can book yourselves in for two and a half months! Small, intimate bar with lots of Victoriana associated with the brewing and licensed trade as decoration. Bar snacks include filled baked potatoes, omelettes, haggis, steak pies and other traditional dishes. The constantly changing ales could include Belhaven 80/-, Smiles Exhibition, McEwans 80/-, Theakstons and five guest beers. Lager is kept for the uninitiated tourist.

OPEN: 11–12.45 (12.30–11 Sun).
Real Ale. Lunchtime snacks.
Children in back room. Dogs on leads.

THE QUIET PINT

EDINBURGH

Starbank   Tel: 0131 552 4141

64 Laverockbank Road, Edinburgh EH5 3BZ
Free House. Valerie West, licensee.

If you want to sample a selection of the beers brewed in Scotland, this is the place to come. The pub keeps approximately ten on handpump which change frequently, but you can be assured of a well chosen range. There is also a good choice of bar food: home-made soup, paté, trout fillet with tarragon cream sauce, mixed seafood salad, boiled ham salad, steak and ale casserole, ploughmans, a vegetarian dish of the day and daily specials. Wines by the glass and a selection of malt whiskies. Views over the Firth of Forth from the pub and seats on the terrace out of the prevailing wind.

OPEN: 11–11 (11–midnight Thurs–Sat; 12.30–11 Sun).
Real Ale. No smoking restaurant.
Children welcome. Dogs on leads.
Wheelchair access.

ELIE

Ship Inn   Tel: 01333 330 246

The Toft, Elie, Fife, KY9 1DT
Free House. Richard & Jill Philip, licensees.

Very near the Watersports Centre, so you will be surrounded by people who do energetic things and recover in the Ship Inn. Windsurfing, waterski-ing and sailing in the Bay, the pub also organises its own cricket fixtures and even Rugby matches on the sandy beach beyond the beer garden. When you are totally exhausted even thinking about it, be assured that the whole family is welcome here to relax. Licensed since 1838, they have perfected the art of catering for the traveller. Big downstairs bar, three dining areas – one upstairs. They serve lunchtime and evening bar food and a three-course lunch or à la carte dinner. There is also a children's menu. In July and August the beer garden is covered by a marquee in which they have a bar and barbecue and hold the occasional beer and jazz festivals. Bar food could include sweet herring salad, garlic mushrooms, seafood crepes, spicy fried chicken, poached salmon with a lime mayonnaise, home-made beef steak pie and lots of steaks. There is also a roast Sunday lunch. Courage Directors, Belhaven 80/- and Boddingtons. Choice of wines and malt whiskies. The big beer garden overlooks a sandy bay and the Firth of Forth.

SCOTLAND

OPEN: 11–midnight (12.30–11 Sun).
Real Ale. Restaurant (not Sun eve).
Children in restaurant and lounge bar. Dogs on leads.
Occasional jazz outside.
Wheelchair access.

GLASGOW

Babbity Bowster   Tel: 0141 552 5055

16/18 Blackfriars Street, Glasgow, Strathclyde G1 1PE
Free House. Fraser Laurie, licensee.

A fine renovated Adam town house in a quiet pedestrianised street in the business centre of the city. Understandably popular with journalists, businessmen and students, or anyone wanting a refreshing drink from a cup of tea to a glass of the Babbity Bowsters' very own beer. Breakfast is served at 8.30 and bar snacks from 12 until 9 at night. More a café/bar with a restaurant and hotel attached, than a pub. Bar food includes filled baguettes, spicy chicken, haggis neeps and tatties. Specials from the blackboard include lots of fish dishes: langoustines, oysters, prawns, fresh fish – all with home-baked bread. Barbecued dishes in the summer. Maclays 80/-, 70/-, and a guest beer. This is the only pub in the city centre which has an outside drinking area. There are seats and tables on the small terrace.

OPEN: 8–midnight
Real Ale. Restaurant. N.B. Music in the restaurant.
Children in restaurant. No dogs.
Bedrooms.

GLASGOW

The Horseshoe   Tel: 0141 248 4467

17 Drury Street, Glasgow, G2 5AE.
Bass Taverns. David Smith, manager.

I don't know whether this is a recommendation or not, but the Horseshoe is supposed to be Keith Floyd's favourite place in Glasgow! I say that, as I didn't think he liked quiet-ish places. We'll give him the benefit of the doubt –but as there is a kareoke bar upstairs, that could be where he would be aiming for. Hidden down a side street, it is worth searching out as an example of an immaculately preserved, un-modernised Victorian town bar

429

– stained glass and all. Popular, roomy and not far from Central Station. The TV is turned up for all the big games – you have been warned. Solid, sustaining pub grub of the haddock and chips, steak pie and two veg. sort. Draught Bass, Broughton Green Mantle and Caledonian 80/-. Selection of malt whiskies.

OPEN: 11–midnight Mon–Sat. 12.30–midnight Sun.
Real Ale.
Children welcome until 8pm. Only Guide Dogs.

GLASGOW

Press Bar   Tel: 0141 552 5142

199 Albion Street, Glasgow G1 1RU
Free House. Mr McEntee, licensee.

As the name suggests, it is surrounded by various newspaper offices and as our researcher says "caters largely for thirsty male hacks." On the edge of the 80's named "Merchant City", only 10 minutes walk from the city centre and near High Street station. It's a small, no frills sort of place, dominated by its regulars escaping the high-tec bustling news rooms. Usual range of bar snacks, some chicken dishes and lasagne and, I have on good authority, "a pie and peas to die for". Draught Bass, Beamish, Guinness, Tennents lagers and Dry Blackthorn cider.

OPEN: 11–midnight. 12.30–midnight Sun.
Real Ale
No children. Dogs on leads.

GLASGOW

Tennents Bar   Tel: 0141 3390649

191 Byres Road, Glasgow, G12 8TN
Bass Taverns. Alison O'Connor, licensee.

Large traditional pub in the heart of Glasgow's West End. The original Tennents pub. It has a wide clientele, though rarely overcrowded. A bit of a chaps place this. Vast selection of beers at very reasonable prices. As with many of the Glasgow pubs the television set is prominent, and the sound is turned up for the big games. Sandwiches, toasties, filled baked potatoes – usual bar snacks. Tennents and lots of other lagers, Guinness, Beamish, Dry

Blackthorn cider, 12 real ales, nine regulars and three guests. About 40 malt whiskies. Handy for the buses and Hillhead Underground.

OPEN: 11–11 Mon.–Thurs. 11–12 Fri. Sat. 12.30–11 Sun.
Real Ale.
No Children. Dogs on leads.

GLASGOW

Three Judges   Tel: 0141 337 3055

141 Dumbarton Road (Partick Cross) Glasgow G11 6PR
Maclay-Alloa. Helen McCarroll, manager.

Very much a down to earth, no nonsense sort of local, which has over the years won awards for the best pub and landlord in Glasgow. In Partick Cross, which is the place to go if you want to hear Gaelic. They say more Gaelic is spoken here than in the Western Isles. Only bar snacks are available – toasties, ploughmans – that sort of thing – a crisp or nut goes without saying. Maclay 80/-, Wallace IPA and guest beers plus a draught farm cider. More than 1,000 different beers have been brought in as guests over the last three years, the number rises by about 250 a year. Range of whiskies: they feature a "malt of the month". Very near the University and the Kelvin Grove Art Gallery; the Botanical Gardens are 200 yards away and the Transport Museum just 100 yards along the road.

OPEN: 11–11 (11–12 Sat), (12.30–11 Sun).
Real Ale.
No children. Dogs on leads.

GLASGOW

Ubiquitous Chip   Tel: 0141 334 5007

12 Ashton Lane, Glasgow G12
Free House. Ronnie Clydesdale, licensee.

On good authority this is "the trendy place to hang out". Situated in a cobbled lane in the very heart of Glasgow, it was originally a Victorian coach house, but is now a well-known restaurant, with the addition of an upstairs bar serving imaginative bar food. There is a daily changing menu, but food could include home-made soup, oak smoked fillet of mackerel, chicken and ham paté with Cumberland sauce, honey roast ham, rare roast Scotch beef, vegetarian haggis with neeps and tatties, roast chicken piri piri, a fish dish, choice of salads and home-made puddings. A two or three course lunch is served in the restaurant. The wine selection is reputed to be the best in Scotland (they have their own wine shop). 120 malt whiskies and, last but not least, real ales: Caledonian 80/- and Deuchars IPA. Bulmers cider and Furstenberg lager.

OPEN: 11 – 11 (11–12 Fri & Sat; 12.30 – 12 Sun)
Real Ale. Restaurant.
Children welcome. Dogs on leads in bar.
Wheelchair access.

INNERLEITHEN

Traquair Arms Hotel   Tel: 01896 830229

Traquair, Innerleithen, Borders EH44 6PD
Free House. Hugh Anderson, licensee

Innerleithen was reputedly the model for "St Ronan's Well" in Sir Walter Scott's Waverley novels. The Traquair Arms is a good, solidly dependable stone inn, with a comfortable main bar serving generous portions of popular bar food and an interesting range of ales. Food includes soups, sandwiches, omelettes, filled baked potatoes, baked smoked haddock with cream and cheese, chicken and pasta, vegetarian dishes and steak & ale pie. There is a greater variety of dishes during the evening. Broughton Greenmantle Ale, and Traquair House, sometimes Traquair Bear Ale and Guinness. The 18th century brewery is situated in a wing of Traquair House. They resumed brewing in 1965 with the original equipment which hadn't been used since the middle of the last century. Traquair House itself, dating back to the 10th century, is one of Scotland's oldest inhabited houses. The iron gates have remained closed since 1745 and will do so until the Stuarts return.

OPEN: 11–midnight (12–12 Sun).
Real Ale. Restaurant.
Children welcome. Dogs on leads.
Bedrooms.
(1st Sun in month Scottish music and story telling)

KILBERRY

Kilberry Inn   Tel: 01880 770223

Kilberry by Tarbert, Strathclyde PA29 6YD
Free House. John & Kathy Leadbeater, licensees.

This inn is halfway round the single track road from Tarbert (overlooked by the stronghold of Robert the Bruce) and Lochgilphead (B8024) and well worth the trip. Feast your eyes on the spectacular views across the loch to Gigha and work up an appetite for the delights on offer at the Kilberry Inn. Formerly a croft, it is now a "dining pub" offering interesting award-winning, home-cooked food – you can even buy the marmalade and chutneys. They have a constantly changing menu, but favourites can always be found: different mousses and paté, layers of sausage stuffing and apple in a pie, beef cooked in Old Peculiar Ale, venison in red wine, salmon fish pie, not forgetting soups, ploughmans, all with home-baked bread. Desserts include apple pie, lemon meringue pie and shortcakes. Scottish bottled beers, Jennings Oatmeal Stout and Broughton Old Jock Strong Ale. A choice of malt whiskies.

OPEN: 11–2. 5–10 (closed Sun)
Children in no-smoking family room. No dogs.
Bedrooms, home-made jam or marmalade with breakfast.

KILLIECRANKIE

Killiecrankie Hotel   Tel: 01796 473220

Killiecrankie, Nr Pitlochry, Tayside PH16 5LG
Free House. Colin & Carole Anderson, licensees.

In four acres of its own land, overlooking the River Garry and the Pass of Killiecrankie, this fine hotel occupies an enviable position in a beautiful area of Perthshire. It has a panelled bar where they provide bar lunches and suppers, and there is a table d'hôte menu in the elegant dining room. Bar food includes the stalwarts: soups, ploughmans, paté, roulade of smoked salmon with dill filling, sweet cured herrings and also hot dishes such as braised pheasant in red wine, grilled fish, venison casserole, local trout, salmon and a choice of puddings. Good wine list and a selection of malt whiskies. You are surrounded by lovely countryside with lots of things to see. The 17th century mill at Blair Atholl is still working and the smallest distillery in Scotland is north east of Pitlochry. Pitlochry also has a theatre festival every year. Go at the right time of the year and you can watch the salmon struggle up a "fish ladder" at the southern end of Loch Faskally.

OPEN: 11–2.30. 6–11 (closed Jan–Feb). No-smoking evening restaurant.
Children welcome. No dogs where food is served.
Bedrooms.

KINNESSWOOD

Lomond Country Inn
Tel: 01592 840253

Main Street. Kinnesswood, Kinross-shire, KY13 7HN
Free House. David Adams, licensee.

Cosy and friendly, this family-run Inn has magnificent views over Loch
Leven. Loch Leven Castle on Castle island is where Mary Queen of Scots
was imprisoned, and in 1568, made her escape. Big open log fires in the bar
where they serve bar snacks and meals all day. Simply prepared, using fresh
ingredients, the set price "Scottish Menu" is very popular. Local venison and
wild salmon are frequently featured. Jennings, Draught Bass and Caledonian
IPA. Seats in the garden to enjoy the view.

OPEN:11–11 (midnight Fri & Sat.)
Real Ale. Restaurant.
Children welcome. Dogs on leads.
Wheelchair access. Bedrooms.

KIPPEN

Cross Keys Hotel
Tel: 01786 870293

Main Street, Kippen, Central FK8 3DN
Free House. Angus and Sandra Watt, licensees.

Small, well-run hotel situated in the centre of a small village near Stirling.
Food is served in the lounge bar or the restaurant. It has a family room and
a simply furnished public bar with the pool table and dreaded juke box.
Home-cooked bar food includes soup, smoked salmon and prawn cornets,
lasagne, steak pie plus daily specials which could include poached Scottish
salmon in lemon sauce, breast of chicken in mushroom and cream sauce
plus vegetarian dishes and traditional puddings. Children's portions. An
evening restaurant offers a more elaborate menu. Broughtons Green Mantle
and lots of malt whiskies. Seats in the garden.

OPEN: 12–2.30. 5.30–11 (5.30 – 12 Sat)
Real Ale. Restaurant.
Children in restaurant/family room only. Dogs on leads.
Bedrooms.

SCOTLAND

MELROSE

The Kings Arms Hotel   Tel: 01896 822143

High Street, Melrose, Roxburghshire TD6 9PB
Free House. Jim Rattray, manager.

You could say this is a 'themed' place, the theme being rugby. They are very serious about the game. The first seven-a-side rugby match was played in Melrose; as the landlord says "we're famous for our Abbey and rugby club." Even more famous now that Robert the Bruce's heart has been found in the Abbey. In the centre of Sir Walter Scott country, Melrose is a small town surrounded by wonderful countryside on the banks of the river Tweed, The Kings Arms, originally a coaching inn, is a lively local dating back to the 17th century. One à la carte menu with dishes ranging from filled baguettes to a sirloin steak. The prawn club sandwiches are the size of a full meal, but you could have fish and chips, or something Italian like salmon and prawn tagliatelle; vegetarian dishes too. Ind Coope Burton, Tetley Bitter and a guest beer from one of the Border breweries.

OPEN: 11–11. (11–midnight Fri & Sat. 12–11 Sun)
Real Ale. Dining rooms.
Children until 8pm. Dogs on leads.
Car park. Wheelchair access to bars.
Six en-suite bedrooms.

MOUNTBENGER

Gordon Arms Hotel   Tel: 01750 82232

Yarrow Valley, Mountbenger, Selkirk TD7 5LE
Free House. Harry Mitchell, licensee

It's in the remote rolling Border hills near St Mary's Loch and the River Yarrow, next to a well-positioned 'stop' sign at the junction of the A708 and B709. Ideally placed for any traveller on the Southern Upland Way or on the direct route between Land's End and John O'Groats. Friendly, accommodating, with open fires in the bars in cold weather, and a range of home-cooked meals and choice of real ales. Breakfast is served all day. Bar snacks include soups, sandwiches, filled baked potatoes, grills, fish and traditional puddings. Children's portions, and in summer high tea in the lounge. Particularly geared up to the walker/cyclist/bird watcher with a cleverly converted bunkhouse which offers clean, warm, basic accommodation. So, not only big boots and hairy socks, but back-packs the size of a Wendy House too. Broughtons Greenmantle ales, one guest and Scottish Oatmeal Stout. Over 50 malt whiskies. Trout and salmon fishing can be arranged. Fantastic, wild scenery.

OPEN: 11–11 (midnight Sat). 11–3. 6.30–11 winter weekdays.
Real Ale. Restaurant (not Sun eve). Closed Tuesday mid Oct–Easter.
Children in eating area lounge & dining room until 8 pm. Dogs on leads.
Accordion & Fiddle Club 3rd Wed each month.

SHEILDAIG

Tigh an Eilean Hotel   Tel: 01520 755251

Sheildaig, Strathcarron, Ross-shire.
Free House. Mrs E Stewart, licensee.

The village was only created in 1800 by the Admiralty who offered grants to entice people to live here and work for the Navy. Spectacular scenery surrounds this small village and its hotel, built on the edge of the sea, with views towards the National Trust "Island of Pines". The non-residents side has no more than a small bar whose windows look out to sea. Well chosen bar food ranges from sandwiches, soups and salmon salad to hot weekly specials which could include chicken in white wine, rabbit or game casserole and a choice of fish. There is a comprehensive wine list. Tables and chairs in a side courtyard. Excellent walking country.

OPEN: 11–11 (11–2.30 Sun) Winter: 11–2.30. 5–11. closed Sun. night.
Evening restaurant summer only.
Children until 8 pm. No dogs.

ST MARY'S LOCH

Tibbie Shiels Inn   Tel: 01750 42231

St Mary's Loch, Selkirk, Borders TD7 5NE
Free House. Jack & Jill Brown, licensees.

Named after Isabella Shiel, landlady for 55 years, it was originally a tiny inn built on the finger of land that separates St Mary's Loch and the Loch of the Lowes. After her husband died, she supported herself and six children by taking in "gentlemen lodgers". Thirteen beds were somehow distributed between what is now the bar and the attic – increasing to 35 in the shooting season! The inn has been somewhat extended since then so there is a little more room to move around. Bar food includes: soups, ploughmans, Holy Mole chilli salad and garlic bread, spicy chicken, fresh local Yarrow trout, salmon, escalope of pork with ginger wine sauce, queen scallops with a bacon and cream sauce are among the favourites. Some vegetarian dishes and a variety of puddings. Broughton Green Mantle and Belhaven 80/- on hand pump. Selection of wines and over 50 malt whiskies. Lots of walks, the Southern Upland Way is close by – too energetic? Tables and chairs at the front of the pub.

OPEN: 11–11 (11–12 Sat). Closed Mon Nov–March.
Real Ale. Restaurant.
Children welcome. No dogs.
Bedrooms, all en-suite.
Wheelchair access throughout the inn.

SWINTON

Wheatsheaf Hotel   Tel: 01890 860257

Main Street, Swinton, Berwickshire TD11 3JJ
Free House. Alan Read, licensee.

Popular with everyone: locals, tourists, fishermen – close to the River Tweed – and between Coldstream (Battle of Flodden Field, 1513) and Duns. Food is an important feature: the landlord is a dedicated chef and offers a daily changing menu which, as well as the usual lunchtime favourites, could include fresh quail salad in Thai dressing, hot baked avocado with seafood in cheese sauce, warm widgeon salad, devilled whitebait, pork and apricot strogonoff with rice, peppered sirloin steak in a cream and brandy sauce and broccoli and oyster mushroom fricassee with rice. Imaginative puddings. Broughton Green Mantle ale and one guest beer. Good wine list and choice of malt whiskies.

OPEN: 11–2.30 (11–3 Sat); 6–11. Tues–Sun, closed Monday. Closed Sun eve Nov–March. Closed two weeks Feb and last week Oct.
Real Ale. Restaurant.
Children welcome. Dogs on leads.
Bedrooms. Wheelchair access.

TAYVALLICH

Tayvallich Inn   Tel: 01546 870282

Tayvallich by Lochgilphead, Strathclyde PA31 8PL
Free House. John Grafton, licensee.

More a restaurant and bar than a conventional inn. It was built on a natural
harbour on Loch A'Bhealaich and in good weather the glass doors in the bar
are opened onto the terrace from where you can sit and admire the view.
Wonderful variety of shellfish on the menu: Loch Sween mussels and
oysters, Sound of Jura scallops with parsley and lemon, West coast prawns
thermidor, seafood platter and of course smoked salmon. Not forgotten
though is the peppered chicken, grilled prime Scottish sirloin or fillet steak
and last but not least home-made puddings. Choice of wines and malt
whiskies plus keg beers: Calders 70/-, Dryboroughs Heavy, Labatts Lager,
Old English Cider, Kilkenny Irish Ale and Guinness. There are walks along the
edge of the loch, and to Knapdale Forest.

OPEN: 11–midnight (11–1am Sat). Closed Mon Nov–March.
Restaurant.
Children in eating areas. Dogs on leads.
Wheelchair access to pub.

TWEEDSMUIR

Crook Inn   Tel: 0189 97272

Tweedsmuir, Nr Biggar, Borders MLR 6QN
Free House. Stuart Reid, licensee.

Built in 1604 and situated on the scenic route between Moffat and
Edinburgh, this was originally a drovers' inn, now a welcoming, friendly pub
in the lovely Tweed Valley. Simply furnished bars with cosy fires on colder
days. Traditional bar food – home-made soup and chicken liver paté – with
the addition of local trout with almonds, poached salmon with creamy dill
sauce, grilled lambs liver, supreme of chicken , steaks, mixed grills and
vegetarian dishes. They also serve high tea. Childrens' menu too. Broughton
Green Mantle and McEwans 80/- on hand pump. Good range of wines and
malt whiskies. Seats and children's play area in the garden. Daily trout
fishing permits are available from the inn.

OPEN: 11–midnight.
Real Ale. Restaurant.
Children welcome. Dogs on leads.
Bedrooms

439

WALES

ABERDOVEY

Penhelig Arms Hotel   Tel: 01654 767215

Aberdovey, Gwynedd LL35 0LT
Free House. Robert & Sally Hughes, licensees.

Beside Penhelig Harbour and near the mouth of the River Dyfi, this delightful hotel has everything you could wish for: comfortable bars, imaginative lunchtime and evening bar menus, an excellent restaurant, above average accommodation, fantastic views over the harbour and last but not least, good ales. From the Fishermen's Bar, the bar food could include seafood vol-au-vent, tomato, basil and cream cheese roulade, omelettes with a variety of fillings, chicken cooked with apricots in a cream and brandy sauce served with rice, fish pie, a choice of fish, char-grilled sirloin steak, salads, sandwiches and a variety of puddings. An imaginative, reasonably priced three-course dinner is available in the no-smoking restaurant; also a three-course Sunday lunch. Champagne by the glass if you want to be indulgent. Well chosen wine list. Felinfoel Double Dragon, Morlands Old Speckled Hen, Smiles Best, Tetleys and Brains SA ales. In warm weather you can sit outside on the sea wall and admire the view or tuck yourself up near the fire in the bar if the Welsh winds blow. Good walks along the sea front in both directions.

OPEN: 11–3. 6–11.
Real Ale. Restaurant. Sunday lunch in bar or restaurant.
Children in restaurant. Dogs in bar and bedrooms.
Bedrooms

AMROTH

Amroth Arms   Tel: 01834 812480

Amroth, Narberth, Pembrokeshire SA67 8NG
Free House. Roger Harries, licensee.

Only the width of the road separates the Amroth Arms from the beach in this seaside village on the shores of Camarthen Bay. There was a forest here 4,000 years ago – engulfed by the sea, its petrified stumps are often exposed after stormy weather. Several houses have been lost too over the years, but the Amroth Arms stands firm: a bar, and an ante-room with pool, dart-board and bar skittles. The television will be on when there is a rugby international, or Glamorgan are playing cricket: a deathly 'ush will tell you they're losing, so you are advised to change the subject. Lots of other things to talk about here. The pub is the centre for the Pembrokeshire League of Sea-Angling clubs. "Pathological liars" and I quote, "may care to notice that weighing scales are in operation." Teams are entered in the Bar Skittles League, the Pool League and the Darts League. There is also a Clay Pigeon shooting team. Finally, and they said it "the mentally unbalanced, which is to say the majority, dash into the sea for a Christmas swim, collecting money from the less mentally unbalanced to give to charity." Seems quite mundane to talk about food but they do feed you. Bar snacks, local fresh fish, (see above), traditional Welsh dishes and a lamb and meat pie. Seasonal variations determine the beers, so there might be Worthington Best, Draught Bass and guest beers. Finally, seats in front of the pub, to watch all the comings and goings.

OPEN: 11–3. 6–11
Real Ale. Restaurant.
Quiet children welcome, and dogs as long as they don't argue with the resident canines.

BANGOR

Union Hotel   Tel: 01248 362462

Garth Road, Bangor, Gwynedd LL57 2SF
Burtonwood. John Duggan, tenant.

They say they are open all hours here – all permitted hours, that is. Adjoining the local boatyard – "Dickies"– and the yacht basin, the Union Garth, as it is known, claims to be the only quiet pub in this cathedral city. Certainly anyone wanting to hire a room for a party goes through the third degree, and his DJ has to promise that any music played is sotto voce. It has a distinctly nautical atmosphere – the view of Snowdonia from the small garden at the back of the pub is viewed through a forest of yacht masts, accompanied by that evocative slap of rigging on main masts that is the only music you need on a summer's evening. Good, reliable, traditional bar food: soups, ploughmans, paté, smoked mussels and salads, omelettes, grilled gammon, steaks, filled baked potatoes and steak and kidney pie. Burtonwood Ales. Seats in the small garden.

OPEN: All permitted hours. No food Tues evenings.
Real Ale
Quiet children welcome, but not in bar. Dogs on leads.
Bedrooms. Wheelchair access quite easy, but no special facilities.

BEAUMARIS

Ye Olde Bulls Head   Tel: 01248 810329

Castle Street, Beaumaris, Anglesey LL58 8AP
Free House. David Robertson, licensee.

An attractive small town which is dominated by the castle built by Edward
I in the 13th century. The pub is a little younger than the Castle, but still of
venerable age, dating back to the 15th century. The interior of the Bulls Head
reflects its long history: panelled, beamed, with open fires and full of
interesting artefacts which include the towns' original ducking stool – a use
for which could still be found I'm sure. There is a daily changing menu, but
bar food is only available at lunchtimes: sandwiches and ploughmans (with
local cheeses), soups, omelettes, braised chicken in wine and mustard
sauce, crab or smoked trout salad among other dishes. A three-course
Sunday lunch is served in the no-smoking restaurant. Bass, Worthingtons
and a guest beer. Good choice of wines.

OPEN: 11–11 (no bar meals/snacks Sun lunchtime. Sunday lunch in
restaurant).
Real Ale. Restaurant.
Children until 8 pm (none under 7 in restaurant). No dogs.
Bedrooms.

CILCAIN

White Horse   Tel: 01352 740142

The Square, Cilcain, Flintshire CH7 5NN
Free House. Peter Jeory, licensee.

Near Mold, a busy market town, two country parks and the River Alyn, the
creeper-covered White Horse is in an enviable position. This old stone pub
has several bars, one with an inglenook fireplace – go into the back one if
you have your dog with you. Local produce – including free range eggs and
organically grown vegetables – is mostly used to create a varied selection

of home-made bar food: filled rolls, omelettes, the ham to go with the eggs is home-baked, chicken and herb pie, lamb cobbler, game pie, grilled trout, various pasta and vegetarian dishes, plus a variety of puddings. the home-made specials change weekly. Thwaites ale plus two weekly changing guests. No keg bitters here. Selection of wines, farm ciders. Seats at the side of the pub.

OPEN: 12–3.30. (12–4 Sat). 7–11.
Real Ale.
No children inside pub. Dogs on leads.
Wheelchair access into pub.

CILGERRAN

Pendre Inn   Tel: 01239 614223

Cilgerran, Nr Cardigan, Dyfed SA43 2SL
Free House. Robert Lowe & Miranda Cobb, owners/licensees.

Cilgerran lies in a lovely wooded area off the A478 near Cardigan. Nearby is the River Teifi, which is overlooked by the remains of a 13th century castle that was built about 100 years before the Pendre. The pub, low beamed with polished slate and flagstone floors has loads of what the Welsh call 'hwyl' – meaning atmosphere. No frozen food passes the door. "I make everything as I go along", said Miranda Cobb. "I've been a cook for a long time, and even if I say so myself, I have quite a reputation." The menu changes constantly; lots of specials and lots of fish: mackerel, trout, sea bass and grey mullet. In winter the farmers are out shooting, particularly the pesky pigeons, so 'twenty ways to cook a pigeon' may feature on the menu! Other local game goes into the homemade game pies and local produce accompanies them. Worthington BB, Draught Bass and Crown Buckley's Reverend James Bitter. There are seats outside in the big garden which you share with 8 hens and a cockerel. (Rumours abound: by the time you get to the Pendre he may have gone to the big perch in the sky but not into a pie!)

OPEN: 11.30–3. 6–12. (6–10.30 Sun)
Real Ale. Restaurant.
Children welcome. Dogs firmly on leads, remember the hens.
Car park.

CLYTHA

Clytha Arms   Tel: 01873 840206

Clytha, Nr Abergavenny, Monmouthshire NP7 9BW
Free House. Andrew & Beverley Canning, licensees.

On the Abergavenny/Raglan road, close to Clytha Castle, this nice old country inn, which has only re-opened in the last few years, has a good-sized country bar and a smaller, lounge bar. The blackboard menu lists dependable, reasonably-priced, country dishes: the usual sandwiches and ploughmans, faggots and peas, venison sausages, potato pancakes and larva bread are just a selection of those available. The restaurant, (with napkins, candles and fresh flowers), has a separate, more expensive menu featuring regional specialities. They have a set Sunday lunch. Hook Norton, Bass and Brains ales plus an interesting selection of guest beers. There are wonderful walks along the banks of the River Usk and also through the grounds of Clytha Castle.

OPEN: 11.30–3.30. 6–11 (11–11 Sat). Closed Mon lunchtimes except Bank Hols.
Real Ale. No bar snacks or restaurant Sun. eve.
Children welcome until 8 (not in bar). Dogs if well behaved.
Bedrooms.

CRESSWELL QUAY

Cresselly Arms   Tel: 01646 65121

Cresswell Quay, Kilgetty, Dyfed SA68 0TE
Free House. Maurice and Janet Cole, licensees.

Near Carew, its ruined 13th century castle, and the only 19th century Welsh tidal mill on the Carew River, the Cresselly Arms is a timeless place, little changed since early this century. You can arrive by car, or by boat (depending on the tide), to enjoy your pint – still served from the cask into large jugs, and from there into your glass. A friendly, traditional pub serving good beer as well as a crisp or a nut. Flowers Original, also Guinness or Heineken. Seats outside to watch the tides and the boats.

OPEN: 11–3. 5–11.
Real Ale. No food.
No children. No dogs.

KENFIG

Prince of Wales Inn Tel: 01656 740356

Ton Kenfig, Mid-Glamorgan CF33 4PR
Free House. Jeremy Evans, lease.

Off the M4 at junction 37, Kenfig is about 2.5 miles further on, off the A4429 towards Porthcawl, signposted Mawdlem/Kenfig, on the fringes of the Kenfig Burrows Nature Reserve. Eight hundred years ago Kenfig was a thriving community but by the 16th century the shifting sands had all but engulfed the town. Only the ruins of the castle are left to remind you of what has been lost. The Prince of Wales was made of sterner stuff. Five hundred years old, the Inn has many tales to tell; the 'ghost room' has featured on the BBC TV production "Out of this World". Lots of strange noises emanating from the limestone walls were recorded for the programme. Troubled spirits or not, this is a popular, successful pub. Only a small bar area, but many rooms full of old fashioned settles. Three real fires. All the vegetables are home grown. The pub has an acre of land across the road, so fresh vegetables to go with the home-made steak and onion pie, chicken and mushroom pie, daily roast or fresh fish. Bar snacks too – ploughmans, sandwiches and basket meals. Draught Bass, Worthington BB and several guest beers. Large sitting out area. Just in case you and your friends want to ghost watch, the "ghost room" is the function room and can be hired.

OPEN: 11.30–4. 6–11. (Sunday hours a bit flexible and longer)
Real Ale. Restaurant.
Children welcome. Dogs in games room only.

LLANGATTOCK

Vine Tree Inn Tel: 01873 810514

The Leager, Llangattock, Crickhowell, Powys NP8 1HG
Free House. I.S. Lennox, licensee.

This village of old weavers' cottages with its tiny paved square and 16th century church, is fortunate to be so near the lovely Monmouth Brecon Canal and the River Usk. Food is all important in this efficient and very busy pub. Freshly cooked, using local produce and fish from Cornwall. The menu is extensive: hot curried prawns, baked egg provençal, smoked trout, fillet steak stuffed with paté in a port wine sauce, rabbit in a wine, celery and almond sauce, lots of chicken dishes including Vine Tree chicken – (chicken breast stuffed with prawns, wrapped in bacon in a seafood sauce), steaks, fish – including salmon – a variety of vegetarian dishes, also Sunday roasts. Even the bread is home-made. Boddingtons, Wadworths 6X and Fremlins Bitter. Seats outside over look the river and there are wonderful walks along the canal.

OPEN: 12–3. 6–11.
Real Ale. Restaurant.
Children welcome. Dogs on leads (well behaved).

LLANSANTFFRAID-YM-MECHAIN

The Lion Hotel Tel: 01691 828207

Llansantffraid-Ym-Mechain, Powys SY22 6AQ
Free House. Mr Ron Edwards, owner/licensee.

To reach some country pubs you have to be an expert map-reader, so with this one. You need to know it's close to the Shropshire border, on the A495, which is off the A483 Oswestry/Welshpool road – in a lovely part of Wales. A Georgian hotel, The Lion was built in 1740. Inside is a country bar, public bar, lounge and dining room. Interesting, home-made food: ratatouille topped with cheese, garlic mushrooms or deep-fried Camembert, honey-baked ham, chicken à la crème, barbecue spare ribs, (a huge spare rib, not the usual bones), duckling, several chicken dishes and pork. Fruit puddings and crumbles. Bar menu gives you a choice of sandwiches, ploughmans, curry, plaice and chips, lasagne, scampi and home-made steak pie. Bass Special and Worthington Best Bitter from the cask. Draught lagers, Guinness and Ciders.

OPEN: 12–2.30ish 6.30–11. (6.30–10.30 Sun)
Real Ale. Restaurant.
Children welcome. No dogs, except guide dogs.
Six en suite bedrooms.

LLANTHONY

Abbey Hotel Tel: 01873 890487

Llanthony, Nr Abergavenny, Monmouthshire NP7 7NN
Free House. Ivor Prentice, licensee.

Ruins set amid the quiet beauty of the Vale of Ewyas, and among the ruins in a truly magical setting is the Abbey Hotel which incorporates parts of the Prior's house, and includes an atmospheric vaulted crypt bar. Simple furnishings in the main flagstoned bar where the food is plain and traditional: home-made soups, toasted sandwiches, home-made burgers, veggy ones too; in the evening dishes include casseroles, local lamb in garlic or a nut roast. Ruddles County, Draught Bass, Flowers Original and farm ciders. Glorious setting with wonderful walks.

OPEN: 11–3. 6–11 (11–11 Sat & Summer hols) Closed weekdays end Nov–end March. Open Christmas & New Year week
Real Ale.
No children inside. No dogs.
Bedrooms

LLANWNDA

Goat Hotel   Tel: 01286 830256

Llanwnda, Caernarvon, Gwynedd LL54 5SD
Free House. Anne Griffith, licensee.

The walled town of Caernarvon, full of lovely old buildings and dominated by the ruins of Edward I's castle, is in a prominent position overlooking the Menai Strait. It is also your nearest point of contact when searching for this tiny hamlet. Well worth finding for the friendly welcome you get when you arrive. Polish up your Welsh so that you can greet the landlady and the villagers. The Goat has a fair sized main bar and a no-smoking parlour. On high days and holidays an impressive, very reasonable buffet is available, with a choice of starters, many fish dishes, cold meats and pies; otherwise there are home-made soups, interesting sandwiches, ploughmans with local cheeses, home-cooked ham and salads – good substantial fare. Draught Bass, Whitbread and Boddingtons Bitter. Tables on the terrace at the front of the pub.

OPEN: 11–4. 6–11
Real Ale. (No lunchtime food Sun).
Children welcome. Dogs on leads.
Bedrooms

LLYSWEN

Griffin Inn   Tel: 01874 754241

Llyswen, Brecon, Powys LD3 0UR.
Free House. Richard Stockton, licensee.

The creeper covered Griffin is one of those places you wish you lived next

447

to. In the upper Wye valley, seven miles from Hay-on-Wye, it is an old, long-established, sporting inn, fishing and shooting to the fore. Inside, there is a comfortable bar with a huge inglenook fireplace. It is the centre of village life where everyone meets. If you are eating, this is the sort of place where you know the ingredients are as fresh as they could possibly be. Fish from the river, well hung game from the hills, fruit and veg from local gardens and local cheeses. Roast lunch Sunday. Pub food at its best. Beers are largely guests; there could be Boddingtons and Flowers IPA, but go and be surprised. A varied wine list includes some half bottles. Glorious countryside, lots of lovely walks.

OPEN: 12–3. 7–11
Real Ale. Restaurant. No food Sun eve. unless resident.
Children welcome. Dogs on leads.

MAENTWROG

Grapes   Tel: 01766 590208

Maentwrog, Blaenau Ffestiniog, Gwynedd, LL14 4HN
Free House. Brian & Gill Tarbox, licensees.

Built in an attractive alpine-like valley with cottages clinging to its sides and from where there are magnificent views of the mountains, is The Grapes – a popular old coaching inn with comfortable pine-panelled bars and big fires, serving well presented, generous bar food. This could include lunchtime soups – changing daily, seafood pancakes, a medley of mushrooms in garlic butter with french bread, filled jacket potatoes, their very own proper beef burgers, French bread filled with steak and mushrooms or onions, smoked bacon or veggie sausage, steak and kidney pies, salads, rack of Welsh lamb and vegetarian dishes. There are lots of fishy specials. Everything is cooked to order. The restaurant is no-smoking and there is a children's menu. Sunday roast. Bass and Worthingtons Best, about five guest beers from a total of 30 or 40 rotating throughout the year. Farm cider. Seats on the verandah which look over the garden to the mountains beyond. Nearby is the Vale of Ffestiniog and the Ffestiniog Railway. Using 1860 locomotives it travels through 14 miles of breathtaking scenery, and is well worth a ride.

OPEN: 11–11.
Real Ale. Restaurant (not Sun eves)
Children in family room, and on the veranda. Dogs on leads.
Bedrooms. Wheelchair access no problem.

MENAI BRIDGE

Liverpool Arms   Tel: 01248 712453

St George's Pier, Menai Bridge, Anglesey, North Wales
Greenalls. Tony Thickett, tenant.

Overlooking the Menai Bridge – the graceful suspension bridge Thomas
Telford built in 1826 to link the Welsh mainland to the Island of Anglesey –
the Liverpool Arms, a stone-built early 19th century pub, is full of nautical
artefacts. It has two comfortable bars, dining room and a conservatory
seating 38. The food in the restaurant and the bar is all home-made and
could include: leek and ham mornay, cod and prawn mornay, baked ham
salad, sirloin steak, salmon, prawn and fresh Cromer crab salads. Thomas
Greenalls Original, Greenalls and Tetleys Bitters and one guest beer a week.
No garden, just a patio.

OPEN: 11–11 (12–3. 7–10.30 Sun)
Real Ale.
Children welcome. No dogs.

NANTGWYNANT

Pen-y-Gwryd Hotel   Tel: 01286 870211

Nantgwynant, Gwynedd LL55 4NT. at junction of A498 and A4086.
Free House. Jane Pullee, licensee.

Surrounded by mountains, steep valleys and close to Snowdon – at 3560ft
the highest mountain in England and Wales – this is serious climbing
country: never mind the big boots and hairy socks, you'll need all weather
gear, with ironmongery and ropes attached to various parts of your body.
The Hotel even has a climbers' bar which also serves as the headquarters
of the local Mountain Rescue team. There is an interesting collection of
boots that have made famous (accompanied) climbs, and this was where
the successful 1953 Everest team based itself. A jolly, friendly inn serving
hearty home-made bar food, including special pies which change daily,
casseroles in winter, as well as soups, sandwiches and home-made bread
to go with the home-made paté and the local cheeses for the ploughmans.
No bar food in the evening, just meals in the no-smoking restaurant. Bass
and Theakstons ales.

THE QUIET PINT

OPEN: 11–11 (closed Nov–New Year. Open weekends only Jan–Feb)
Real Ale. Evening restaurant.
Well behaved children welcome, not in residents' bar. Dogs on leads.
Bedrooms. Wheelchair access.

OLD RADNOR

The Harp Inn   Tel: 01544 350655

Old Radnor, Presteigne, Powys LD8 2RH
Free House. Stephen & Dee Cope, licensees.

Wonderful panoramic views from this 15th century hillside inn, situated next to the church, overlooking the village green. You'll get a warm welcome from the landlord who first came here as a customer 20 years ago; 17 years later he ended up buying it. Inside there is a cosy old-fashioned feel to the place provided by the beams, slate floors, some nice pieces of antique furniture and log fires in both the public and lounge bars. The landlady does all the cooking with a little help at the weekends. There is a lunchtime snack menu: home-made soup of the day, filled baked potatoes, Harp paté, mushrooms on toast, sandwiches, lasagne, home-made curry and daily specials such as faggots. Woods Special, Wye Valley HPA and a guest beer. Lots of outside seating so you can admire the view. Good walking country too.

OPEN: 11.30–11
Real Ale. Small Restaurant.
Children & Dogs welcome.
Bedrooms.

PENRHYNSIDE

Penrhyn Arms   Tel: 01492 540809

Pendre Road, Penrhynside, Llandudno, Gwynedd LL30 3BY
Free House. Mick Morris, licensee.

"No music, no food and no customers!" was how the owners of the Penrhyn Arms introduced themselves. The first two statements are correct, but not the third. Near the slate quarries, and now part of Llandudno, the village of Penrhynside and the Penrhyn Arms were built at the turn of the century to cater for the quarry workers. A small pub, just one bar and a pool room. The treasured bagatelle board is nearly as old as the pub; they also play bar skittles and the next purchase is going to be a shove h'penny board so they can join the Welsh league. Bought off the brewery, the landlord is hoping to

450

put back some of the character previous owners have removed; the garden is due some attention too. "Vaste range of food" says the landlord, "three types of crisps and two of nuts. Occasionally things get really exciting and I change the flavour of the crisps." This is a traditional ale house, with the sort of friendly, ebullient landlord you would wish for all village pubs. Marstons ales from the cask, lagers and cider from the pumps and a guest ale. Water and biscuits under the counter for the dog.

OPEN: Mon–Fri : 12–2.30. 5.30–11ish. Sat–Sun : 12–11ish.
Real Ale. Crisps and nuts.
Children if well behaved. Dogs very welcome.

PONTFAEN

Dyffryn Arms   Tel: 01348 881305

Pontfaen, Dyfed SA65 9SE
Free House. Bessie Davis, licensee.

Find Fishguard on the map and look left a bit. Pontfaen seems to be in the middle of a fairly empty bit of Wales, but only a mile or so off the B4314, surrounded by woodland and in an area where there is lots of rushing water. The Dyffryn Arms, a tiny, unspoilt pub – just two rooms – has been in Bessie Davis' family for 151 years. Well kept Draught Bass still served from the jug. Only one real beer, the rest are bottled or canned. To eat? Well, crisps, nuts and a pickled egg!

OPEN: 12–12
Real Ale. Children in the garden. Dogs on leads.
Car park.

PRESTEIGNE

Radnorshire Arms   Tel: 01544 267406

The High Street, Presteigne, Powys LB8 2BE
Free House. Aidan Treacy, manager.

This small, Welsh market town has an interesting part-Saxon church, which the Normans, Tudors and Georgians have all added to, or altered during their times. In Elizabeth I's reign, the Radnorshire Arms was a private house, complete with secret passages and a priest's chamber; it became a coaching inn in 1792 and since then has perfected the art of looking after the needs of the traveller. A wonderful example of Elizabethan timbering outside, with oak beams and panelling inside, it has been successfully modernised without losing its age old charm and welcoming atmosphere. The bar menu, served in the oak-panelled bar, is all home-made, offering a choice of both local and regional specialities. They have a no-smoking restaurant. Marstons Pedigree, Banks's Bitter, Ruddles County and a guest beer plus wines by the glass. Seats outside in the sheltered garden.

OPEN: 11–11.
Real Ale. Restaurant (not Sun eves).
Children welcome. No dogs.
Bedrooms

ST ASAPH

Farmers Arms   Tel: 01745 582190

The Waen, Nr St. Asaph, Denbighshire.(on the B5429 between the Expressway A55, and Tremeirchion)
Free House. B Seaman, licensee.

A delightful country pub which leans more towards a restaurant than a pub. There is a public bar with all the noisy bits, situated well away from the bar in the main lounge; a small snug and a room for parties, which is also used for meetings by the Rotary Club and local Young Farmers. Fractionally borderline in our case, there certainly isn't any piped music but early in the evening when the bar is still fairly empty, there could be very quiet "cocktaily" music on tape. This is turned off as the pub fills up, and the landlord, a classically trained musician, can sometimes be persuaded to play the grand piano in the lounge bar. The home-cooked food ranges from simple bar food to an elaborate à la carte menu in the dining room. Theakstons is the main ale, and two others are chosen by the landlord.

OPEN: 12–3. 7–11 (12–3. 7–10.30 Sun)
Real Ale
No Children, No Dogs.

STACKPOLE

Armstrong Arms   Tel: 01646 672324

Stackpole, Pembroke, Dyfed SA71 5DF
Free House. Senga & Peter Waddilove, licensees.

Just three miles south of Pembroke – which boasts the largest Norman castle in Britain and is reputed to be the birthplace of Henry VII in 1457 – the Armstrong Arms is a mere 400 years old and has been a pub for only a few years. Friendly and welcoming, in this short time it has nevertheless created a niche for itself as one of the few pubs with a deserved reputation for serving imaginative and interesting home-cooked food: curried parsnip soup with parsnip crisps, croissant filled with smoked salmon and egg, Welsh cheese platter, flat mushrooms stuffed with spinach and stilton, home-made meatballs in a tomato salsa with fresh spaghetti, fillet steak with mushrooms in a brandy and cream sauce, grilled supreme of chicken wrapped in Parma ham, served with a red wine sauce. Impressive home-made puddings. Menus change daily. Worthingtons Best Bitter and another ale which could be Charles Wells Bombadier, Mansfield Bitter, Caledonian Deuchars IPA or a choice of six others. Over 40 malt whiskies. Seats outside in the flowery garden.

OPEN: 11–3. 6–11
Real Ale. (No meals/snacks winter Sun eves).Must book for Sat. eve and Sunday lunch. No credit cards.
Children welcome. Dogs in bar.
Wheelchair access.

TUDWEILOG

Lion Hotel   Tel: 01758 770244

Nefyn Road, Tudweilog, Gwynedd LL53 8ND
Free House. Andrew Lee, licensee.

A popular, village inn not far from the sandy beaches and windsurfing seas around the Lleyn Peninsula. Comfortable and friendly, it has a good-sized main bar, no-smoking family dining room and a public bar with a juke box (not used much we hope). Satisfying bar menu includes home-made soups, sandwiches, ploughmans, baked potatoes with various fillings, lasagne, steaks, and several vegetarian dishes. There is a daily specials board with extra main dishes and puddings. Children's portions too. Theakstons Best and Mild, Boddingtons, Marstons Pedigree and guest beers during spring and summer. A number of malt whiskies. Children's play area and tables in the front garden and courtyard.

OPEN: 11–3. 5.30–11.(12–2. 7–11 winter). Closed Sun.
Real Ale.
Children in family dining room. No dogs.

WINE BARS & PUB GROUPS

DAVYS

Lunching on a slice of traditional English pie taken with chilled champagne from a pewter tankard is an experience you won't easily forget. Of course, to savour it to the full, it helps to be surrounded by old oak barrels and freshly sawdusted floors, which evoke an atmosphere of times gone by. This cellar imagery is one Davys have cultivated successfully since they opened The Boot and Flogger wine bar in 1965. Today, they own 54 establishments, of which all but seven are in London. Davys have been one of Britain's major wine shippers for over 125 years. While other establishments fall out of favour, Davys remains constantly popular, distinctive and welcoming.

LONDON

Bangers
2 Wilson Street
London EC2
Tel: 0171 377 6326

Bangers Too
1 St Mary-at-Hill
London EC3
Tel: 0171 283 4443

Bishop of Norwich
91/93 Moorgate
London EC2
Tel: 0171 920 0857

Bishops Parlour
91/93 Moorgate
London EC2
Tel: 0171 588 2581

Bottlescrue
Bath House
53/60 Holborn Viaduct
London EC1
Tel: 0171 248 2157

Bung Hole
57 High Holborn
London WC1
Tel: 0171 242 4318

Bung Hole Cellars
Hand Court
57 High Holborn
London WC1
Tel: 0171 831 8365

City Pipe
Foster Lane off Cheapside
London EC1
Tel: 0171 606 2110

City Vaults
2 St Martins-le-Grand
London EC1
Tel: 0171 606 8721

Colonel Jaspers
161 Greenwich High Rd
London SE10
Tel: 0181 853 0585

WINE BARS & PUB GROUPS

Colonel Jaspers
190 City Road
London EC1
Tel: 0171 608 0925

The Cooperage
48–50 Tooley Street
London SE1
Tel: 0171 403 5775

Crown Passage Vaults
20 King Street St James's
London SW1
Tel: 0171 839 8831

Crusting Pipe
27 The Market
Covent Garden
London WC2
Tel: 0171 836 1415

Burgundy Bens
102/108 Clerkenwell Road
London EC1 Tel: 0171 251 3783

The Chiv
90/92 Wigmore Street
London W1
Tel: 0171 224 0170

Champagne Charlies
Villiers Street
London WC2
Tel: 0171 930 7737

Chopper Lump
10c Hanover Square
London W1
Tel: 0171 499 7569

City Boot
7 Moorfields
High Walk
London EC2
Tel: 0171 588 4766

City Flogger
Fenn Court
120 Fenchurch Street
London EC3
Tel: 0171 623 3251

City F.O.B.
Below London Bridge
Lower Thames Street
London EC3
Tel: 0171 621 0619

Davys at Creed Lane
10 Creed Lane
London EC4
Tel: 0171 236 5317

Davys Wine Vaults
161 Greenwich High Rd
London SE10
Tel: 0181 858 7204

Dock Blida
50/54 Blandford St
London W1
Tel: 0171 486 3590

Grapeshots
2/3 Artillery Passage
London E1
Tel: 0171 247 8215

Gyngleboy
27 Spring Street
Paddington
London W2
Tel: 0171 723 3351

Guinea Butt
White Hart Yard
Borough High Street
London SE1
Tel: 0171 407 2829

The Habit
Friary Court
65 Crutched Friars
London EC3
Tel: 0171 481 1131

Lees Bag
4 Great Portland Street
London W1
Tel: 0171 636 5287

The Mug House
1–3 Tooley Street
London SE1
Tel: 0171 403 8343

The Pulpit
63 Worship Street
London EC2
Tel: 0171 377 1574

Shotberries
167 Queen Victoria Street
London EC4
Tel: 0171 329 4759

Skinkers
42 Tooley Street
London EC1
Tel: 0171 407 9181

The Spittoon
15/17 Long Lane
London EC1
Tel: 0171 726 8858

Tappit-Hen
5 William 1V St
Strand
London WC2
Tel: 0171 836 9839

Tappit-Hen Cellars
5 William 1V St
Strand
London WC2
Tel: 0171 836 9839

Tapster
3 Brewers Green
Buckingham Gate
London SW1
Tel: 0171 222 0561

Truckles of Pied Bull Yard (Ale &
Port House)
off Bury Place
Bloomsbury
London WC1
Tel: 0171 404 5338

Truckles of Pied Bull Yard (Wine
Rooms)
off Bury Place
Bloomsbury
London WC1
Tel: 0171 404 5334

Tumblers
1 Kensington High St
London W8
Tel: 0171 987 0393

Udder Place
Russia Court
Russia Row
1/6 Milk Street
London EC2
Tel: 0171 606 7252

Udder Place
(Wine Rooms)
Russia Court
Russia Row
1/6 Milk Street
London EC2
Tel: 0171 600 2165

The Wine Vaults
122 North End
Croydon
Tel: 0181 680 2419

The Vineyard
International House
1 St Katherine's Way
London E1
Tel: 0171 480 6680

The Vineyard Coffee House
International House
1 St Katherine's Way
London E1
Tel: 0171 480 5088

COUNTRY ESTABLISHMENTS

Bottlescrue Bills
66 South Street
Exeter
Devon
Tel: 01392 437511

Colonel Jaspers
3 Beacon House
Queen's Avenue
Clifton
Bristol
Tel: 01272 731289

Colonel Jaspers
15B Longbridge Road
Barking
Essex
Tel: 0181 507 8481

The Crypt
Frewin Court
off Cornmarket Oxford
Tel: 01865 251000

Spotted Dog
15 Longbridge Road
Barking
Essex
Tel: 0181 594 0228

White Hart Hotel
66 South Street
Exeter
Devon
Tel: 01392 79897

YOUNG'S MUSAK FREE PUBS
Some of the pubs listed below are
fully described elsewhere in the
Book

BALHAM
The Nightingale
97, Nightingale Lane SW12

BARNES
Bulls Head
373, Lonsdale Road SW13
Coach & Horses
27 High Street SW13
White Hart
The Terrace, Riverside SW13

BATTERSEA
Duke of Cambridge
228 Battersea Bridge Road SW11

BEDDINGTON
Plough
Croydon Road

BETCHWORTH
Dolphin
The Street

BLOOMSBURY
Calthorpe Arms
252 Gray's Inn Road WC1
Lamb
94 Lamb's Conduit Street WC1
Three Cups
21 Sandland Street WC1

BOROUGH
Bunch of Grapes
2 St Thomas Street SE1

BOW
Coborn Arms
8 Coborn Road E3

457

THE QUIET PINT

BRIXTON
Hope & Anchor
123 Acre Lane SW2
Trinity Arms
24 Trinity Gardens SW9

CHELSEA
Chelsea Ram
32 Burnaby Street SW10
Coopers Arms
87 Flood Street SW3
Finches
190 Fulham Road SW10

CHISWICK
Crown & Anchor
374 High Road W4

CITY OF LONDON
City Retreat
74 Shoe Lane EC4
City House
80 Bishopsgate EC2
Lamb Tavern
10 Leadenhall Market EC3

CLAPHAM COMMON
Windmill Hotel
South Side SW4

CLAPHAM JUNCTION
Plough
89 St John's Hill SW11

CLAPTON
Prince of Wales
145 Lea Bridge Road E5

CLERKENWELL
London Spa
70 Exmouth Market EC1

CROYDON
Dog & Bull
24 Surrey Street
Gloucester
11 White Horse Road
Tamworth Arms
62 Tamworth Road

DARTFORD
Malt Shovel
3 Darenth Road

DULWICH
Dulwich Wood House
39 Sydenham Hill SE26

EAST DULWICH
Clock House
196a Peckham Rye SE22

EAST SHEEN
Hare & Hounds
216 Upper Richmond Road West
SW14

EFFINGHAM
Plough
Orestan Lane

EPSOM
Kings Arms
144 East Street

ESHER
Bear
71 High Street

ETON WICK
Pickwick
71 High Street

EUSTON
Square Tavern
Tolmers Square NW1

FITZROVIA
One Tun
58 Goodge Street W1

GREENWICH
Richard 1st
53/54 Royal Hill SE10

HAMMERSMITH
Brook Green
170 Shepherd's Bush Road W6

HAMPSTEAD
Horse & Groom
68 Heath Street NW3

ISLEWORTH
Castle
18 Upper Square

ISLINGTON
Marquess Tavern
32 Canonbury Street N1

KENSINGTON
Brittania
1 Allen Street W8
Brittania Tap
150 Warwick Road W14

KEW
Coach & Horses
8 Kew Greene

KILBURN
Queens Arms
1 High Street NW6

KINGSTON
Albert Arms
57 Kingston Hill
Norbiton Grey Horse
46 Richmond Road

LAMBETH
Plough
518 Wandsworth Road SW8
Surprise
16 Southville SW8

LEE
Crown
117 Burnt Ash Hill SE12

LOUGHBOROUGH JUNCTION
Wickford Tavern
58 Flaxman Road SE5

MARYLEBONE
Wargrave Arms
42 Brendon Street W1

MAYFAIR
Guinea
30 Bruton Place, Berkeley Square W1

MERTON
Prince of Wales
98 Morden Road SW19

MITCHAM
Bull
32 Church Road
Cricketers
340 London Road

MORTLAKE
Charles Butler
40 High Street SW14
Jolly Gardeners
36 Lower Richmond Road SW14

NORWOOD
Hope
49 High Street SE27
Railway Bell
14 Cawnpore Street SE19

NOTTING HILL
Duke of Wellington
179 Portobello Road W11

OXFORD
Angel & Greyhound
30 St. Clements Street
Kings Arms
40 Holywell Street

OXSHOTT
Bear
Leatherhead Road

PLUMPTON GREEN
Fountain
Station Road

PRIMROSE HILL
Queens
49 Regents Park Road NW1

PUTNEY
Castle
220 Putney Bridge Road SW15
Duke's Head
8 Lower Richmond Road SW15
Green Man
Putney Heath SW15

REGENTS PARK
Spread Eagle
141 Albert Street NW1

THE QUIET PINT

RICHMOND
The Fox & Goose
325–327 Petersham Road
Ham Mitre
20 St. Mary's Grove
Old Ship
3 King Street
Red Cow
59 Sheen Road
Shaftesbury Arms
123 Kew Road
Shakespeare
1 Shakespeare Terrace, Lower
Richmond Road
Waterman's Arms
12 Water Lane
White Cross
Riverside

ROEHAMPTON
Angel
11 High Street SW15
Maltese Cat
Aubyn Square SW15

ROTHERHITHE
Ship
39 St. Marychurch Street SE16

SOUTHWARK
Prince William Henry
217 Blackfriars Road SE1
Founder's Arms
52 Hopton Street SE1

STEPNEY
Hollands
7 Exmouth Street, Brayford Sq E1
Queen's Head
8 Flamborough Street E14

STREATHAM
Pied Bull
498 Streatham High Road SW16

SURBITON
Black Lion
58 Brighton Road
Waggon & Horses
1 Surbiton Hill Road

SUTTON
Lord Nelson
32 Lower Road
New Town
7 Lind Road
Robin Hood
52 West Street

SYDENHAM
Bricklayer's Arms
189 Dartmouth Road SE26

TEDDINGTON
Abercorn Arms
75 Church Street
Queen Dowager
49 North Lane

THORNTON HEATH
Fountain Head
114 Parchmore Road
Lord Napier
111 Beulah Road
Railway Telegraph
19 Brigstock Road

TOOTING
Gorringe Park
29 London Road SW17
Leather Bottle
538 Garratt Lane SW17
Prince of Wales
646 Garratt Lane SW17

TWICKENHAM
Old Anchor
71 Richmond Road
Popes Grotto
Cross Deap

WALTON-ON-THAMES
Royal George
130 Hersham Road
Swan
50 Manor Road

WALLINGTON
Duke's Head
6 Manor Road, The Green

WINE BARS & PUB GROUPS

WANDSWORTH
The Alma
499 Old York Road SW18
County Arms
345 Trinity Road SW18
Gardener's Arms
268 Merton Road SW18
Grapes
39 Fairfield Street SW18
King's Arms
96 Wandsworth High Street SW18
Old Sergeant
104 Garratt Lane SW18
Queen Adelaide
35 Putney Bridge Road SW18

Ship
41 Jew's Row SW18
Wheatsheaf
30 Putney Bridge Road

WESTMINSTER
Buckingham Arms
62 Petty France SW1
Royal Oak
2 Regency Street SW1

WIMBLEDON
Hand in Hand
6 Crooked Billet SW19
Rose & Crown
55 High Street SW19

AUGMENTING THE DIRECTORY

This SECOND edition of THE QUIET PINT does not list all Britain's pubs that are free of recorded music. There are hundreds we have not yet tracked down, or which no one has told us about. If you come across any we have not listed, please send us the details on the adjacent forms.

You can get most of the information from the publican or his bar staff, but make sure they understand that an entry in THE QUIET PINT is absolutely FREE. Most will be only too pleased to tell you about their pub, its history, the ales and food they serve, many other fascinating details and, of course, themselves.

Descriptions are up to you. Just report what you see and feel about the pub you are nominating. There are plenty of examples to go by in THE QUIET PINT.

Many thanks.

THE PIPEDOWN CAMPAIGN

The Pipedown Campaign is solely against piped music in all public places, not just in public houses. Music on the telephone is another irritant some members are protesting about. Pipedown may, in some ways, be a crusade, but their aim is to convert, not to exterminate. The world is full of shrill, fanatical, single-issue protesters. Pipedown is not among them.

Everyone who supports their aims should join them. The more support they have, the more they will be able to accomplish.

TEN CASES
TO BE WON

For your chance to win a case of Wadworth
6X Export* simply nominate your favourite
place for a quiet pint and return the form to the address below.

The first ten nominations we receive will each win a case of
Wadworth 6X Export.

NOMINATION FORM

Please check with the licensee before you nominate a pub that he DOES
NOT play any recorded music at any time.

1. Name of pub ....

2. Telephone number ....

3. Postal address, including post code ....

    ....

4. Is pub a Free or Tied House (*delete as appropriate*)

5. If Tied, please name the Brewery or Group it belongs to

    ....

6. Name of Publican and Status ....

    e.g. Tenant, licensee or manager (delete as appropriate)

7. Opening Hours ....

8. Are Children allowed? .... Are Dogs allowed? ....

9.   Is there a garden, or an outside drinking area? ....

Please use the space overleaf to describe the pub.

The Quiet Pint, FREEPOST, Sandwich, Kent CT13 9BR.

(Over 18's only)

DESCRIPTION OF PUB/WINE BAR

NOMINATION FORM

Please check with the licensee before you nominate a pub that he DOES NOT play any recorded music at any time.

1. Name of pub ....

2. Telephone number ....

3. Postal address, including post code ....

   ....

   ....

4. Is pub a Free or Tied House (*delete as appropriate*)

5. If Tied, please name the Brewery or Group it belongs to

   ....

6. Name of Publican and Status ....

   e.g. Tenant, licensee or manager (delete as appropriate)

7. Opening Hours ....

8. Are Children allowed? .... Are Dogs allowed? ....

9. Is there a garden, or an outside drinking area? ....

Please use the space overleaf to describe the pub and its surroundings in your own way. THE QUIET PINT is full of examples of the kind of descriptions we are seeking. The pub may have a brochure and/or menu: if so, please send them with this form to:

The Quiet Pint, FREEPOST, Sandwich, Kent CT13 9BR.

DESCRIPTION OF PUB/WINE BAR

NOMINATION FORM

Please check with the licensee before you nominate a pub that he DOES NOT play any recorded music at any time.

1. Name of pub ....

2. Telephone number ....

3. Postal address, including post code ....

    ....

    ....

4. Is pub a Free or Tied House (*delete as appropriate*)

5. If Tied, please name the Brewery or Group it belongs to

    ....

6. Name of Publican and Status ....

    e.g. Tenant, licensee or manager (delete as appropriate)

7. Opening Hours ....

8. Are Children allowed? .... Are Dogs allowed? ....

9. Is there a garden, or an outside drinking area? ....

Please use the space overleaf to describe the pub and its surroundings in your own way. THE QUIET PINT is full of examples of the kind of descriptions we are seeking. The pub may have a brochure and/or menu: if so, please send them with this form to:

The Quiet Pint, FREEPOST, Sandwich, Kent CT13 9BR.

DESCRIPTION OF PUB/WINE BAR

NOMINATION FORM

Please check with the licensee before you nominate a pub that he DOES NOT play any recorded music at any time.

1. Name of pub ....

2. Telephone number ....

3. Postal address, including post code ....

....

....

4. Is pub a Free or Tied House (*delete as appropriate*)

5. If Tied, please name the Brewery or Group it belongs to

....

6. Name of Publican and Status ....

   e.g. Tenant, licensee or manager (delete as appropriate)

7. Opening Hours ....

8. Are Children allowed? .... Are Dogs allowed? ....

9. Is there a garden, or an outside drinking area? ....

Please use the space overleaf to describe the pub and its surroundings in your own way. THE QUIET PINT is full of examples of the kind of descriptions we are seeking. The pub may have a brochure and/or menu: if so, please send them with this form to:

The Quiet Pint, FREEPOST, Sandwich, Kent CT13 9BR.

DESCRIPTION OF PUB/WINE BAR

PIPEDOWN SUBSCRIPTION FORM

Annual subscription is £10.00, overseas £15.00 payable to:

Pipedown
6 Kingsley Mansions
London W14 9SG
Tel/Fax: 01980 623945

Name ....

Address ....

....

....

Please enclose s.a.e.